PRENTICE HALL MATHEMATICS

GRADE 6 MATH

CALIFORNIA ALL-IN-ONE Student Workbook

VERSION A

Boston, Massachusetts
Upper Saddle River, New Jersey

ISBN-13: 978-0-13-350113-1
ISBN-10: 0-13-350113-2

5 6 7 8 9 10 11 10 09

Daily Notetaking Guide

Daily Notetaking Guide (continued)

Practice, Guided Problem Solving, Vocabulary

Chapter 1: Decimals and Integers

Chapter 2: Exponents, Factors, and Fractions

Chapter 3: Operations with Fractions

Chapter 4: Equations

Chapter 5: Ratios, Rates, and Proportions

Chapter 6: Percents

Chapter 7: Geometry

Chapter 8: Measurement

Chapter 9: Patterns and Rules

Chapter 10: Displaying and Analyzing Data

Chapter 11: Using Probability

A Note to the Student:

This section of your workbook contains notetaking pages for each lesson in your student edition. They are structured to help you take effective notes in class. They will also serve as a study guide as you prepare for tests and quizzes.

Name ______________________ Class ______________ Date ______________

Lesson 1-1

Using Estimation Strategies

Lesson Objective	**California Content Standards**
To use different estimation strategies	Supports AF 2.3

Vocabulary

Compatible numbers are ____

____

Example

1 Estimating by Rounding At the zoo, you see a Colombian black spider monkey. The length of its body is 58.31 cm. The length of its tail is 78.96 cm. To the nearest centimeter, estimate the total length of the monkey's body and tail.

$78.96 + 58.31 \approx$ ☐ + ☐ ← **Round to the nearest whole number.**

$=$ ☐ ← **Add.**

The total length is about ☐ cm.

CA Standards Check

1. Estimate. First round to the nearest whole number.

a. $1.75 + 0.92$

☐

b. $14.34 - 7.8$

☐

c. $4.90 \cdot 6.25$

☐

Name ______________________ Class ______________ Date ______________

Examples

❷ **Estimating by Front-End Estimation** At a snack shop, you order a taco that costs \$3.79, a juice that costs \$.89, and a yogurt that costs \$1.39. Estimate the total cost of your order.

Step 1 Add the front-end digits.

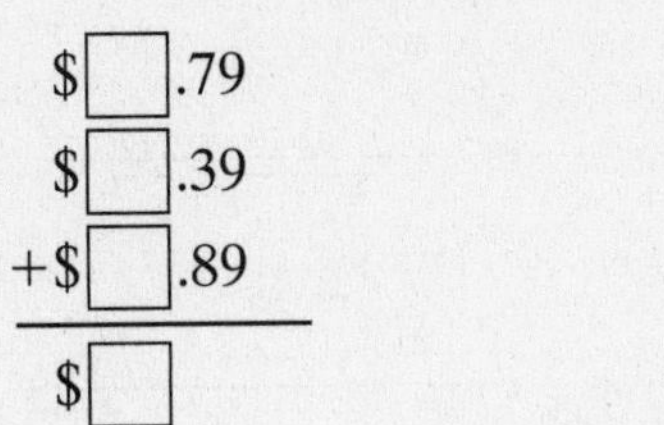

\+

Step 2 Estimate the total amount of cents to the nearest dollar.

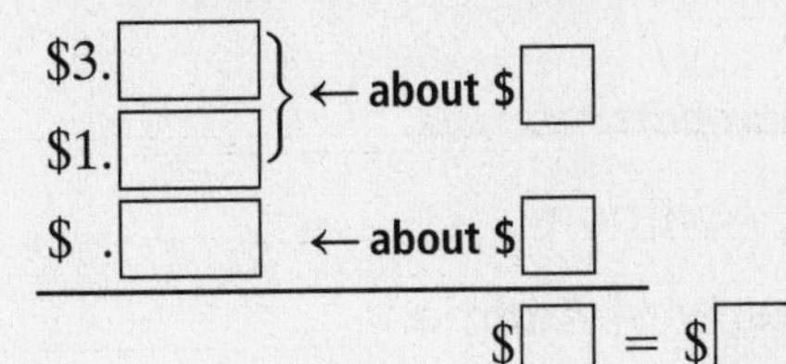

The total cost is about \$☐.

Check Round each cost to the nearest whole dollar.

☐ + \$1 + ☐ = ☐

The answer checks.

❸ **Estimating Using Compatible Numbers** Suppose you save \$61.80. About how many CDs can you buy if each costs \$15.95?

61.8 ÷ 15.95 ← **Use division.**

64 ÷ 16 ← **Choose compatible numbers such as 64 and 16.**

☐ ← **Simplify.**

You can buy about ☐ CDs.

CA Standards Check

2. Estimate to the nearest dollar the total cost of a dog collar for \$5.79, a dog toy for \$2.48, and a dog dish for \$5.99.

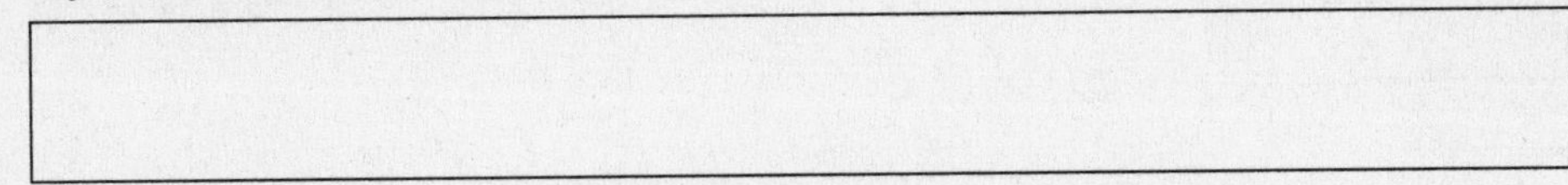

3. Your friend says that you can buy about twice as many CDs priced at \$7.95 each as CDs priced at \$15.95 each. Is your friend correct? Explain.

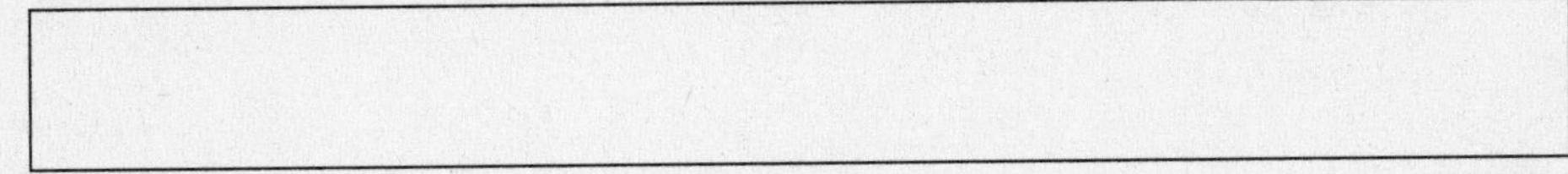

Name ______________________ Class ______________ Date ____________

Lesson 1-2

Adding and Subtracting Decimals

Lesson Objective	California Content Standards
To add and subtract decimals and use properties of addition	AF 1.3

Take Note

Properties of Addition

Identity Property of Addition ______________________

Arithmetic	Algebra
$5.6 + \square = 5.6$	$a + \square = a$

Commutative Property of Addition ______________________

____

Arithmetic	Algebra
$1.2 + 3.4 = \square$	$\square = b + a$

Associative Property of Addition ______________________

____

Arithmetic	Algebra
$(2.5 + 6) + 4 = 2.5 + \square$	$(a + b) + c = a + \square$

Example

1 Adding Decimals Find $2.15 + 7.632 + 16.5$.

Align the decimal points. →

$$\begin{array}{r} 2.150 \\ 7.632 \\ +\underline{16.500} \\ \square \end{array}$$

← Insert zeros so each addend has the same number of decimal places.

CA Standards Check

1. Find $9.75 + 14.851 + 2$.

Name ______________________ Class ______________ Date ____________

Examples

❷ Subtracting Decimals You have 5.08 min left on a CD. How much time will you have left after you record a 2.5-minute song?

$$\begin{array}{r} 5.08 \\ -2.50 \\ \hline \end{array}$$ ← **Align the decimal points.** ← **Insert a zero.**

$$\begin{array}{r} \overset{4\ 10}{\cancel{5}.\cancel{0}8} \\ -2.50 \\ \hline \square \end{array}$$ ← **Regroup.** ← **Subtract.**

You will have ☐ min left on the CD.

❸ Using Properties of Addition Use mental math to find 0.2 + 15.7 + 3.8.

What you think

I should look for compatible numbers. The sum of ☐ and ☐ is 4. Then add ☐ and 15.7 for a total of ☐.

Why it works

0.2 + 15.7 + 3.8 = 0.2 + 3.8 + 15.7 ← ☐ **Property of Addition**

= (0.2 + 3.8) + 15.7 ← ☐ **Property of Addition**

= ☐ + 15.7 ← **Add within parentheses.**

= ☐ ← **Simplify.**

CA Standards Check

2. Find 26.7 − 14.81.

3. Use mental math to find 4.4 + 5.3 + 0.6.

Name ____________________ Class ______________ Date ______________

Lesson 1-3

Multiplying and Dividing Decimals

Lesson Objective	California Content Standards
To multiply and divide decimals and use properties of multiplication	AF 1.3, MR 2.1

Take Note

Properties of Multiplication

Identity Property of Multiplication ______________________________

Arithmetic $5 \cdot ☐ = 5$ **Algebra** $a \cdot ☐ = a$

$☐ \cdot 5 = 5$ $☐ \cdot a = a$

Zero Property of Multiplication ______________________________

Arithmetic $5 \cdot ☐ = 0$ **Algebra** $a \cdot ☐ = 0$

$☐ \cdot 5 = 0$ $☐ \cdot a = 0$

Commutative Property of Multiplication ______________________________

____

Arithmetic $5 \cdot 2 = 2 \cdot ☐$ **Algebra** $a \cdot 2 = 2 \cdot ☐$

Associative Property of Multiplication ______________________________

____

Arithmetic $(3 \cdot 2) \cdot 5 = 3 \cdot ☐$ **Algebra** $(a \cdot b) \cdot c = a \cdot ☐$

Examples

1 Multiplying Decimals Estimate $11.4 \cdot 3.6$. Then find the product.

Estimate $11.4 \cdot 3.6 \approx ☐ \cdot ☐ = ☐$

Step 1 Multiply as with whole numbers.

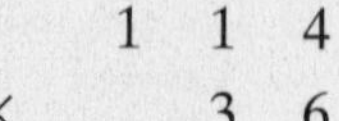

```
    1 1 4
×     3 6
  ☐ ☐ ☐
☐ ☐ ☐
☐ ☐ ☐ ☐
```

Step 2 Locate the decimal point.

```
    1 1 . 4   ←  ☐  decimal place (tenths)
×     3 . 6   ←  ☐  decimal place (tenths)
    ☐ ☐ ☐
  ☐ ☐ ☐
  ☐ ☐ ☐ ☐     ←  ☐  decimal places
```

The product of 11.4 and 3.6 is ☐.

Check for Reasonableness The product ☐ is close to the estimate of ☐. The answer is reasonable.

Name ______________________ Class ______________ Date ______________

❸ Dividing a Decimal by a Decimal Find 1.512 ÷ 0.36.

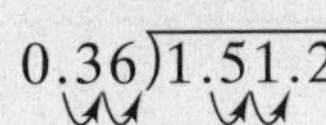

$0.36\overline{)1.51.2}$ ← **Multiply the divisor and the dividend by 100 to make the divisor a whole number.**

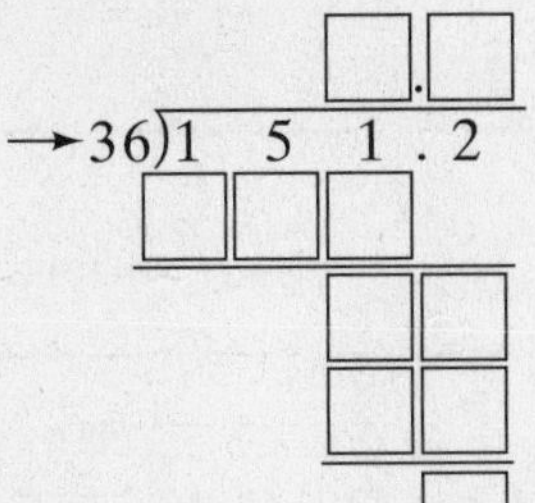

$36\overline{)1\ 5\ 1\ .\ 2}$ ← **Place the decimal point in the quotient above the decimal point in the dividend.**

CA Standards Check

1. Estimate, then find each product.

a. 3.7 · 9 

b. 14.3 · 0.81 

c. 8.73 · 5.4 

2. Use mental math to find 2.5 · 6.3 · 4.

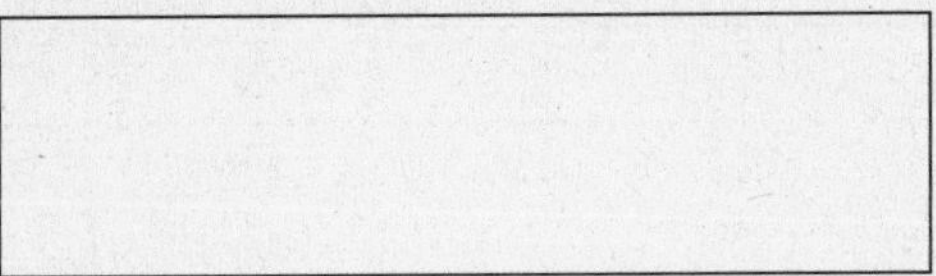

3. Find each quotient.

a. 12.42 ÷ 5.4

b. 67.84 ÷ 0.64

c. 144.06 ÷ 9.8

4. You use 0.6 lb of bananas in each smoothie. How many smoothies can you make with 3.12 lb of bananas?

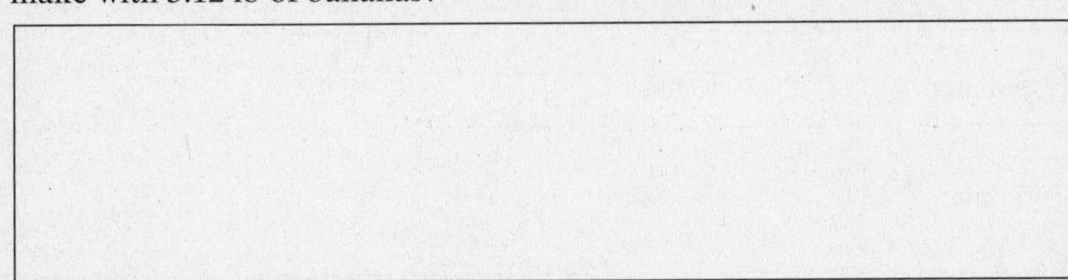

Name ________________ Class ________________ Date ________________

Lesson 1-4

Measuring in Metric Units

Lesson Objective	**California Content Standards**
To use appropriate metric units and convert among metric units	AF 2.1, MR 1.0

Take Note

Unit	kilometer	hecto-meter	deca-meter	meter	deci-meter	centimeter	millimeter
Symbol	km	hm	dam	m	dm	cm	mm
Value	☐ m	100 m	10 m	☐ m	0.1 m	☐ m	☐ m

Example

1 Choosing a Reasonable Estimate Choose a reasonable estimate. Explain your choice.

a. length of a pencil: 19 mm 19 cm 19 m

____

____

____

b. capacity of a bucket: 12 ml 12 L 12 kL

____

____

CA Standards Check

1. Choose a reasonable estimate. Explain your choice.

a. diameter of a soup bowl: 20 mm 20 cm 20 m

b. mass of a butterfly: 500 mg 500 g 500 kg

Examples

2 Multiplying to Change Units Change 871 centimeters to meters.

871 cm = ▢ m

centimeters: 0, 500, 871, 1,000
meters: 0, 5, ▢, 10

1 cm = ▢ m ← **You are starting with centimeters. Complete the relationship 1 cm = ▢ m.**

871 · ▢ = ▢ m ← **To change centimeters to meters, multiply by ▢.**

871 cm equals ▢ m.

3 Multiplying to Change Units Change 40.6 meters to decimeters.

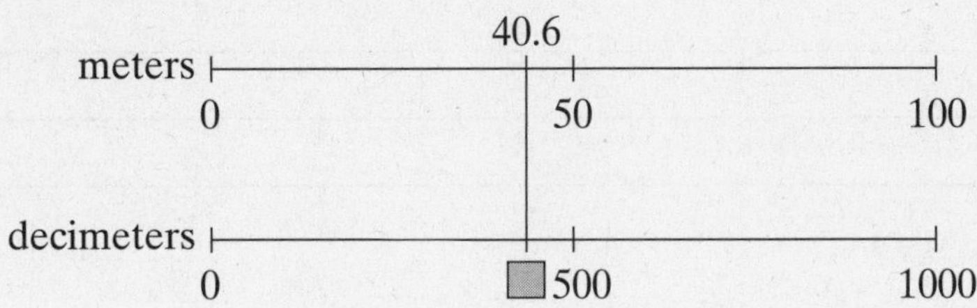

40.6 m = ▢ dm

1 m = ▢ dm ← **You are starting with meters. Complete the relationship 1 m = ▢ dm.**

40.6 · ▢ = ▢ ← **To change meters to decimeters, multiply by ▢.**

40.6 meters equals ▢ decimeters.

CA Standards Check

2. Change 34 liters to milliliters.

3. Change 4,690 grams to kilograms.

Name ______________________ Class ______________ Date ______________

Lesson 1-5

Comparing and Ordering Integers

Lesson Objective	California Content Standards
To use integers and find absolute value	Supports NS 1.1

Vocabulary

Integers are ____

Two numbers are opposites if ____

The absolute value of a number is ____

Example

1 Finding an Opposite Find the opposite of 2.

The opposite of 2 is ☐, because 2 and ☐ are each ☐ units from ☐, but in ☐ directions.

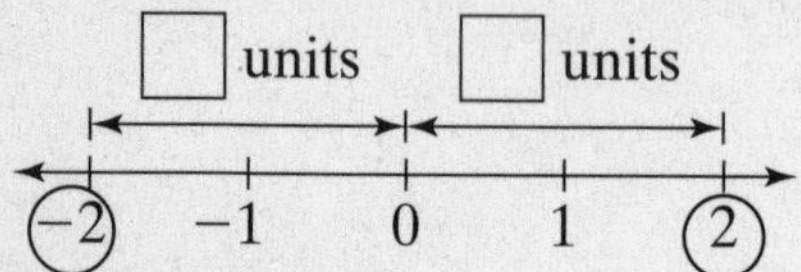

CA Standards Check

1. Find the opposite of each number.

a. −8 **b.** 13 **c.** −22

Name ______________________ Class ______________ Date ______________

Examples

❷ Finding Absolute Value Find $|-5|$ and $|5|$.

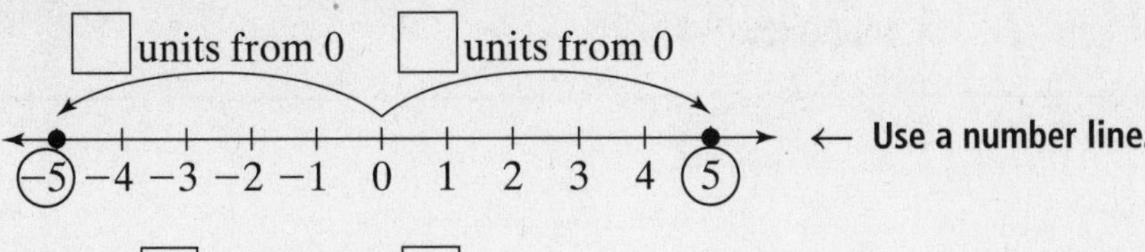

$|-5| = \square$ and $|5| = \square$.

❸ Comparing Integers Compare 3 and −8 using <, =, or >.

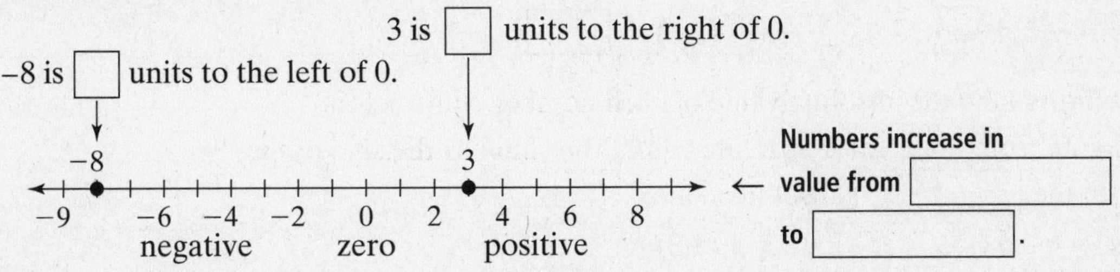

Since 3 is to the ______ of −8 on the number line, 3 ☐ −8.

CA Standards Check

2. Find $|-8|$.

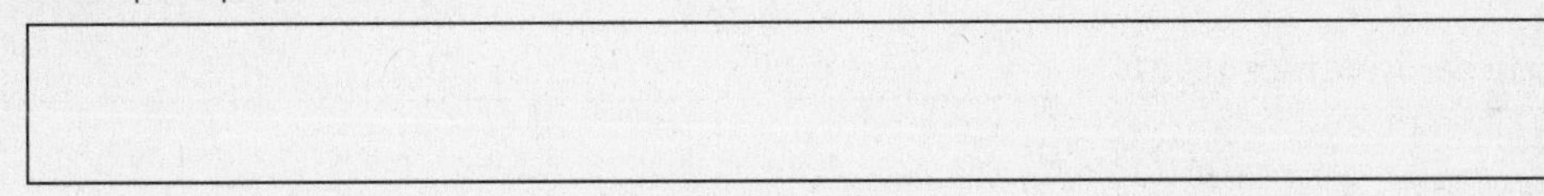

3. Compare −8 and −2 using <, =, or >.

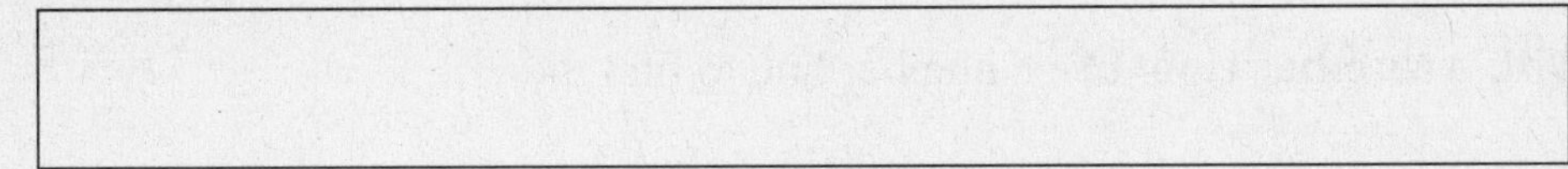

4. Order the numbers 3, −1, −4, and 2 from least to greatest.

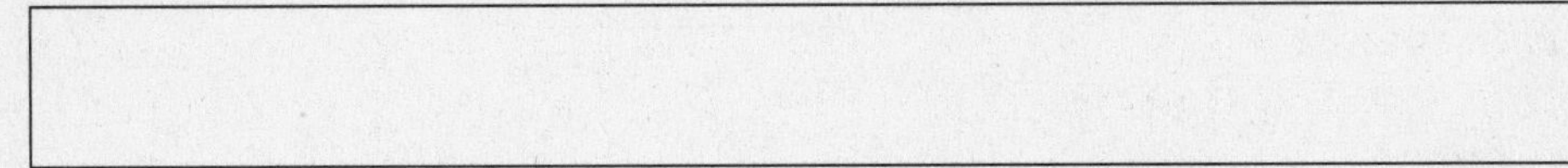

Name ______________________ Class ______________ Date ______________

Lesson 1-6

Adding and Subtracting Integers

Lesson Objective	California Content Standards
To add and subtract integers	NS 2.3

Take Note

Adding Integers

Same Sign The sum of two positive numbers is ☐. The sum of two negative numbers is negative.

Examples $3 + 5 =$ ☐ $\qquad -3 + (-5) =$ ☐

Different Signs Find the absolute value of each number. Subtract the lesser absolute from the greater absolute value. The sum has the sign of the integer with the ☐ absolute value.

Examples $-3 + 5 =$ ☐ $\qquad 3 + (-5) =$ ☐

Subtracting Integers

To subtract an integer, add its ☐.

Examples $3 - 5 = 3 + ($☐$) =$ ☐ $\qquad -3 - 5 = -3 + ($☐$) =$ ☐

Two numbers are additive inverses if ______________________________

____

Example

1 Adding Integers With a Number Line Use a number line to find the sum $-4 + (-2)$.

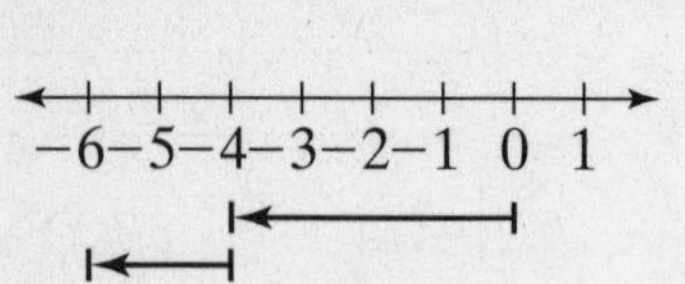

← **Start at** ☐. **Move 4 units** ☐.
Then move another 2 units ☐.

The sum is ☐.

CA Standards Check

1. Use a number line to find each sum.

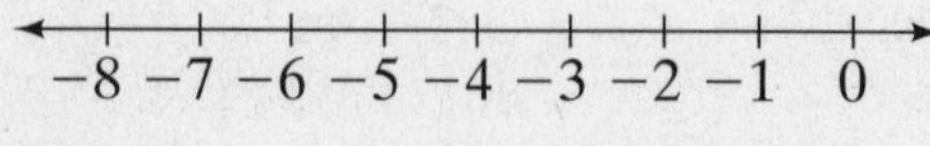

a. $-8 + 1$ ☐ b. $-1 + (-7)$ ☐ c. $-6 + 6$ ☐

Name ______________________ Class ______________ Date ____________

Examples

❷ Adding Integers Find 24 + (−6).

$|24| =$ ☐ and $|-6| =$ ☐ ← **Find the absolute value of each integer.**

$24 -$ ☐ $=$ ☐ ← **Subtract ☐ from 24 because |−6| ☐ |24|.**

$24 + (-6) =$ ☐ ← **The sum has the same sign as ☐.**

❸ Subtracting Integers Find −7 − 2.

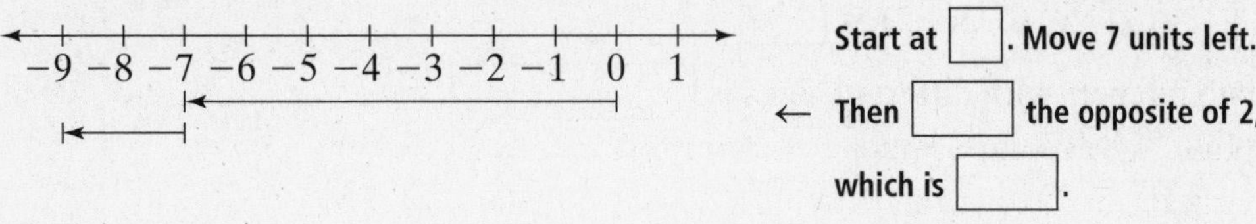

Start at ☐. Move 7 units left.

← **Then ☐ the opposite of 2, which is ☐.**

$-7 - 2 = -7$ ☐ $(-2) =$ ☐

❹ Application Recorded temperatures at Amundsen-Scott Station in Antarctica have ranged from a low of −89°F to a high of −13°F. Find the difference in temperatures.

Subtract to find the difference.

$-13 - (-89) = -13 +$ ☐ ← **Add the ☐ of −89, which is ☐.**

$=$ ☐ ← **Simplify.**

The difference in temperatures is ☐.

CA Standards Check

2. Find each sum.

a. $-97 + (-65)$ **b.** $21 + (-39)$ **c.** $22 + (-22)$

3. Find $-6 - 1$.

4. Find $14 - (-7)$.

5. During the biggest drop of a roller coaster in Ohio, your altitude changes by −155 ft. Another roller coaster in Texas has a −137 ft change. How much farther do you drop on the Ohio roller coaster?

Name ______________________ Class ______________ Date ______________

Lesson 1-7

Multiplying and Dividing Integers

Lesson Objective	California Content Standards
To multiply and divide integers	NS 2.3 ⊃, AF 2.3

Take Note

Multiplying Integers

The product of two integers with the same sign is ________.

Examples $3(2) =$ ____ $\quad -3(-2) =$ ____

The product of two integers with different signs is ________.

Examples $-3(2) =$ ____ $\quad 3(-2) =$ ____

Dividing Integers

The quotient of two integers with the same sign is ________.

Examples $10 \div 2 =$ ____ $\quad -10 \div (-2) =$ ____

The quotient of two integers with different signs is ________.

Examples $-10 \div 2 =$ ____ $\quad 10 \div (-2) =$ ____

Example

1 Multiplying Integers Find each product.

a. $3(7) =$ ____ ← ________ **signs;** ________ **product.** → b. $-3(-7) =$ ____

c. $3(-7) =$ ____ ← ________ **signs;** ________ **product.** → d. $-3(7) =$ ____

CA Standards Check

1. Simplify the expression $-4(-7)$.

Example

❷ Dividing Integers You are riding your bicycle at a speed of 12 ft/s. Four seconds later, you come to a complete stop. Find the acceleration of your bicycle.

$$\text{acceleration} = \frac{\text{final velocity} - \text{initial velocity}}{\text{time}}$$

$$= \frac{\square - \square}{\square}$$ ← **Substitute ☐ for final velocity, ☐ for initial velocity, and ☐ for time.**

$$= \frac{\square}{\square} = \square$$ ← **Simplify. The ☐ sign means the bicycle is slowing.**

The bicycle's acceleration is ☐ ft/s per second.

CA Standards Check

2. Suppose you are running at the rate of 24 ft/s in a 40-yd dash. It takes you 4 s to slow to a stop. Find your acceleration.

Name ______________________ Class ______________ Date ______________

Lesson 1-8

Order of Operations and the Distributive Property

Lesson Objective	California Content Standards
To use the order of operations and the Distributive Property	AF 1.3, AF 1.4

Take Note

Order of Operations

1. Work inside grouping symbols.

2. ☐ and ☐ in order from left to right.

3. ☐ and ☐ in order from left to right.

Distributive Property

Arithmetic	Algebra
$9(4 + 5) = \square(4) + \square(5)$	$a(b + c) = \square(b) + \square(c)$
$5(8 - 2) = 5(\square) - 5(\square)$	$a(b - c) = a(\square) - a(\square)$

Example

1 Using the Order of Operations Find the value of each expression.

a. $9 + 3 \cdot 5 - 1$

☐ ← **Multiply.**

23 ← **Add and subtract.**

b. $9 + 3 \cdot (5 - 1)$

☐ ← **Work inside grouping symbols.**

☐ ← **Multiply.**

21 ← **Add.**

CA Standards Check

1. Find the value of each expression.

a. $7(-4 + 2) - 1$

b. $\frac{-40}{4} + 2 \cdot 5$

c. $\frac{8 + 4}{6} - 11$

Name ______________________ Class ______________ Date ______________

Examples

2 Application You want to buy four CDs at a price of $11.95 each and two DVDs at a price of $18.75 each. What is the total cost of the items?

Words ☐ CDs + ☐ DVDs

Expression ☐ × 11.95 + ☐ × ☐ = ☐ + 37.50 ← **First multiply.**

= ☐ ← **Then add.**

The total cost is $☐.

3 Using the Distributive Property Use the Distributive Property to find 4(4.8).

If I think of 4.8 as (5.0 – 0.2), then, 4(4.8) is the same as 4(☐ – ☐).

4(4.8) = 4(5.0 – 0.2)

= 4(5.0) – 4(0.2) ← **Use the** ☐ **Property.**

= ☐ – ☐ ← **Multiply.**

= ☐ ← **Subtract.**

CA Standards Check

2. What is the total cost of one CD at a price of $11.95 and three DVDs at a price of $18.75 each?

3. Use the Distributive Property and mental math to find 9(14).

Name ______________________ Class ______________ Date ______________

Lesson 1-9

Mean, Median, Mode, and Range

Lesson Objective	California Content Standards
To describe data using mean, median, mode, and range	SDAP 1.0, SDAP 1.1, SDAP 1.3

Vocabulary

The mean of a data set is ______________________________

An outlier is a data item that ______________________________

The median of a data set is ______________________________

The mode of a data set is ______________________________

The range of a data set is ______________________________

Examples

1 Finding the Mean Find the mean of 502, 477, 593, 481, 735, and 614.

$\frac{502 + 477 + 593 + 481 + 735 + 614}{\square}$ ← **Divide the sum by the number of items.**

$\frac{\square}{\square} = \square$ ← **Simplify.**

2 Finding the Median Find the median of the data in the chart. First write the data in order from least to greatest.

18 Responses to "How many pets do you have?"					
2	0	1	2	4	2
1	0	3	2	0	8
0	1	2	3	0	1

____

The two middle values are $\square$ and $\square$.

Find the mean of the two $\square$ values.

$\frac{\square + \square}{\square} = \square$

The median is $\square$.

CA Standards Check

1. Find the mean of 216, 230, 198, and 252. $\square$
2. Find the median in the set of data: −5 −1 3 −18 −2 2

$\square$

Name ______________________ Class ______________ Date ______________

Examples

3 Finding the Mode Find the mode of the data in the chart. Make a table to organize the data.

Peppers	Onions	Mushrooms	Olives

The mode is ☐.

Favorite Pizza Topping of Twelve People Surveyed		
peppers	onions	mushrooms
onions	olives	peppers
onions	peppers	mushrooms
onions	olives	onions

4 Finding Range Elevations in California range from −282 ft (or 282 ft below sea level) at Badwater in Death Valley to 14,495 ft at the top of Mt. Whitney. Find the elevation range in California.

14,495 − (−282) = 14,495 + ☐ ← **Add the ☐ of −282, which is ☐.**

= ☐ ← **Simplify.**

The elevation range in California is ☐ ft.

CA Standards Check

3. Find the modes.

a. 17 16 18 17 16 17

b. 3.2 3.7 3.5 3.7 3.5 3.2

c. pen, pencil, marker, marker, pen, pen, pen, pencil, marker

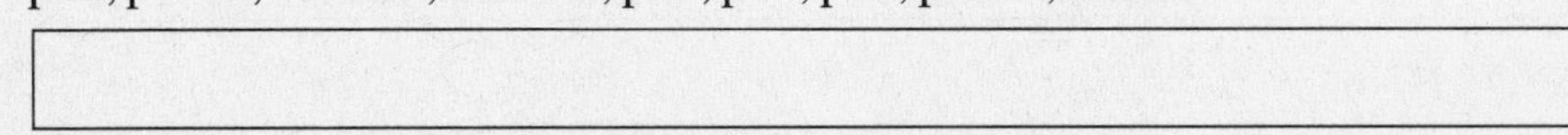

4. Record temperatures in California have ranged from a low of −45°F to a high of 134°F. Find the temperature range.

Name ______________________ Class ______________ Date ____________

Lesson 2-1

Exponents and Order of Operations

Lesson Objective	California Content Standards
To write and simplify expressions with exponents	AF 1.3, AF 1.4

Take Note

Order of Operations

1. Do all operations within [ ] first.
2. Evaluate any term(s) with [ ].
3. [ ] and [ ] in order from left to right.
4. [ ] and [ ] in order from left to right.

An exponent ______________________________

____

exponent → $5^{\square} = 5 \cdot 5 \cdot 5 = \square$ ← value of the expression

base

The base is used as a factor three times.

A power is ______________________________

____

Example

1 Writing Expressions Using Exponents Write 7 · 7 · 7 · 7 using an exponent.

$7 \cdot 7 \cdot 7 \cdot 7 = \square$ ← [ ] is the base. [ ] is the exponent.

CA Standards Check

1. Write using exponents.

a. 44 · 44 · 44 · 44

b. (−2) · (−2)

Name ______________________ Class ______________ Date ______________

Examples

❷ Application A seaside village has an area of 1.3^2 km^2. Find the value of 1.3^2.

Method 1

$(1.3)^2 = (\square)(\square)$ ← **Write as a product of repeated factors.**

$= \square$ ← **Multiply.**

Method 2

Use a calculator.

1.3 $\square$ = $\square$ ← **Use the** $\square$ **key to square numbers.**

The area of the village is $\square$ km^2.

❸ Simplifying Using Order of Operations Simplify $2^3 \cdot (9 - 3)^2$.

$2^3 \cdot (9 - 3)^2 = 2^3 \cdot \square^2$ ← **Do operations in parentheses.**

$= \square \cdot \square$ ← **Find the values of the powers.**

$= \square$ ← **Multiply.**

CA Standards Check

2. Simplify. Use paper and pencil, a model, or a calculator.

a. 3^5

b. 10^9

c. 3.1^2

3. Simplify.

a. $(-2)^3$

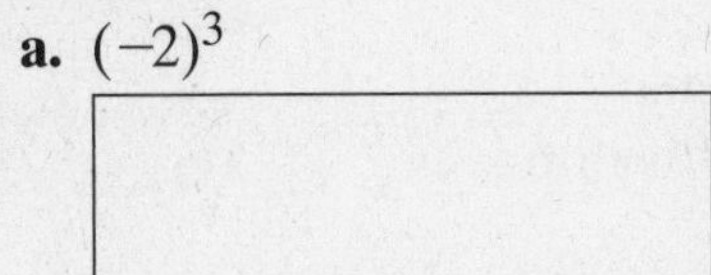

b. -2^3

c. $(3 + 5)^2 - 2$

Name ______________________ Class ______________ Date ______________

Lesson 2-2

Prime Factorization

Lesson Objective	**California Content Standards**
To find multiples and divisors and to use prime factorization	NS 2.4

Vocabulary

A multiple of a number is ______________________

The least common multiple (LCM) of two or more numbers is ______________________

A factor is ______________________

A composite number is ______________________

A prime number is ______________________

Prime factorization is ______________________

The greatest common factor (GCF) of two or more numbers is ______________________

Example

1 Finding the LCM Dan goes to the health club every 4 days. His sister Neesa goes there every 6 days. Dan and Neesa both went to the health club today. When will they both go there on the same day again?

Find the least common multiple of 4 and 6.

Multiples of 4: 4, 8, ☐, ☐, ☐, ...
Multiples of 6: 6, 12, ☐, ☐, ...

← **List the first several multiples of 4 and 6.**

The LCM of 4 and 6 is ☐. Both will go to the health club again in ☐ days.

CA Standards Check

1. Find the LCM of each pair of numbers.

a. 4, 10 ☐

b. 5, 7 ☐

c. 12, 15 ☐

Name ______________________ Class ______________ Date ______________

Examples

❷ Prime Numbers and Composite Numbers Determine whether each number is prime or composite.

a. 17 Factors: [ ] 17 is a [ ] number.

b. 22 Factors: [ ] 22 is a [ ] number.

❸ Writing Prime Factorization Use a factor tree to write the prime factorization of 90.

90

Prime → (2) · [ ] ← **Write 90 as the product of any two of its factors.**

Prime → (5) · [ ] ← **Write [ ] as the product of two factors.**

Prime → (3) · [ ] ← **Write [ ] as the product of two factors.**

90 = [ ]. Using exponents, you can write 90 = 2 · [ ] · 5.

❹ Finding the GCF Find the GCF of 32 and 48.

32 = [ ]

48 = [ ] ← **Write the prime factorizations.**

GCF = [ ] = [ ] ← **Find the product of the common factors.**

The GCF of 32 and 48 is [ ].

CA Standards Check

2. Is 15 prime or composite? Explain.

[ ]

3. Write the prime factorization of 72. Use exponents where possible.

[ ]

4. Find the GCD of 16 and 24.

[ ]

Name ______________ Class ______________ Date ______________

Lesson 2-3

Simplifying Fractions

Lesson Objective	California Content Standards
To write equivalent fractions and to simplify fractions	NS 2.4

Vocabulary

Equivalent fractions are ______________

A fraction is in simplest form when ______________

Examples

1 Using Multiples Use a table of multiples to write three fractions equivalent to $\frac{3}{7}$.

	× 2	× 3	× 4
3			
7			

← **Multiples in the same column form fractions equivalent to $\frac{3}{7}$.**

Three fractions equivalent to $\frac{3}{7}$ are $\frac{\square}{\square}$, $\frac{\square}{\square}$, and $\frac{\square}{\square}$.

2 Using Factors Find three fractions equivalent to $\frac{16}{24}$.

Factors of 16: ______________

Factors of 24: ______________

} ← **List the factors of each number. Look for common factors.**

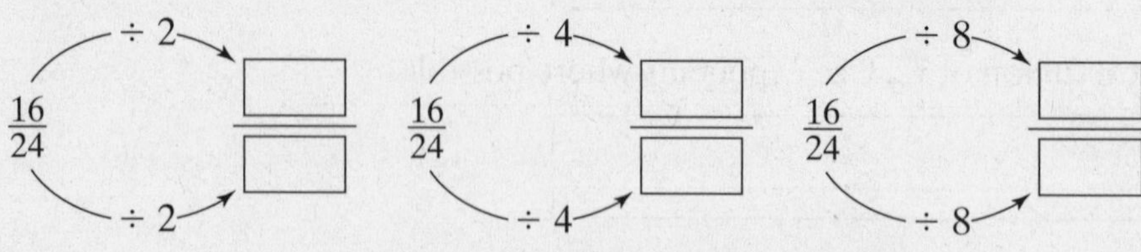

Three fractions equivalent to $\frac{16}{24}$ are $\frac{\square}{\square}$, $\frac{\square}{\square}$, and $\frac{\square}{\square}$.

Name ________________ Class ________________ Date ________________

Examples

3 Simplifying by Dividing Simplify $\frac{12}{30}$.

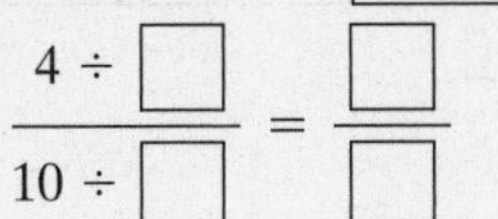

$\frac{12 \div 3}{30 \div 3} = \frac{\square}{\square}$ ← **Divide the numerator and denominator by a common factor.**

$\frac{4 \div \square}{10 \div \square} = \frac{\square}{\square}$ ← **If necessary, divide again by another common factor.**

In simplest form, $\frac{12}{30}$ is $\frac{\square}{\square}$.

4 Using the GCD to Simplify a Fraction There are 28 students in Mai's homeroom. Of these, 20 students have a pet. What fraction of the students have a pet? Write your answer in simplest form.

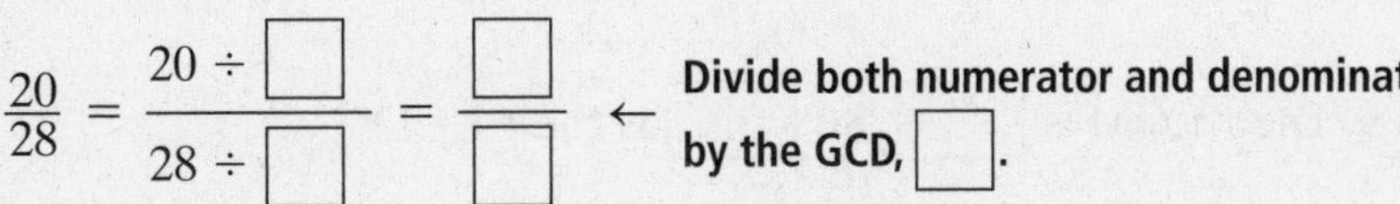

$\frac{20}{28} = \frac{20 \div \square}{28 \div \square} = \frac{\square}{\square}$ ← **Divide both numerator and denominator by the GCD, $\square$.**

The fraction of students that have a pet is $\frac{\square}{\square}$.

CA Standards Check

1. Use multiples to write two fractions equivalent to $\frac{4}{5}$.

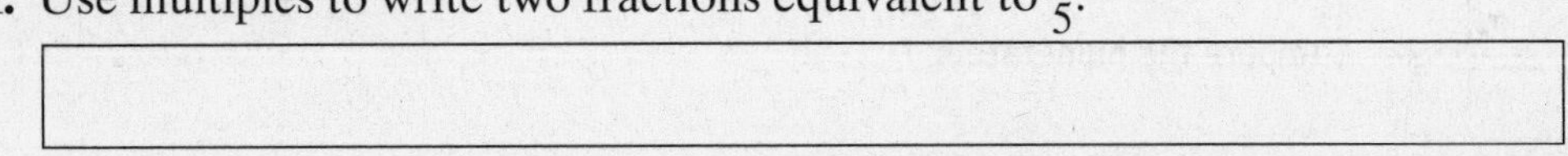

2. Use common factors to write two fractions equivalent to $\frac{18}{30}$.

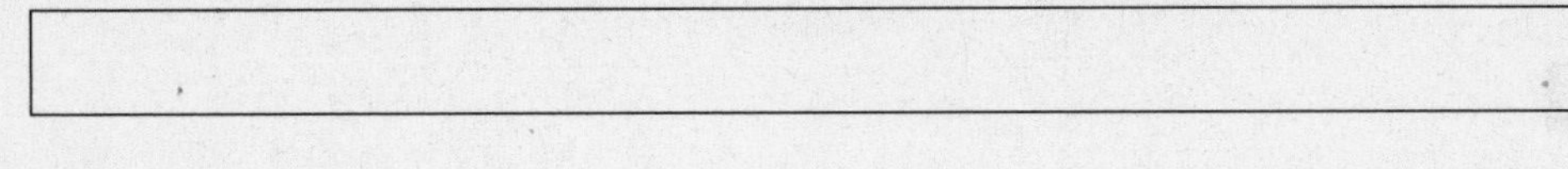

3. Write $\frac{8}{12}$ in simplest form.

4. Your class ordered 45 calculators. Of these, 18 were solar powered. What fraction of the calculators was solar powered?

Name ______________________ Class ______________ Date ____________

Lesson 2-4

Comparing and Ordering Fractions

Lesson Objective	**California Content Standards**
To compare and order fractions	NS 1.1, MR 2.5

Vocabulary

A least common denominator (LCD) of two or more fractions is ______________________

____

Example

1 Comparing Fractions Compare $\frac{7}{12}$ and $\frac{5}{9}$.

The denominators are 12 and 9. Their LCM is ☐. So ☐ is their LCD.

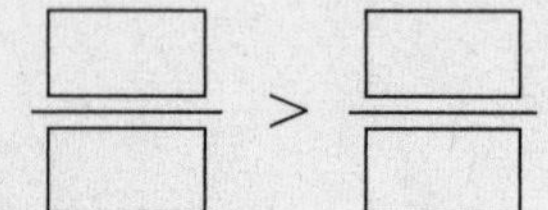

$\frac{7}{12} = \frac{7 \times 3}{12 \times 3} = \frac{\square}{\square}$

← **Write equivalent fractions with a denominator of ☐.**

$\frac{5}{9} = \frac{5 \times 4}{9 \times 4} = \frac{\square}{\square}$

$\frac{\square}{\square} > \frac{\square}{\square}$ ← **Compare the numerators.**

So $\frac{7}{12}$ ☐ $\frac{5}{9}$.

CA Standards Check

1. Compare each pair of fractions. Use <, =, or >.

a. $\frac{3}{4}$ ☐ $\frac{5}{6}$

b. $\frac{1}{6}$ ☐ $\frac{2}{9}$

c. $\frac{4}{10}$ ☐ $\frac{3}{8}$

Name ______________________ Class ______________ Date ______________

Example

2 Application Giselda wants to paint her room. She found $\frac{3}{5}$ gal of yellow paint, $\frac{2}{3}$ gal of blue paint, and $\frac{1}{2}$ gal of green paint. Which of these amounts is the smallest? Which is the largest? Order the colors from least to greatest amount of paint.

Order $\frac{3}{5}$, $\frac{2}{3}$, and $\frac{1}{2}$.

The LCM of 5, 3, and 2 is ☐. So ☐ is the LCD.

Yellow → $\frac{3}{5} = \frac{3 \times \square}{5 \times \square} = \frac{\square}{\square}$

Blue → $\frac{2}{3} = \frac{2 \times \square}{3 \times \square} = \frac{\square}{\square}$ ← **Write equivalent fractions with a denominator of ☐.**

Green → $\frac{1}{2} = \frac{1 \times \square}{2 \times \square} = \frac{\square}{\square}$

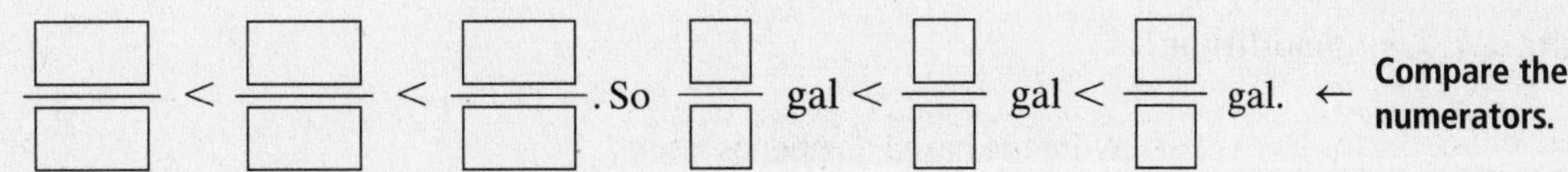

$\frac{\square}{\square} < \frac{\square}{\square} < \frac{\square}{\square}$. So $\frac{\square}{\square}$ gal < $\frac{\square}{\square}$ gal < $\frac{\square}{\square}$ gal. ← **Compare the numerators.**

The green paint is the smallest amount. The blue paint is the largest amount.

CA Standards Check

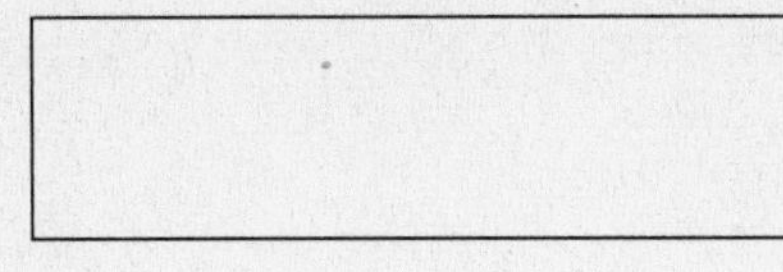

2. Order $\frac{1}{5}$, $\frac{2}{6}$, $\frac{1}{15}$ from least to greatest.

Name ______________________ Class ______________ Date ______________

Lesson 2-5

Mixed Numbers and Improper Fractions

Lesson Objective	California Content Standards
To write mixed numbers and improper fractions	NS 1.1

Vocabulary

An improper fraction has ____

A mixed number is ____

Examples

1 Writing an Improper Fraction Write $3\frac{2}{5}$ as an improper fraction.

Method 1 Using addition

$3\frac{2}{5} = 3 + \frac{2}{5}$ ← **Write the mixed number as a sum.**

$= \frac{\square}{\square} + \frac{2}{5}$ ← **Change 3 to a fraction with the same denominator as $\frac{2}{5}$. Substitute $3 = 3 \cdot \frac{\square}{\square} = \frac{\square}{\square}$.**

$= \frac{\square + \square}{5}$ ← **Add the numerators.**

$= \frac{\square}{\square}$ ← **Simplify.**

Method 2 Using multiplication

Multiply the denominator by the whole number. **Add the numerator.**

$3\frac{2}{5} = \square \frac{\square}{5} = \frac{(5 \times \square) + \square}{5} = \frac{\square}{\square}$

The denominator stays the same.

Name ______________________ Class ______________ Date ______________

❷ **Writing a Mixed Number** Karl needs $\frac{18}{4}$ cups of milk to make several loaves of bread. Express the amount of milk as a mixed number in simplest form.

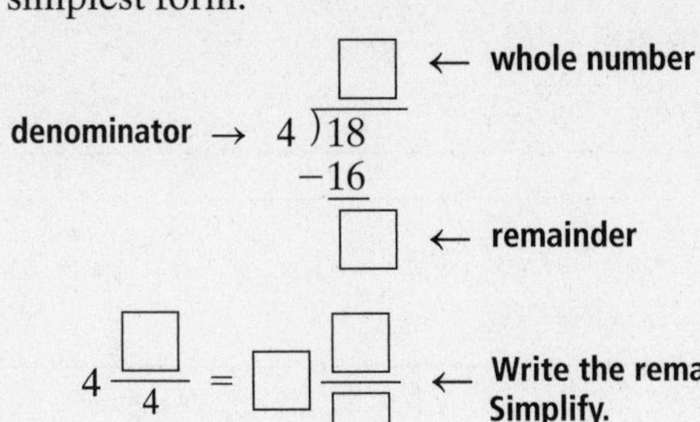

$4\frac{\square}{4} = \square\frac{\square}{\square}$ ← **Write the remainder as a fraction, $\frac{\text{remainder}}{\text{denominator}}$. Simplify.**

Karl needs $\square\frac{\square}{\square}$ cups of milk.

CA Standards Check

1. **Choose a Method** Write $2\frac{5}{8}$ as an improper fraction.

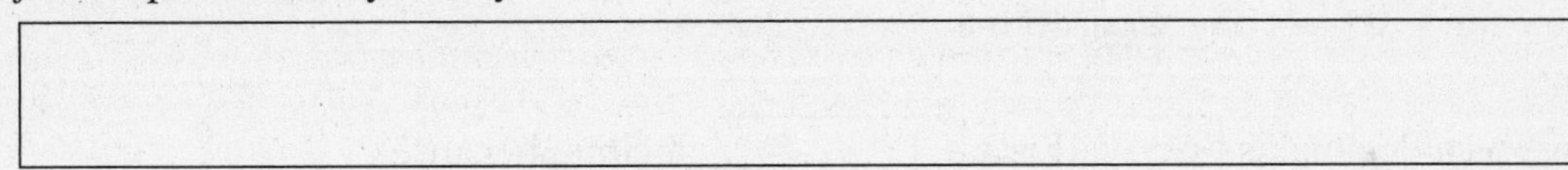

2. A bakery sells a jumbo pie with 12 slices. If you need 30 slices, how many jumbo pies should you buy?

Name ______________________ Class ______________ Date ______________

Lesson 2-6

Fractions and Decimals

Lesson Objective	**California Content Standards**
To convert between fractions and decimals	NS 1.1 🔑, MR 3.2

Vocabulary

A terminating decimal is ____

____

A repeating decimal is ____

____

Examples

1 Writing a Terminating Decimal Write the fraction $\frac{1}{4}$ as a decimal.

$\frac{1}{4}$ or $1 \div 4 = 4\overline{)1.00}$ ← **quotient** [ ]

− [ ]

20

−20

0 ← **The remainder is 0.**

The fraction $\frac{1}{4}$ as a decimal is [ ]. It is a [ ] decimal because the division process stops when the remainder is [ ].

2 Writing a Repeating Decimal Write $\frac{7}{15}$ as a decimal.

Method 1: Paper and Pencil

$\frac{7}{15}$ or $7 \div 15 = 15\overline{)7.0000}$ ← **The digit 6 repeats.** [ ]

−60

100

− 90

[ ] ← **There will always be a remainder of** [ ].

So $\frac{7}{15} =$ [ ].

Method 2: Calculator

7 ÷ 15 = [ ]

Name ________________ Class ________________ Date ________________

3 Writing a Decimal as a Fraction Write 4.105 as a fraction in simplest form.

Since $0.105 = \frac{105}{1000}$, $4.105 = \square \frac{\square}{\square}$.

$4\frac{105}{1,000} = 4\frac{105 \div \square}{1,000 \div \square}$ ← **Use the GCD to write the fraction in simplest form.**

$= \square \frac{\square}{\square}$

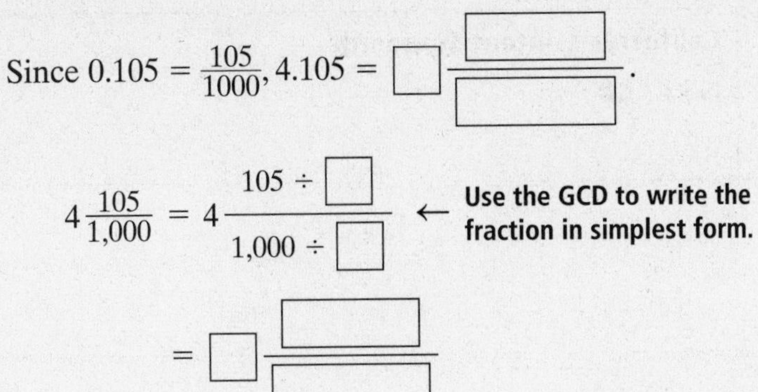

4 Application In a survey of next year's seventh-grade students, 0.25 said they will come to school by bus, $\frac{5}{24}$ said they will walk, 0.375 said they will come in a car, and $\frac{1}{16}$ said they will ride their bicycles. Order the means of transportation from most used to least used.

walk $\frac{5}{24} = \square$ ← **Rewrite the fractions as decimals.** bicycles $\frac{1}{16} =$

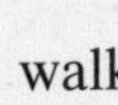

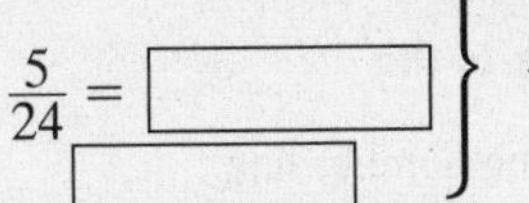

Since 0.375 $\square$ 0.25 $\square$ 0.208 $\square$ 0.0625, the means of transportation are $\square$, $\square$, $\square$, and $\square$.

CA Standards Check

1. Write $\frac{5}{8}$ as a decimal.

2. Write $\frac{5}{9}$ as a decimal.

3. Write 1.364 as a mixed number with a fraction in simplest form.

4. Order from greatest to least: $1\frac{3}{8}$, $1\frac{7}{15}$, 1.862

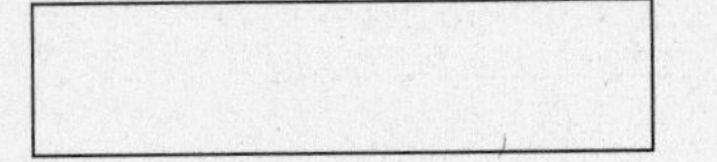

5. In a survey about pets, $\frac{2}{5}$ of the students prefer cats, 0.33 prefer dogs, $\frac{3}{25}$ prefer birds, and 0.15 prefer fish. List the choices in order of preference.

Name ______________________ Class ______________ Date ____________

Lesson 2-7

Rational Numbers

Lesson Objective	**California Content Standards**
To compare and order rational numbers	NS 1.1

Vocabulary

A rational number is ____

____

Example

1 Comparing Rational Numbers Compare $-\frac{1}{4}$ and $-\frac{3}{8}$.

Method 1

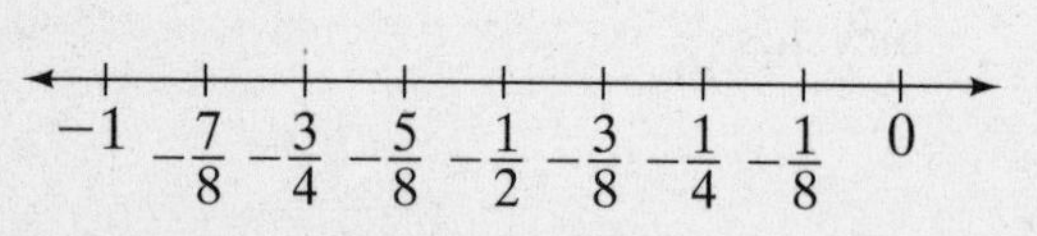

← **Since** $-\frac{3}{8}$ **is farther to the** ☐ **on the number line, it is the** ☐ **number.**

So, $-\frac{1}{4}$ ☐ $-\frac{3}{8}$.

Method 2

$-\frac{1}{4} = \frac{1 \times \square}{4 \times \square}$ ← **The LCD is** ☐**. Write an equivalent fraction.**

$= -\frac{2}{8}$ ← **Simplify.**

Since $-\frac{2}{8}$ ☐ $-\frac{3}{8}$, $-\frac{1}{4}$ ☐ $-\frac{3}{8}$.

CA Standards Check

1. Compare $-\frac{2}{3}$ and $-\frac{1}{6}$. Use <, =, or >.

☐

Name ______________________ Class ______________ Date ______________

Examples

❷ Comparing Decimals Compare. Use <, = , or >.

a. 8.7 and 8.1

8.7 $\square$ 8.1 ← **Both numbers are positive. Compare the digits.**

b. −8.7 and 8.1

−8.7 $\square$ 8.1 ← **Any negative number is less than a positive number.**

c. −8.7 and −8.1

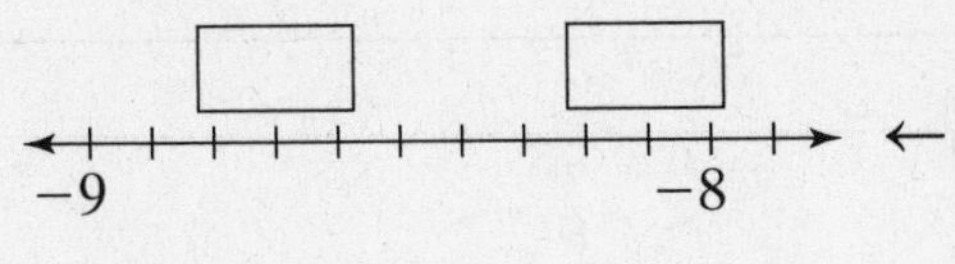

← **Place the decimals on a number line and compare their locations.**

−8.7 $\square$ −8.1

❸ Ordering Rational Numbers Order these numbers from least to greatest: $-\frac{3}{5}$, 0.625, $\frac{2}{3}$, and −0.5.

$-\frac{3}{5} = -3 \div 5 = -0.6$ ← **Write as a decimal.**

$\frac{2}{3} = 2 \div 3 = 0.66666\ldots = 0.\overline{6}$ ← **Write as a repeating decimal.**

$-0.6 \;\square\; -0.5 \;\square\; 0.625 \;\square\; 0.\overline{6}$ ← **Compare the decimals.**

From least to greatest, the numbers are 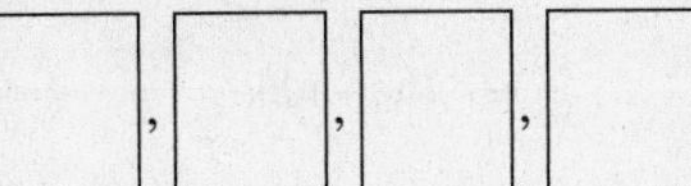

CA Standards Check

2. Compare −4.2 and −4.9. Use <, = , or >.

3. Order from least to greatest,

a. $\frac{2}{3}$, −0.1, $-\frac{5}{8}$, 2.2

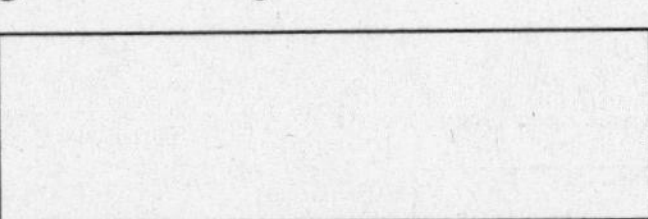

b. 0.625, $\frac{1}{8}$, $\frac{1}{32}$, 0.025

Name ______ Class ______ Date ______

Lesson 3-1

Estimating With Fractions and Mixed Numbers

Lesson Objective	California Content Standards
To estimate sums, differences, products, and quotients involving fractions	NS 2.0

Vocabulary

A benchmark is ______

______

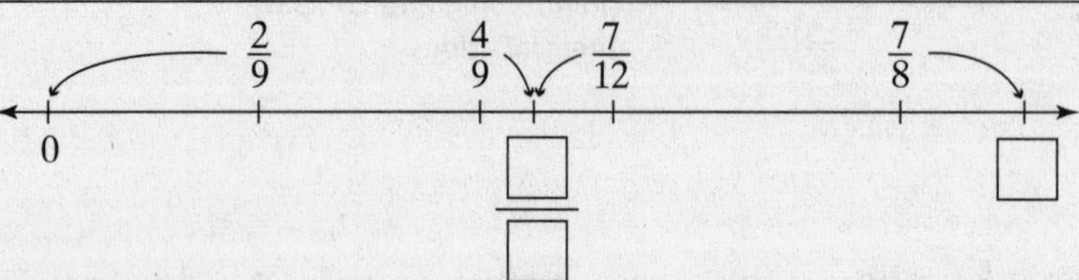

Examples

1 Using Benchmarks With Fractions Use benchmarks to estimate $\frac{4}{7} + \frac{4}{5}$.

$\frac{4}{7} + \frac{4}{5} \approx \frac{\square}{\square} + \square$ ← **Use ______ to estimate each fraction.**

$= 1\frac{1}{2}$ ← **Then add.**

2 Estimating With Mixed Numbers Estimate $5\frac{1}{9} - 2\frac{5}{6}$.

$5\frac{1}{9} - 2\frac{5}{6}$

↓ ↓

$\square - \square = \square$ ← **Round each mixed number. Then subtract.**

CA Standards Check

1. Use benchmarks to estimate.

 a. $\frac{3}{10} + \frac{7}{9}$

 b. $\frac{3}{5} - \frac{1}{8}$

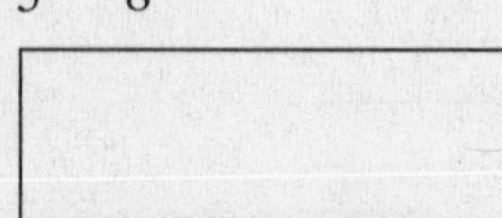

2. Marsha bought $1\frac{3}{8}$ lb of snow peas and $3\frac{1}{10}$ lb of carrots at the market. About how many more pounds of carrots did she buy?

Name ______________________ Class ______________ Date ______________

Examples

❸ Estimating With Mixed Numbers Estimate the product $6\frac{1}{8} \cdot 6\frac{5}{8}$.

$6\frac{1}{8} \cdot 6\frac{5}{8}$

↓ ↓

$\square \cdot \square = 42$ ← **Round each mixed number. Then multiply.**

❹ Estimating With Compatible Numbers Estimate the quotient $26\frac{1}{4} \div 8\frac{2}{3}$.

$26\frac{1}{4} \div 8\frac{2}{3}$

↓ ↓

$\square \div \square = 3$ ← **Use ______ numbers.**
Use ☐ for $26\frac{1}{4}$ and use ☐ for $8\frac{2}{3}$

CA Standards Check

3. Use rounding to estimate each product.

a. $3\frac{5}{6} \cdot 5\frac{1}{8}$

b. $8\frac{1}{8} \cdot 5\frac{11}{12}$

c. $7\frac{1}{3} \cdot 1\frac{13}{16}$

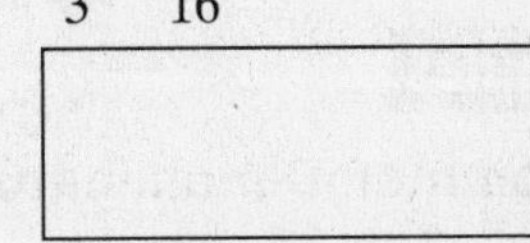

4. Use compatible numbers to estimate each quotient.

a. $35\frac{3}{4} \div 5\frac{11}{12}$

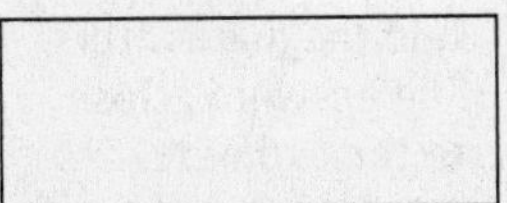

b. $22\frac{7}{8} \div 3\frac{5}{6}$

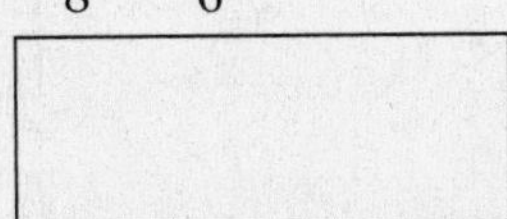

c. $46\frac{2}{5} \div 5\frac{1}{10}$

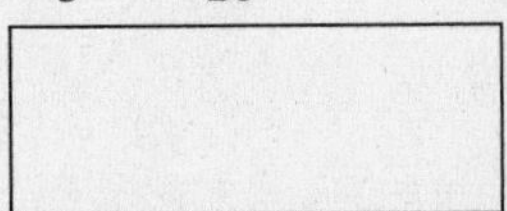

Name ________________ Class ________________ Date ________________

Lesson 3-2

Adding and Subtracting Fractions

Lesson Objective	**California Content Standards**
To add and subtract fractions and to solve problems involving fractions	NS 2.1, NS 2.4 (key), MR 2.1

Take Note

Adding and Subtracting Fractions

You can use models to add or subtract fractions with different denominators. The models below show

$\frac{1}{4} + \frac{1}{3} = \frac{\square}{\square}$ and $\frac{1}{2} - \frac{1}{3} = \frac{\square}{\square}$.

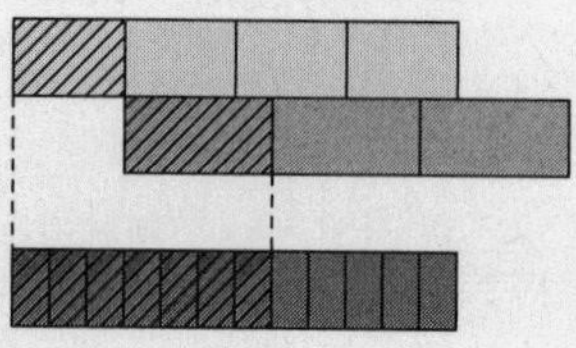

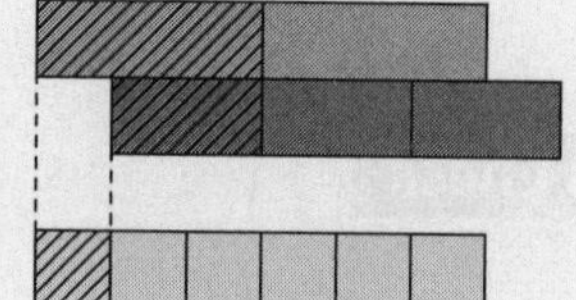

Examples

1 Common Denominators Find $\frac{2}{7} + \frac{3}{7}$.

Estimate $\frac{2}{7} + \frac{3}{7} \approx \square + \frac{\square}{\square}$, or $\frac{1}{2}$

$\frac{2}{7} + \frac{3}{7} = \frac{\square + \square}{\square}$ ← **Keep the denominator the same.**

$= \frac{\square}{\square}$ ← **Add the numerators. The answer is close to the estimate.**

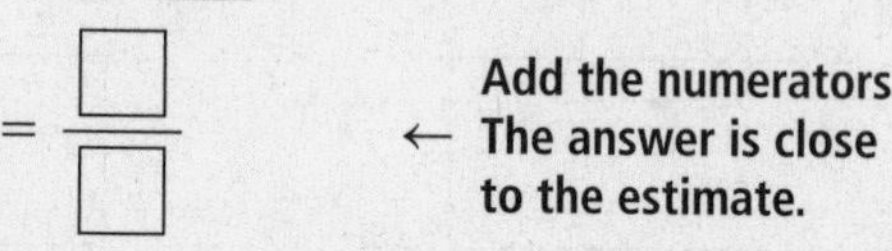

2 Different Denominators Find $\frac{5}{9} + \frac{1}{6}$.

Estimate $\frac{5}{9} + \frac{1}{6} \approx \frac{\square}{\square} + \square$, or $\frac{1}{2}$

$\frac{5}{9} = \frac{5 \cdot \square}{9 \cdot \square} = \frac{\square}{\square}$ ← **The LCD is $\square$. Write an equivalent fraction.**

$+\frac{1}{6} = \frac{1 \cdot \square}{6 \cdot \square} = +\frac{\square}{\square}$ ← **Write an equivalent fraction.**

$\frac{\square}{\square}$ ← **Add the numerators. The answer is close to the estimate.**

Name ____________________ Class ____________ Date ____________

❸ Application A carpenter begins with a board that is $\frac{3}{4}$ in. thick. She removes $\frac{1}{16}$ in. from its thickness. How thick is the board now?

Estimate $\frac{3}{4} - \frac{1}{16} \approx \frac{\square}{\square} - \square$, or $\frac{3}{4}$.

$\frac{3}{4} = \frac{3 \cdot \square}{4 \cdot \square} = \frac{\square}{\square}$ ← **The LCD is** $\square$. **Write an equivalent fraction.**

$-\frac{1}{16} = -\frac{\square}{\square} = -\frac{\square}{\square}$ ← **Write an equivalent fraction.**

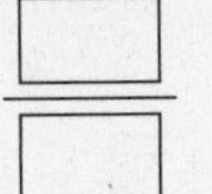

$\frac{\square}{\square}$ ← **Subtract the numerators.**

The board is now $\frac{\square}{\square}$ in. thick.

Check for Reasonableness The answer $\frac{\square}{\square}$ is close to the estimate $\frac{\square}{\square}$.

CA Standards Check

1. Find each sum or difference.

a. $\frac{3}{5} + \frac{1}{5}$ **b.** $\frac{13}{16} - \frac{9}{16}$ **c.** $\frac{1}{4} + \frac{3}{4}$

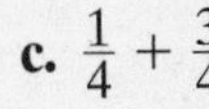

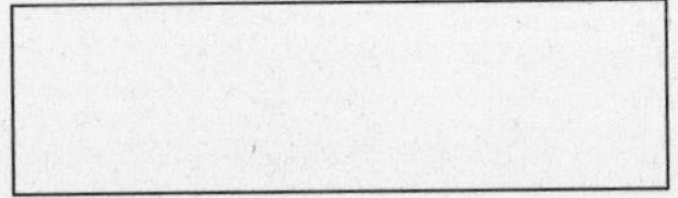

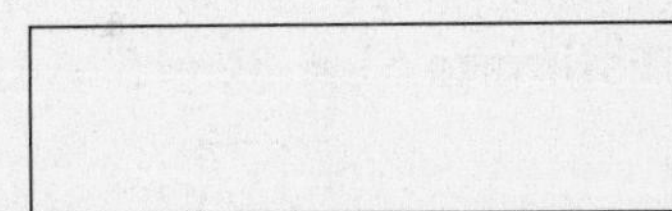

2. Find each sum or difference.

a. $\frac{3}{4} - \frac{1}{6}$ **b.** $\frac{3}{7} + \frac{5}{14}$ **c.** $\frac{1}{4} + \frac{7}{12}$

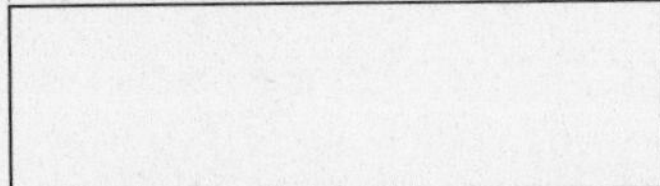

3. You hiked $\frac{5}{8}$ mi and $\frac{1}{4}$ mi in the afternoon. How far did you hike?

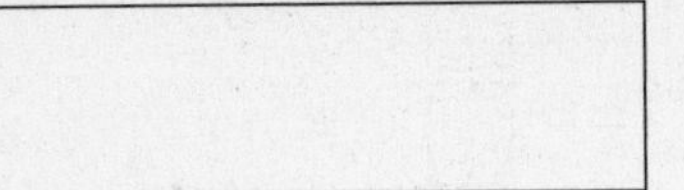

Name ______________ Class ______________ Date ______________

Lesson 3-3

Adding and Subtracting Mixed Numbers

Lesson Objective	**California Content Standards**
To add and subtract mixed numbers and to solve problems involving mixed numbers	NS 2.0, NS 2.4

Examples

1 Same Denominators You are training for a race. You run $2\frac{3}{5}$ mi in the morning and $1\frac{4}{5}$ mi in the afternoon. What is your total mileage?

$2\frac{3}{5} + 1\frac{4}{5} = \square\,\frac{7}{5}$ ← **Add the fractions. Add the whole numbers.**

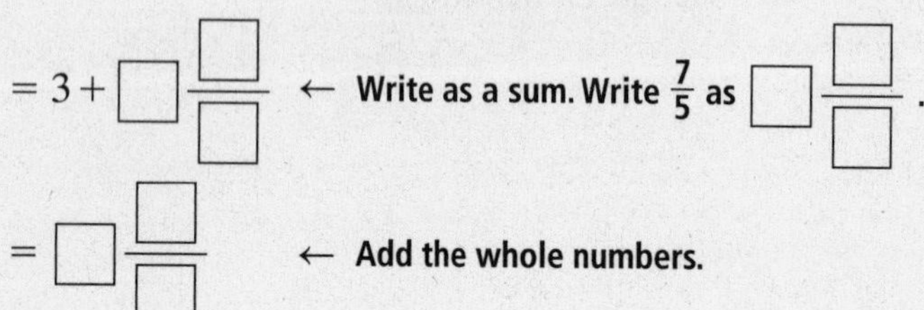

$= 3 + \square\,\frac{\square}{\square}$ ← **Write as a sum. Write $\frac{7}{5}$ as $\square\,\frac{\square}{\square}$.**

$= \square\,\frac{\square}{\square}$ ← **Add the whole numbers.**

Your total mileage is $\square\,\frac{\square}{\square}$ mi.

2 Different Denominators Find $5\frac{1}{2} + 3\frac{2}{3}$.

Estimate $5\frac{1}{2} + 3\frac{2}{3} \approx 5 + 4$, or 9

$5\frac{1}{2} = 5\frac{\square}{\square}$ ← **The LCD is $\square$. Write an equivalent fraction.**

$+3\frac{2}{3} = +\,3\frac{\square}{\square}$ ← **Write an equivalent fraction.**

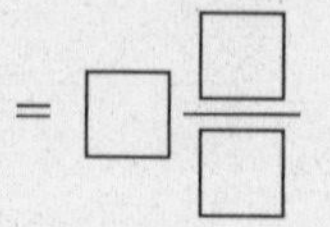

$= \square\,\frac{\square}{\square}$ ← **Add the fractions. Add the whole numbers.**

$= 8 + \square\,\frac{\square}{\square}$ ← **Write the mixed number as a sum. Write $\frac{7}{6}$ as $\square\,\frac{\square}{\square}$.**

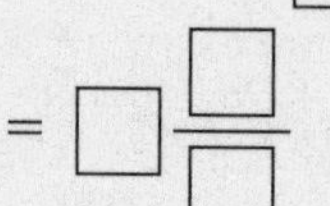

$= \square\,\frac{\square}{\square}$ ← **Add the whole numbers.**

Check for Reasonableness The answer $\square\,\frac{\square}{\square}$ is close to the estimate 9. The answer is reasonable.

Name ______________________ Class ______________ Date ______________

3 Subtracting With Renaming You bought $6\frac{1}{4}$ ft of rope and used $4\frac{3}{8}$ ft. How many feet of rope did you have left?

Find $6\frac{1}{4}$ ☐ $4\frac{3}{8}$.

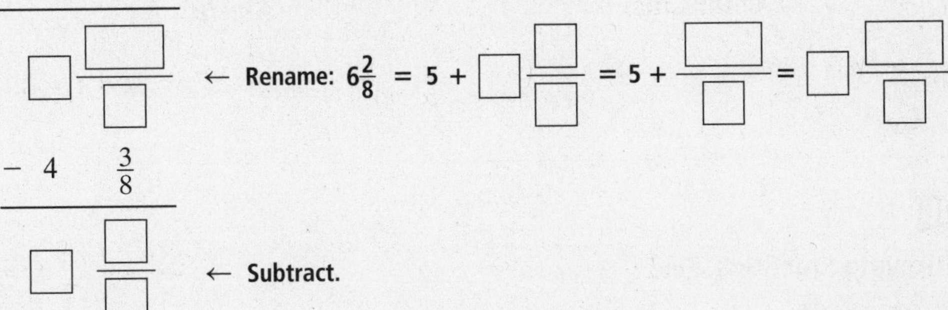

You have ☐ $\frac{☐}{☐}$ feet of rope left.

CA Standards Check

1. Find each sum or difference.

a. $1\frac{2}{3} + 2\frac{2}{3}$

b. $1\frac{2}{5} + 3\frac{2}{5}$

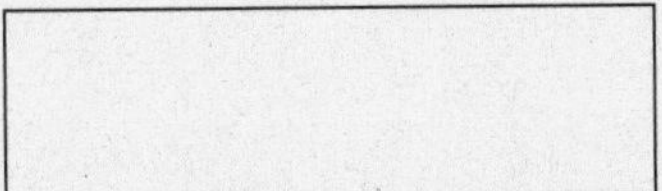

c. $5\frac{1}{2} - 4\frac{1}{2}$

2. Find each sum or difference.

a. $2\frac{3}{4} - 1\frac{3}{4}$

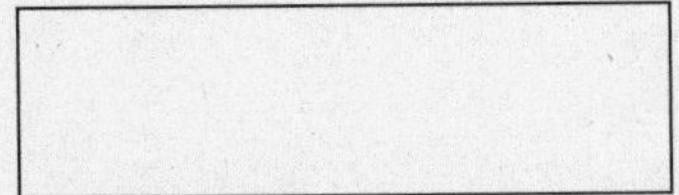

b. $3\frac{1}{6} + 8\frac{7}{8}$

c. $6\frac{1}{2} - 2\frac{1}{5}$

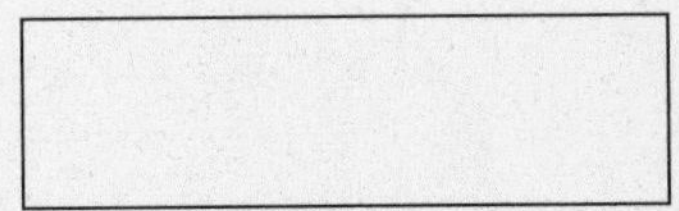

3. Your friend bought $4\frac{1}{3}$ ft of gift wrap and used $2\frac{5}{6}$ ft to wrap a gift. How many feet of gift wrap did your friend have left?

Name ______________________ Class ______________ Date ______________

Lesson 3-4

Multiplying Fractions and Mixed Numbers

Lesson Objective	California Content Standards
To multiply fractions and mixed numbers and to solve problems by multiplying	NS 2.1, NS 2.2

Take Note

Multiplying Fractions

Arithmetic	Algebra
$\frac{1}{3} \cdot \frac{1}{2} = \frac{\square}{\square} = \frac{1}{6}$	$\frac{a}{b} \cdot \frac{c}{d} = \frac{\square}{\square}$, $b \neq 0$ and $d \neq 0$.

Example

1 Multiplying Fractions Find $\frac{3}{5} \cdot \frac{5}{6}$.

$\frac{3}{5} \cdot \frac{5}{6} = \frac{\square \cdot \square}{5 \cdot 6}$ ← **Multiply the numerators. Multiply the denominators.**

$= \frac{\square}{\square}$ ← **Find the two products.**

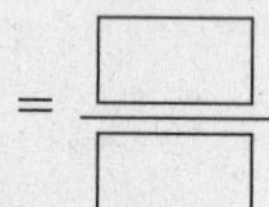

$= \frac{\square}{\square}$ ← **Simplify.**

CA Standards Check

1. a. Find $\frac{3}{5} \cdot \frac{1}{4}$. **b.** Find $\frac{5}{6} \cdot \frac{4}{5}$. **c.** Find $\frac{2}{3} \cdot \frac{4}{5}$.

Name ____________________ Class ____________________ Date ____________________

Examples

2 Multiplying by a Whole Number Ebony biked 12 miles on Saturday. Kate biked $\frac{2}{3}$ of Ebony's distance. How far did Kate bike?

Find $\frac{2}{3}$ of 12 miles, or $\frac{2}{3} \cdot 12$.

$\frac{2}{3} \cdot 12 = \frac{2}{3} \cdot \frac{12}{\square}$ ← **Write 12 as $\frac{12}{1}$.**

$= \frac{2}{\not{3}_{\square}} \cdot \frac{\not{12}^{\square}}{1}$ ← **Simplify before multiplying.**

$= \frac{8}{1}$ ← **Multiply the numerators. Multiply the denominators.**

$= \square$ ← **Simplify. Kate biked $\square$ miles.**

3 Multiplying Mixed Numbers Find $5\frac{1}{2} \cdot 3\frac{1}{3}$.

Estimate $5\frac{1}{2} \cdot 3\frac{1}{3} \approx \square \cdot \square$, or $\square$

$5\frac{1}{2} \cdot 3\frac{1}{3} = \frac{\square}{2} \cdot \frac{\square}{3}$ ← **Write the mixed numbers as improper fractions.**

$= \frac{\square \cdot \square}{2 \cdot 3}$ ← **Multiply the numerators. Multiply the denominators.**

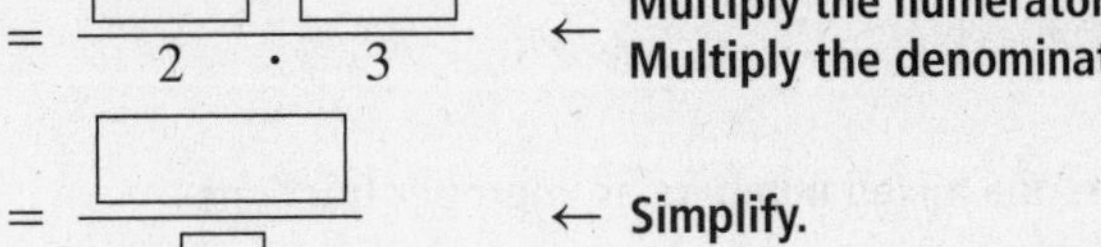

$= \frac{\square}{\square}$ ← **Simplify.**

$= \frac{\square}{\square}$ ← **Simplify.**

$= \square\frac{\square}{\square}$ ← **Write as a mixed number.**

Check for Reasonableness $\square\frac{\square}{\square}$ is close to the estimate $\square$.

CA Standards Check

2. There are 168 members in an orchestra, and $\frac{3}{8}$ of them play the violin. How many members play the violin?

3. a. Find $2\frac{1}{3} \cdot 4\frac{5}{8}$. **b.** Find $3\frac{3}{5} \cdot 1\frac{3}{10}$. **c.** Find $5\frac{3}{4} \cdot 2\frac{5}{8}$.

Name ______________________ Class ______________ Date ____________

Lesson 3-5

Dividing Fractions and Mixed Numbers

Lesson Objective	California Content Standards
To divide fractions and mixed numbers to solve problems	NS 2.1, NS 2.2

Take Note

Dividing by Fractions

Arithmetic

$3 \div \frac{3}{4} = 3 \cdot \frac{\square}{\square} = 4$

Algebra

$\frac{a}{b} \div \frac{c}{d} = \frac{a}{b} \cdot \frac{\square}{\square}$ for b, c and $d \neq 0$.

Two numbers are reciprocals if ____

____

Examples

1 Dividing Mixed Numbers Find $4\frac{2}{3} \div 1\frac{3}{4}$.

$4\frac{2}{3} \div 1\frac{3}{4} = \frac{\square}{\square} \div \frac{\square}{\square}$ ← **Write the mixed numbers as improper fractions.**

$= \frac{14}{3} \cdot \frac{\square}{\square}$ ← **Multiply by $\frac{\square}{\square}$, the $\square$ of $\frac{7}{4}$.**

$= \frac{\overset{\square}{\cancel{14}} \cdot 4}{3 \cdot \underset{\square}{\cancel{7}}}$ ← **Divide 14 and 7 by their GCD, $\square$.**

$= \frac{\square}{\square}$ ← **Multiply.**

$= \square\frac{\square}{\square}$ ← **Write as a mixed number.**

Name ______________________ Class ______________ Date ______________

❷ Application You have a piece of fabric that is $12\frac{1}{2}$ ft long. You need to cut it into strips that are $1\frac{1}{4}$ ft long. How many strips will you have?

To find how many $1\frac{1}{4}$-ft long strips are in $12\frac{1}{2}$ ft, divide $\square\frac{\square}{\square}$

by 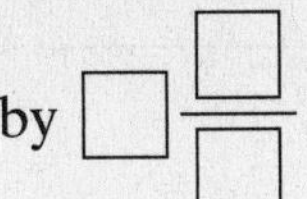.

Estimate $12\frac{1}{2} \div 1\frac{1}{4} \approx \square \div \square$, or $\square$

$12\frac{1}{2} \div 1\frac{1}{4} = \frac{\square}{\square} \div \frac{\square}{\square}$ ← **Write the mixed numbers as improper fractions.**

$= \frac{25}{2} \cdot \frac{\square}{\square}$ ← **Multiply by $\frac{\square}{\square}$, the reciprocal of $\frac{5}{4}$.**

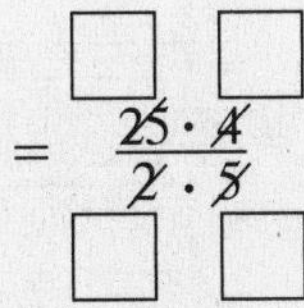

$= \frac{25 \cdot 4}{2 \cdot 5}$ ← **Divide 25 and 5 by their GCD, $\square$. Divide 4 and 2 by their GCD, $\square$.**

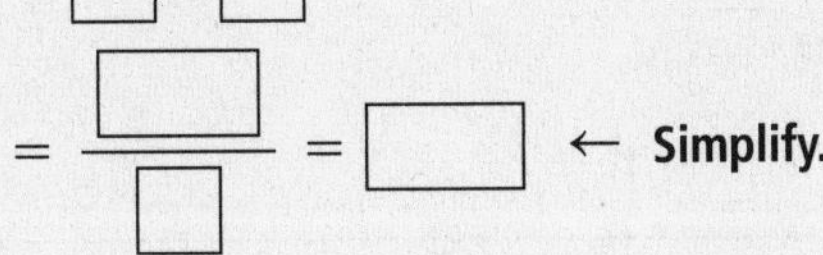

$= \frac{\square}{\square} = \square$ ← **Simplify.**

There are $\square$ $1\frac{1}{4}$-ft strips of fabric in $12\frac{1}{2}$ ft.

Check for Reasonableness $\square$ is close to $\square$. The answer is reasonable.

CA Standards Check

1. a. Find $5\frac{3}{4} \div 3\frac{2}{3}$.

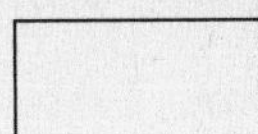

b. Find $4\frac{1}{8} \div 5\frac{1}{2}$.

c. Find $3\frac{9}{16} \div 3$.

2. One can of iced tea holds 12 fl oz. A 2-liter bottle holds $67\frac{3}{5}$ fl oz. How many cans of iced tea will you need to fill a 2-liter bottle?

Name ______________________ Class ______________________ Date ______________________

Lesson 3-6

Changing Units in the Customary System

Lesson Objective	California Content Standards
To change units in the customary system	AF 2.1

Take Note

Customary Units of Measure

Type	Length	Capacity	Weight
Unit	inch (in.) foot (ft) yard (yd) mile (mi)	fluid ounce (fl oz) cup (c) pint (pt) quart (qt) gallon (gal)	ounce (oz) pound (lb) ton (t)
Equivalents	1 ft = ☐ in. 1 yd = ☐ ft 1 mi = ☐ ft	1 c = ☐ fl oz 1 pt = ☐ c 1 qt = ☐ pt 1 gal = ☐ qt	1 lb = ☐ oz 1 t = ☐ lb

Examples

❶ **Changing Units of Length** A carpenter cuts a piece 4 ft 10 in. long from an 8-ft board. What is the length in feet of the remaining piece?

You need to subtract ☐ from ☐ ft.

$4 \text{ ft } 10 \text{ in.} = 4\frac{\square}{\square} \text{ ft} = 4\frac{\square}{\square} \text{ ft}$ ← **Write 10 in. as a fraction of a foot.**

$8 - 4\frac{\square}{\square} = 7\frac{\square}{\square} - 4\frac{\square}{\square}$ ← **Rename 8 as $7\frac{\square}{\square}$.**

$= \square\frac{\square}{\square}$ ← **Subtract.**

The remaining piece is $\square\frac{\square}{\square}$ ft long.

❷ Changing Units of Capacity How many 2-cup servings are in a 36-fluid-ounce sports drink bottle?

First find the number of fluid ounces in 2 cups. Since there are 8 fluid ounces in 1 cup, you know there are ☐ ounces in 2 cups.

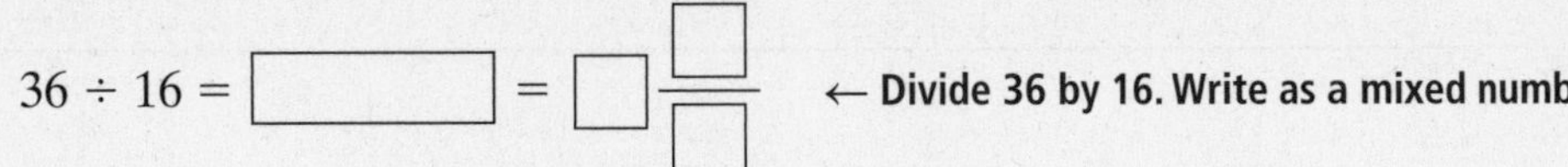

$36 \div 16 =$ ☐ $=$ ☐ $\frac{☐}{☐}$ ← **Divide 36 by 16. Write as a mixed number.**

There are ☐ $\frac{☐}{☐}$ servings in a 36-fl oz of sports drink bottle.

❸ Changing Units of Weight Which weighs more, a $1\frac{3}{4}$-lb book or a 24-oz catalog?

Think of the relationship between pounds and ☐.   1 lb = ☐ oz (× ☐)

To change $1\frac{3}{4}$ lb to ounces, multiply $1\frac{3}{4}$ by ☐.

$1\frac{3}{4} \cdot 16 = \frac{7 \cdot \cancel{16}^{☐}}{\cancel{4}_{☐} \cdot 1}$ ← **Write $1\frac{3}{4}$ as a(n) ☐ fraction.**

$=$ ☐

The $1\frac{3}{4}$-lb book weighs ☐ oz. It is ☐ than the 24-oz catalog.

CA Standards Check

1. How much shorter than a board 10 ft long is a board 8 ft 5 in. long?

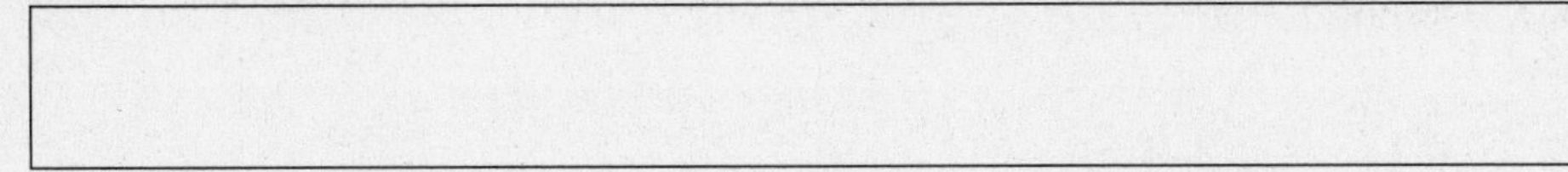

2. How many 1-cup servings are in 50 fluid ounces of juice?

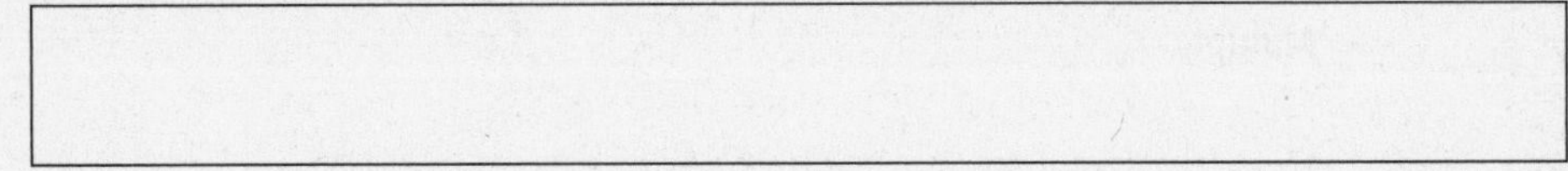

3. Find the number of ounces in $4\frac{5}{8}$ lb.

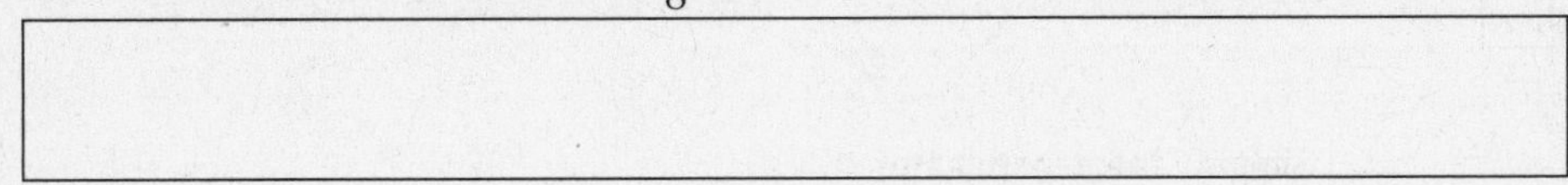

Name ______________________ Class ______________ Date ______________

Lesson 4-1

Evaluating and Writing Algebraic Expressions

Lesson Objective	California Content Standards
To write and evaluate algebraic expressions	AF 1.0, AF 1.2

Vocabulary

A variable is ____

____

An algebraic expression is ____

____

Examples

1 Writing Algebraic Expressions Write an algebraic expression for each word phrase.

a. 6 less than d dollars [ ]

b. the sum of s students and 9 students [ ]

c. 12 times b boxes [ ]

d. 20 hours of work divided equally among w workers [ ]

2 Evaluating Algebraic Expressions Evaluate each expression. Use the values $r = 8$, $s = 1$, and $t = 3$.

a. $6(t - 1)$

$6(t - 1) = 6(\square - 1)$ ← **Substitute.**

$= 6(\square)$ ← **Subtract.**

$= \square$ ← **Multiply.**

b. $\frac{r}{s + t}$

$\frac{r}{s + t} = \frac{\square}{\square + \square}$ ← **Substitute.**

$= \frac{\square}{\square}$ ← **Simplify the denominator.**

$= \square$ ← **Divide.**

3 Application The cost of a package of markers is d dollars. Write an algebraic expression for the total cost in dollars of 7 packages of markers.

a. **Words** number of packages times cost per package

Let d = cost per package.

Expression ☐ · ☐

An algebraic expression for the total cost in dollars is ☐.

b. Suppose that each package of these markers costs \$3.75, and suppose that packages of colored pencils cost \$2.20 each. Write and evaluate the expression to find the total cost of 7 packages of markers and 6 packages of colored pencils.

Let p = cost per package of colored pencils

$7m$ + ☐ = 7(☐) + 6(☐) ← **Substitute 3.75 for *m* and 2.20 for *p*.**

= ☐ + ☐ ← **Multiply.**

= ☐ ← **Add.**

The total cost of the materials will be ☐.

CA Standards Check

1. Write an expression for each word phrase.

a. a temperature of t degrees increased by 5 degrees

b. a price p decreased by 16

c. the product of 5 and n nickels

2. Use the values $n = 3, t = 5$, and $y = 7$ to evaluate $(n + t) \cdot y$.

3. a. A group of friends go out to lunch; n people buy sandwiches and m people buy salads. Each sandwich costs \$4.50 and each salad costs \$5. Write an expression for the total cost of the sandwiches and salads.

b. Use the expression you wrote in Part (a) to find the total cost if 6 people buy sandwiches and 3 people buy salads.

Name ______________________ Class ______________ Date ____________

Lesson 4-2

Using Number Sense to Solve Equations

Lesson Objective	California Content Standards
To solve one-step equations using number sense	AF 1.1

Vocabulary

An equation is ______________________

An open sentence is ______________________

A solution of an equation is ______________________

Example

1 Solving Equations Using Substitution Find the solution of $h - 18 = 54$ from the numbers 3, 36, 62, and 72. You can test each number by substituting for h in the equation.

$3 - 18 \stackrel{?}{=} 54$

$\square = 54$ False

$36 - 18 \stackrel{?}{=} 54$

$18 = 54$ $\square$

$62 - 18 \stackrel{?}{=} 54$

$\square = 54$ $\square$

$72 - 18 \stackrel{?}{=} 54$

$\square = 54$ $\square$

Since the equation is ☐ when you substitute ☐ for ☐, the solution is ☐.

CA Standards Check

1. Find the solution of each equation from the given numbers.

a. $24n = 120$; 3, 5, or 11

b. $124p = 992$; 4, 6, or 8

Name ______________ Class ______________ Date ______________

Examples

❷ Solving Equations Using Mental Math Use mental math to solve each equation.

a. $s - 9 = 5$

What You Think

What number minus ☐ equals ☐?

Since ☐ $- 9 = 5$,

$s =$ ☐.

b. $4z = 28$

What You Think

What number times ☐ equals ☐?

Since $4 \cdot$ ☐ $= 28$,

$z =$ ☐.

❸ Estimating Solutions The weight of a packing crate is 14.65 lb. The crate and its contents together weigh 85.21 lb. Which is the best estimate of the weight of the contents?

A. about 70 lb **B.** about 80 lb

C. about 100 lb **D.** about 110 lb

Words	crate's weight	plus	contents' weight	equals	total weight

Let c = the weight of the contents.

Equation	☐	+	☐	=	☐

$14.65 + c = 85.21$

$14.65 \approx 15 \quad 85.21 \approx 85$ ← **Choose compatible numbers.**

$15 + c = 85$ ← **What number added to 15 is 85?**

$c = 70$ ← **Use mental math.**

The contents of the crate weigh about ☐ lb. The correct answer is choice ☐.

CA Standards Check

2. Use mental math to solve each equation.

a. $t - 3 = 7$ ☐

b. $7x = -63$ ☐

c. $n + 6 = -10.1$ ☐

3. A box of machine parts weighs 14.7 lb. A forklift has a maximum weight limit of 390 lb. About how many boxes of parts can the forklift carry at one time?

☐

Name ______________ Class ______________ Date ______________

Lesson 4-3

Solving Equations by Adding

Lesson Objective	California Content Standards
To solve one-step equations using addition	AF 1.0, AF 1.1

Take Note

Addition Property of Equality

If you ☐ the same value to each side of an equation, the two sides remain ☐.

Arithmetic	Algebra
$\frac{20}{2} = 10$,	If $a = b$,
so $\frac{20}{2} + 3 = 10 + \square$.	then $a + c = b + \square$

Inverse operations are ______________

Example

1 Solving Equations by Adding Solve $t - 58 = 71$. Check your solution.

$t - 58 = 71$

$t - 58 + \square = 71 + 58$ ← ☐ **Property of Equality:** **Add** ☐ **to each side.**

$t + \square = 129$ ← **The numbers 58 and −58 are** ☐.

$t = 129$ ← ☐ **Property**

Check ☐ ← **Check the solution in the original equation.**

$\square - 58 \stackrel{?}{=} 71$ ← **Substitute 129 for *t*.**

$\square = 71$ ← **Subtract.**

CA Standards Check

1. Solve the equation $x - 104 = 64$.

☐

Name ______________________ Class ______________ Date ____________

Example

❷ A pair of shoes costs \$11.35 more than a pair of jeans. The pair of shoes costs \$49. How much does the pair of jeans cost?

Words ☐ is ☐ more than ☐.

↓

Equation

Let j = the cost of the pair of jeans.

$\square = 11.35 + \square$

$49 = 11.35 + j$ ← **Write the equation.**

$49 - \square = 11.35 - \square + j$ ← **Subtract 11.35 from each side.**

$\square = j$ ← **Simplify.**

The pair of jeans cost ☐.

CA Standards Check

2. The temperature dropped 9°F between 7 P.M. and midnight. It was 54°F at midnight. Write and solve an equation to find the temperature at 7 P.M.

☐

Lesson 4-4

Solving Equations by Subtracting

Lesson Objective	California Content Standards
To solve one step equations using subtraction	AF 1.1 🔑, MR 3.0

Take Note

Subtraction Property of Equality

If you ☐ the same value from each side of an equation, the two sides remain ☐.

Arithmetic	Algebra
$\frac{12}{2} = 6$,	If $a = b$,
so $\frac{12}{2} - 4 = 6 - \square$.	then $a - c = b - \square$.

Examples

1 Solving Equations by Subtracting Solve $q + 77 = 129$.

$q + 77 = 129$

$q + 77 - \square = 129 - \square$ ← **Subtract ☐ from each side using the Subtraction Property of Equality.**

$q = \square$ ← **Simplify.**

Check $q + 77 = 129$ ← **Check the solution in the original equation.**

$\square + 77 = 129$ ← **Substitute ☐ for *q*.**

$\square = 71$ ← **Add.**

Name ______________________ Class ______________ Date ______________

❷ **Application** Your friend purchased a DVD and a CD. The DVD cost \$6 more than the CD. The DVD cost \$22. How much did the CD cost?

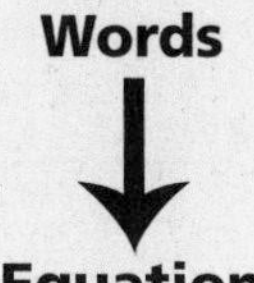

Words ______ is \$6 more than ______.

Let c = the cost of the CD.

Equation ______ $= 6 +$ ______

$$22 = 6 + c$$

$22 -$ ______ $= 6 -$ ______ $+ c$ ← **Subtract** ______ **from each side.**

______ $= c$ ← **Simplify.**

The CD cost ______.

CA Standards Check

1. Solve each equation.

a. $b + 58 = 93$ **b.** $g + 12 = 35$ **c.** $31 = t + 18$

  ______

2. A hardcover book costs \$19 more than its paperback edition.
The hardcover book costs \$26.95. How much does the paperback cost?

______

Name ______________________ Class ______________ Date ______________

Lesson 4-5

Solving Equations by Multiplying

Lesson Objective	**California Content Standards**
To solve one step equations using multiplication	AF 1.1, AF 2.3, MR 2.7

Take Note

Multiplication Property of Equality

If you ______ each side of an equation by the same number, the two sides remain ______.

Multiplication is the inverse operation of division. When a variable is divided by a number, you can use multiplication to undo the division.

Arithmetic	**Algebra**
$\frac{12}{2} = 6$, so $\frac{12}{2} \cdot 2 = 6 \cdot \square$.	If $a = b$, then $a \cdot c = b \cdot \square$.

Multiplication Undoes Division

$\frac{3}{5} \cdot 5 = 3 \qquad \frac{n}{3} \cdot 3 = n$

Examples

1 Solving Equations by Multiplying Solve $\frac{m}{-3} = 27$.

$\frac{m}{-3} = 27$ ← **Notice that m is ______ by −3.**

$\square \cdot \frac{m}{-3} = \square \cdot 27$ ← **______ each side by ______.**

$m = -81$ ← **Simplify.**

Name ______________________ Class ______________ Date ______________

Example

❷ Application Suppose you and your sister go bicycling at a steady rate of 18 miles per hour. You ride your bicycles for 1.4 hours. How far do you travel in miles?

The equation $\frac{d}{t} = r$ relates distance d, rate r, and time t.

$$\frac{d}{t} = r$$

$$\frac{d}{1.4} = 18 \qquad \leftarrow \textbf{Substitute 1.4 for } t\textbf{, and 18 for } r\textbf{.}$$

$$\square \cdot \frac{d}{1.4} = \square \cdot 18 \qquad \leftarrow \textbf{Multiply both sides by } \square\textbf{.}$$

$$d = \square \qquad \leftarrow \textbf{Simplify.}$$

You and your sister travel ______ miles.

CA Standards Check

1. Solve each equation. Check your answer.

a. $\frac{w}{26} = -15$

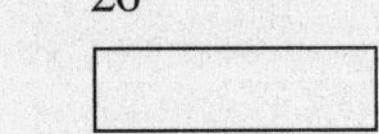

b. $\frac{y}{-9} = 17$

______

2. a. A train travels at an average rate of 72 miles per hour. How far has the train traveled after 1.25 hours?

______

b. Reasoning In Example 2, would you get a different answer if you used the equation $\frac{d}{r} = t$? Explain.

______

3. Solve each equation. Check your answer.

a. $\frac{7}{8}x = 42$

______

b. $\frac{3}{5}p = 48$

______

Name ______________________ Class ______________ Date ______________

Lesson 4-6

Solving Equations by Dividing

Lesson Objective	California Content Standards
To solve one-step equations using division	AF 1.1

Take Note

Division Property of Equality

If you ______ each side of an equation by the same nonzero number, the two sides remain ______.

Arithmetic

Since $3(2) = 6$,

$\frac{3(2)}{2} = \frac{6}{\square}$.

Algebra

If $a = b$ and $c \neq 0$

then $\frac{a}{c} = \frac{b}{\square}$.

Division is the inverse operation of multiplication. When a variable is multiplied by a number, you can use division to undo the multiplication.

Division Undoes Multiplication

$(4 \cdot 9) \div 4 = 9$

$5x \div 5 = x$

Examples

1 Solving Equations by Dividing Solve $-3j = 44.7$. Check your solution.

$-3j = 44.7$ ← Notice j is being ______ by −3.

$\frac{-3j}{\square} = \frac{44.7}{\square}$ ← ______ each side by ______ to get j alone.

$j =$ ______ ← Simplify.

Check ______ ← Check your solution in the original equation.

$-3(\square) \stackrel{?}{=} 44.7$ ← Replace j with ______.

$\square = 44.7$ ✓ ← The solution checks.

2 Application The Art Club must buy 84 pieces of poster board. There are 6 pieces of poster board in a package. How many packages of poster board must the Art Club buy?

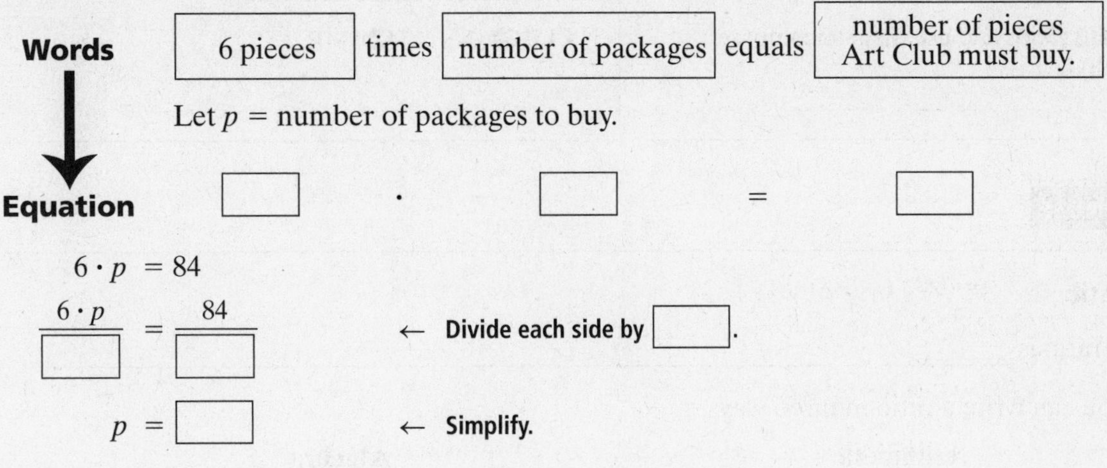

$6 \cdot p = 84$

$\frac{6 \cdot p}{\square} = \frac{84}{\square}$ ← **Divide each side by** ☐.

$p = \square$ ← **Simplify.**

The Art Club must buy ☐ packages of poster board.

CA Standards Check

1. Solve each equation. Check your answer.

a. $3x = -21.6$ ☐

b. $-12y = -108$ ☐

c. $104x = 312$ ☐

2. Suppose you and four friends go to a baseball game. The total cost for five tickets is $110. Write and solve an equation to find the cost of one ticket.

☐

Name ______________________ Class ______________ Date ______________

Lesson 5-1

Ratios

Lesson Objective	**California Content Standards**
To write ratios and use them to compare quantities	NS 1.0, NS 1.2, MR 2.5

Take Note

Ratio

A ratio is ______________________________

You can write a ratio in three ways.

	Arithmetic			**Algebra**	
5 to 7	☐	☐/☐	☐	$a : b$	☐/☐, where $b \neq 0$

Equivalent ratios are ______________________________

Example

1 Writing Ratios There are 7 red stripes and 6 white stripes on the flag of the United States. Write the ratio of red stripes to white stripes in three ways.

red stripes → ☐ ← white stripes

red stripes → ☐ ← white stripes

☐ ← red stripes

☐ ← white stripes

CA Standards Check

1. Write each ratio in three ways. Use the pattern of piano keys shown at the right.

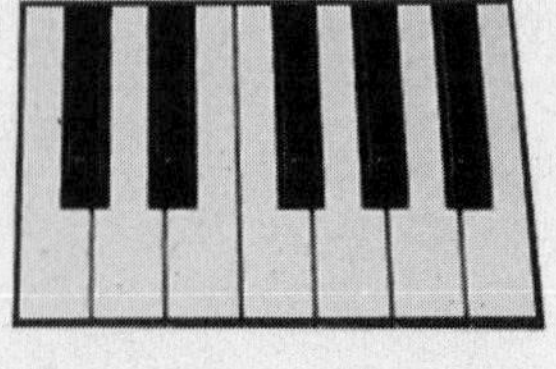

a. white keys to all keys

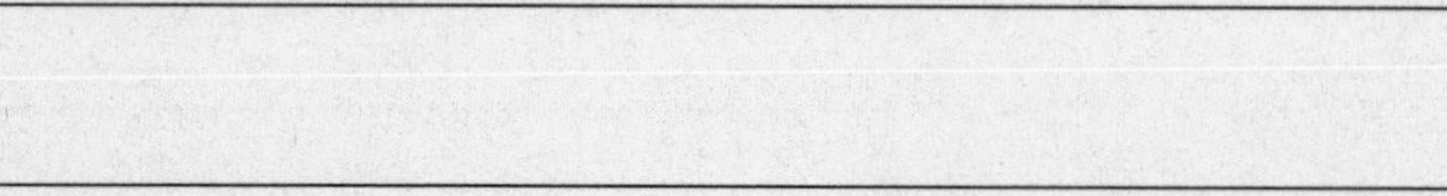

b. black keys to white keys

Name ______________ Class ______________ Date ______________

Examples

2 Writing Equivalent Ratios Find a ratio equivalent to $\frac{14}{4}$.

$$\frac{14 \div \square}{4 \div \square} = \frac{\square}{\square}$$ ← **Divide the numerator and denominator by 2.**

3 Writing Equivalent Ratios Write the ratio 2 lb to 56 oz as a fraction in simplest form.

$$\frac{2 \text{ lb}}{56 \text{ oz}} = \frac{2 \times 16 \text{ oz}}{56 \text{ oz}}$$ ← **There are 16 oz in each pound.**

$$= \frac{\square \text{ oz}}{56 \text{ oz}}$$ ← **Multiply.**

$$= \frac{\square \div \square \text{ oz}}{56 \div \square \text{ oz}}$$ ← **Divide by the GCF, $\square$ oz.**

$$= \frac{\square}{\square}$$ ← **Simplify.**

4 Comparing Ratios The ratio of girls to boys enrolled at King Middle School is 15 : 16. There are 195 girls and 208 boys in Grade 8. Is the ratio of girls to boys in Grade 8 equivalent to the ratio of girls to boys in the entire school?

Entire School		**Grade 8**
$\square$ ←	**girls**	→ $\square$
$\square$ ←	**boys**	→ $\square$

$\frac{\square}{\square} = \square$ ← **Write as a decimal.** → $\frac{\square}{\square} = \square$

Since the two decimals are ______, the ratio of girls to boys in Grade 8 is ______ the ratio of girls to boys in the entire school.

CA Standards Check

2. Find a ratio equivalent to $\frac{7}{9}$.

3. Write the ratio 3 gal to 10 qt as a fraction in simplest form.

4. Tell whether the ratios below are *equivalent* or *not equivalent*.

a. 7 : 3, 128 : 54 **b.** $\frac{180}{240}, \frac{25}{34}$ **c.** 6.1 to 7, 30.5 to 35

Name ______________________ Class ______________ Date ______________

Lesson 5-2

Unit Rates and Proportional Reasoning

Lesson Objective	California Content Standards
To find unit rates and unit costs using proportional reasoning	AF 2.1, AF 2.2

Vocabulary

A rate is ____

____

A unit rate is ____

A unit cost is ____

Examples

1 Finding a Unit Rate You earn \$33 for 4 hours of work. Find the unit rate of dollars per hour.

dollars → hours → $\frac{33}{4}$ = ☐ ← **Divide the first quantity by the second quantity.**

The unit rate is $\frac{☐}{☐}$, or ☐ per hour.

2 Using Unit Cost to Find Total Cost Use the unit cost to find the total cost of 7 yd of ribbon at \$.39 per yard.

Estimate $\$.39 \cdot 7 \approx \$.40 \cdot 7$, or \$2.80.

$\$.39 \cdot 7 =$ ☐ ← **unit cost · number of units = total cost**

The total cost of 7 yd of ribbon is ☐.

Check for Reasonableness The total cost of ☐ is close to the estimate of \$2.80. So, ☐ is reasonable.

CA Standards Check

1. Find the unit rate for 210 heartbeats in 3 minutes.

2. Dog food costs \$.35/lb. How much does a 20-lb bag cost?

Example

3 Using Unit Cost to Compare Find each unit cost. Which is the better buy?

3 lb of potatoes for \$.89

5 lb of potatoes for \$1.59

Divide to find the unit cost of each size.

cost → $\frac{\$.89}{3\text{ lb}} \approx$ ______
size →

cost → $\frac{\$1.59}{5\text{ lb}} \approx$ ______
size →

Since ______ < ______, ______ for ______ is the better buy.

CA Standards Check

3. Which bottle of apple juice is the better buy: 48 fl oz for \$3.05 or 64 fl oz for \$3.59?

Name ______________________ Class ______________ Date ____________

Lesson 5-3

Proportions

Lesson Objective	California Content Standards
To test whether ratios form a proportion	NS 1.2, NS 1.3

Take Note

Proportion

A proportion is ____

Arithmetic	**Algebra**
$\frac{6}{8} = \frac{9}{12}$	$\frac{a}{b} = \frac{c}{d}, b \neq 0, d \neq 0$

Cross Products Property

Cross products are ____

____

If two ratios form a proportion, the cross products are equal. If two ratios have equal cross products, they form a proportion.

Arithmetic	**Algebra**
$\frac{6}{8} = \frac{9}{12}$	$\frac{a}{b} = \frac{c}{d}$
$6 \cdot 12 = 8 \cdot 9$	$ad = bc$, where $b \neq 0$, and $d \neq 0$

Example

1 Writing Ratios in Simplest Form Do the ratios $\frac{42}{56}$ and $\frac{56}{64}$ form a proportion?

$\frac{42}{56} = \frac{42 \div \square}{56 \div \square} = \frac{\square}{\square}$ ← **Divide the numerator and denominator by the GCF.** → $\frac{56}{64} = \frac{56 \div \square}{64 \div \square} = \frac{\square}{\square}$

The ratios in simplest form are not equivalent. They ________ form a proportion.

CA Standards Check

1. Do $\frac{10}{12}$ and $\frac{40}{56}$ form a proportion?

Example

2 Using Cross Products Do the ratios in each pair form a proportion?

a. $\frac{4}{10}, \frac{6}{15}$ **b.** $\frac{8}{6}, \frac{9}{7}$

$\frac{4}{10} \stackrel{?}{=} \frac{6}{15}$ ← **Test each pair of ratios.** → $\frac{8}{6} \stackrel{?}{=} \frac{9}{7}$

$4 \cdot$ ☐ $\stackrel{?}{=} 10 \cdot$ ☐ ← **Write cross products.** → $8 \cdot$ ☐ $\stackrel{?}{=} 6 \cdot$ ☐

☐ ☐ 60 ← **Simplify.** → ☐ ☐ 54

☐, $\frac{4}{10}$ and $\frac{6}{15}$ ☐, $\frac{8}{6}$ and $\frac{9}{7}$

☐ a proportion. ☐ a proportion.

CA Standards Check

2. Determine whether the ratios form a proportion.

a. $\frac{3}{8}, \frac{6}{16}$

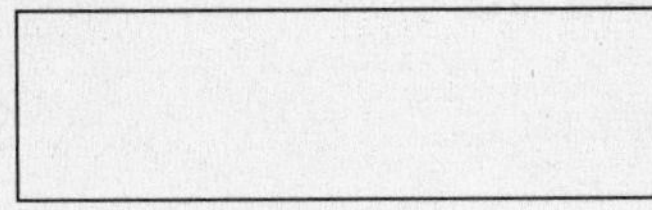

b. $\frac{6}{9}, \frac{4}{6}$

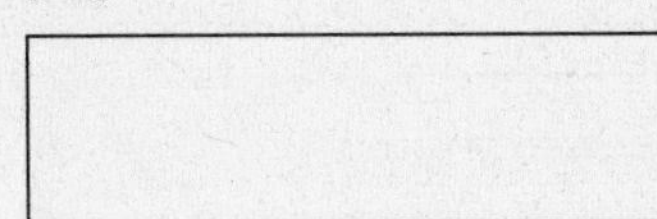

c. $\frac{4}{8}, \frac{5}{9}$

Name ______________________ Class ______________ Date ____________

Lesson 5-4

Solving Proportions

Lesson Objective	**California Content Standards**
To solve proportions using unit rates, mental math, and cross products	NS 1.3

Examples

1 Using Unit Rates The cost of 4 lightbulbs is $3. Use the information to find the cost of 10 lightbulbs.

Step 1 Find the unit price.

$\frac{3 \text{ dollars}}{4 \text{ lightbulbs}} = \$3 \div 4$ lightbulbs ← **Divide to find the unit price.**

☐/lightbulb

Step 2 You know the cost of one lightbulb. Multiply to find the cost of 10 lightbulbs.

☐ · ☐ = ☐ ← **Multiply the unit rate by the number of lightbulbs.**

The cost of 10 lightbulbs is ☐.

2 Solving Using Mental Math Solve each proportion using mental math.

a. $\frac{5}{c} = \frac{30}{42}$

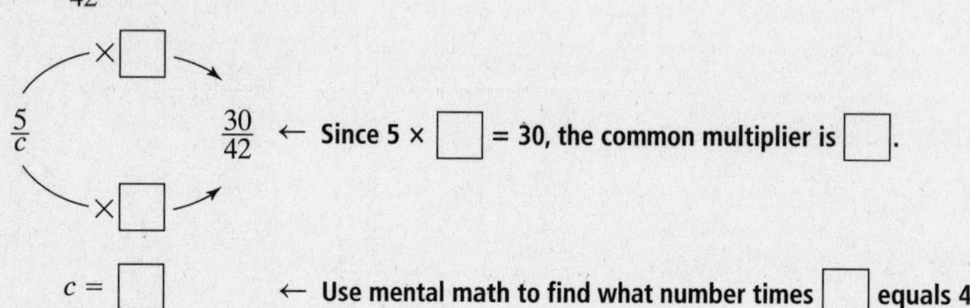

← **Since 5 × ☐ = 30, the common multiplier is ☐.**

$c =$ ☐ ← **Use mental math to find what number times ☐ equals 42.**

b. $\frac{9}{4} = \frac{72}{t}$

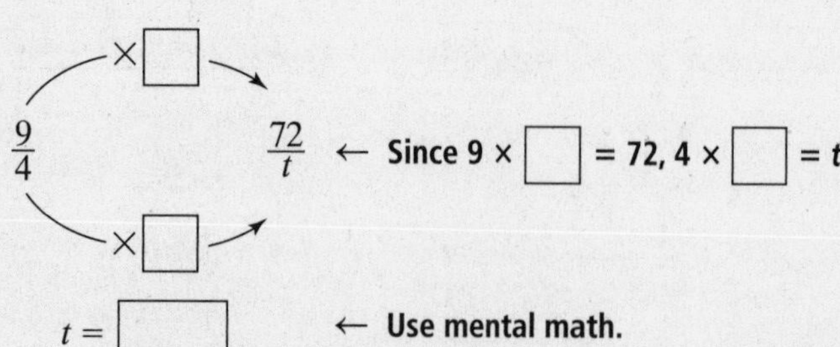

← **Since 9 × ☐ = 72, 4 × ☐ = t.**

$t =$ ☐ ← **Use mental math.**

Name ________________ Class ________________ Date ________________

❷ **Multiple Choice** A 5-ft person standing near a tree casts a shadow 12 ft long. At the same time, the tree casts a shadow 42 ft long. What is the height of the tree?

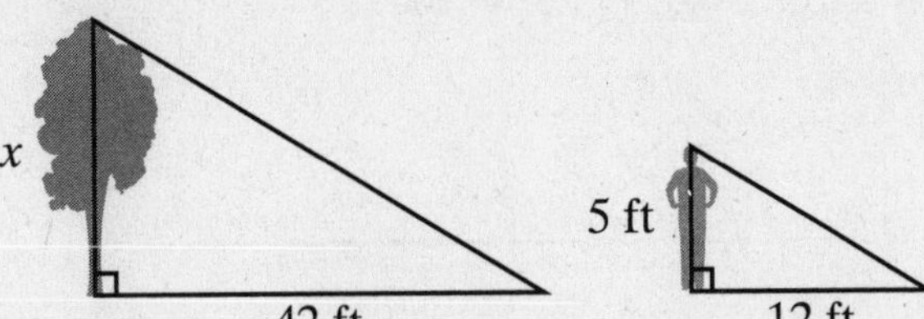

Draw a picture and let x represent the height of the tree.

$\frac{x}{\square} = \frac{42}{\square}$ ← **Write a proportion.**

$\square x = \square \cdot 42$ ← **Write the cross products.**

$\frac{12x}{12} = \frac{5 \cdot 42}{12}$ ← **Divide each side by 12.**

$x = \square$ ← **Simplify.**

The height of the tree is $\square$ ft.

CA Standards Check

1. The trapezoids below are similar. Find x.

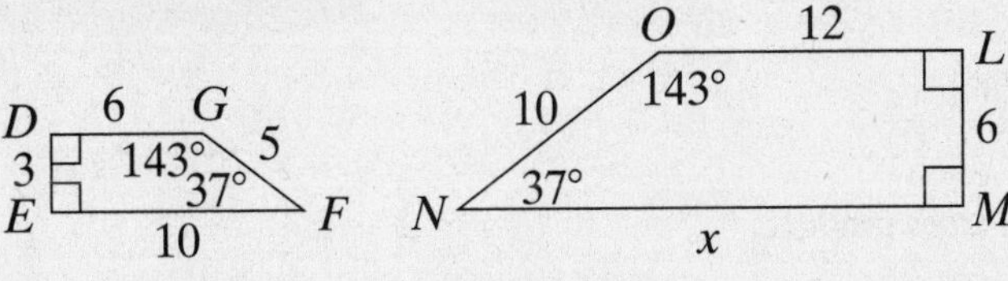

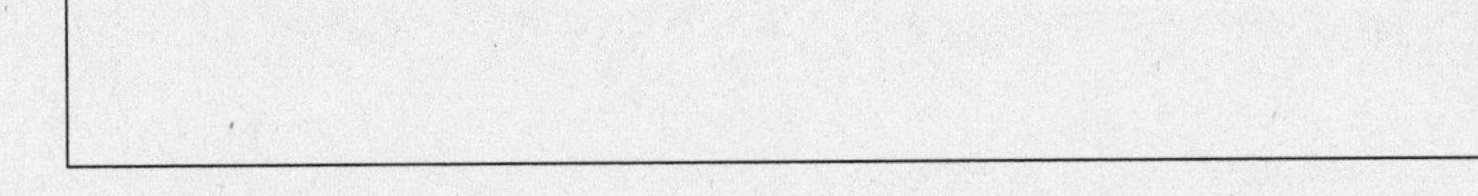

2. A 6-ft person has a shadow 5 ft long. A nearby tree has a shadow 30 ft long. What is the height of the tree?

Name ______________________ Class ______________ Date ______________

Lesson 5-6

Maps and Scale Drawings

Lesson Objective	**California Content Standards**
To use proportions to solve problems involving scale	NS 1.2 ⬭, NS 1.3 ⬭, MR 2.5

Vocabulary

A scale drawing is ____

____

A scale is ____

____

Example

1 **Using a Scale** The scale of a drawing is 1 in. : 6 ft. The length of a wall is 4.5 in. on the drawing. Find the actual length of the wall.

You can write the scale of the drawing as $\frac{1 \text{ in.}}{6 \text{ ft}}$. Then write a proportion.

Let n represent the actual length.

drawing (in.) → / **actual (ft)** → $\frac{1}{6} = \frac{\square}{n}$ ← **drawing (in.)** / ← **actual (ft)**

$\square n = \square(4.5)$ ← **Write the cross products.**

$n = \square$ ← **Simplify.**

The actual length is $\square$ ft.

CA Standards Check

1. Use the same scale as in Example 1. If an object is 2.5 in. long on the drawing, how long is the actual object?

$\square$

Name ______________________ Class ______________ Date ______________

Example

❷ Application Find the actual distance from Asheville to Raleigh.

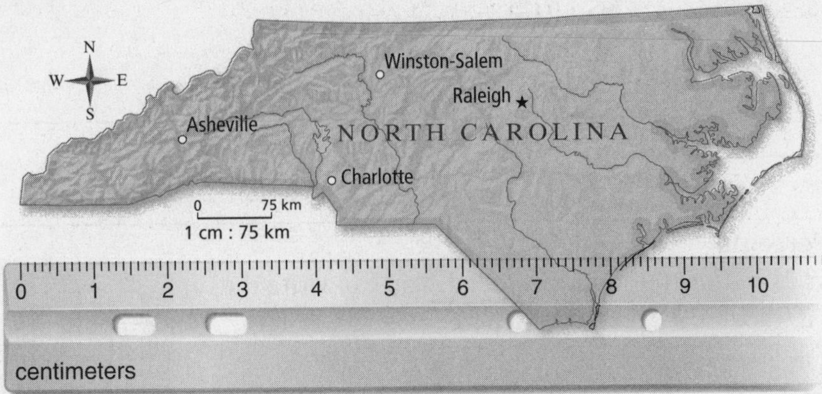

Step 1 Use a centimeter ruler to find the map distance from Asheville to Raleigh. The map distance is about 4.4 cm.

Step 2 Use a proportion to find the actual distance. Let n represent the actual distance.

map (cm) → / actual (km) → $\frac{1}{75} = \frac{\square}{n}$ ← map (cm) / ← actual (km) ← **Write a proportion.**

$1\square = \square(4.4)$ ← **Write the cross products.**

$n = \square$ ← **Simplify.**

The actual distance from Asheville to Raleigh is about ______ km.

CA Standards Check

2. Find the actual distance from Charlotte to Raleigh.

____

Name ______________ Class ______________ Date ______________

Lesson 6-1

Percents, Fractions, and Decimals

Lesson Objective	California Content Standards
To connect percents, fractions, and decimals	NS 1.0

Take Note

Fractions, Decimals, and Percents

The model at the right shows 21 out of 100 squares shaded. You can write the shaded part of the model as a fraction, a decimal, or a percent.

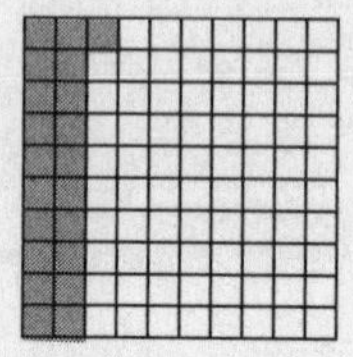

Fraction	Decimal	Percent
$\frac{\square}{\square}$	$\square$	$\square$

Examples

1 Writing Decimals as Percents Write 0.101 as a percent.

$0.101 = \frac{101}{\square}$ ← **Write as a fraction.**

$= \frac{\square}{\square}$ ← **Write an equivalent fraction with** $\square$ **in the denominator.**

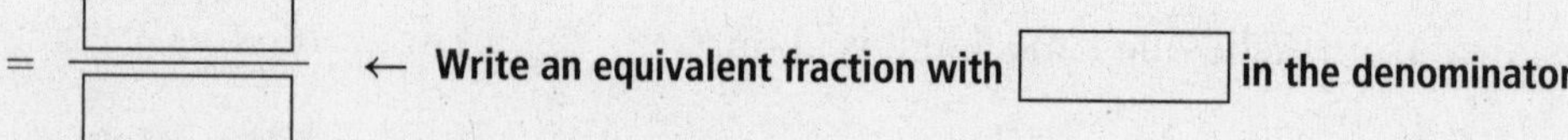

$= \square$ ← **Write as a percent.**

2 Writing Percents as Decimals Write 6.4% as a decimal.

$6.4\% = \frac{\square}{\square}$ ← **Write the percent as a fraction.**

$= \square$ ← **Divide.**

CA Standards Check

1. a. Write 0.62 as a percent. $\square$

   b. Write 0.526 as a percent. $\square$

2. Write each percent as a decimal.

   a. 35% $\square$

   b. 9% $\square$

   c. 12.5% $\square$

   d. 7.8% $\square$

Name ______________________ Class ______________ Date ______________

Examples

❹ Writing Percents as Fractions

Write each percent as a fraction in simplest form.

a. 12%

$12\% = \frac{12}{\square}$ ← Write as a fraction with a denominator of $\square$. →

$= \frac{12 \div \square}{100 \div \square}$ ← Divide the numerator and the denominator by the GCD. →

$= \frac{\square}{\square}$ ← Simplify the fraction. →

b. 45%

$45\% = \frac{45}{\square}$

$= \frac{45 \div \square}{100 \div \square}$

$= \frac{\square}{\square}$

CA Standards Check

3. Write each as a percent. When necessary, round to the nearest tenth of a percent.

a. $\frac{3}{5}$ $\square$ **b.** $\frac{21}{40}$ $\square$

c. $\frac{11}{16}$ $\square$ **d.** $\frac{19}{80}$ $\square$

4. a. An elephant eats about 6% of its body weight in vegetation every day. Write this as a fraction in simplest form.

$\square$

b. During the winter, weasels eat up to 40% of their body weight each day. Write this as a fraction in simplest form.

$\square$

Name ____________ Class ____________ Date ____________

Lesson 6-2

Percents Greater Than 100% or Less Than 1%

Lesson Objective	California Content Standards
To use percents greater than 100% or less than 1%	NS 1.0

Examples

1 Rewriting Percents Write 140% as a decimal and as a fraction.

140% = ____ ← **Move the decimal point ____ places to the ____.**

$140\% = \frac{140}{\square}$ ← **Use the definition of percent.**

$= \frac{\square}{\square}$ or $\square\frac{\square}{\square}$ ← **Simplify the fraction.**

140% equals ____ in decimal form and ____ in fraction form.

2 Rewriting Percents Write 0.75% as a decimal and as a fraction in simplest form.

0.75% = ____ ← **Move the decimal point ____ places to the ____.**

$0.75\% = \frac{0.75}{\square}$ ← **Use the definition of percent.**

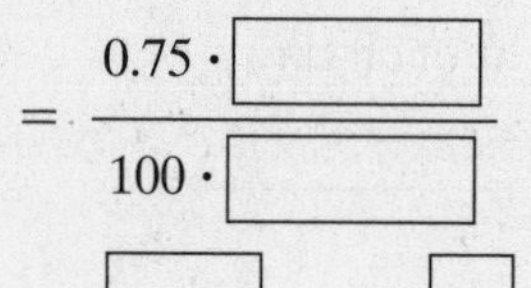

$= \frac{0.75 \cdot \square}{100 \cdot \square}$ ← **Multiply numerator and denominator by ____ to get a whole number numerator.**

$= \frac{\square}{10{,}000} = \frac{\square}{\square}$ ← **Simplify.**

0.75% equals ____ in decimal form and ____ in fraction form.

CA Standards Check

1. Write 125% as a decimal and as a fraction.

2. Write 0.35% as a decimal and as a fraction in simplest form.

Name ______________________ Class ______________ Date ______________

Examples

3 **Writing Mixed Numbers as Percents** The sports stadium at a school has $4\frac{2}{3}$ as many seats as the auditorium. Write this mixed number as a percent. Round to the nearest hundredth.

$4\frac{2}{3} = \square + \square \div \square = \square$ ← Use a calculator.

$\approx 4.6667 = \square\ \%$ ← Move the decimal point $\square$ places to the $\square$.

The number of seats in the stadium is $\square$ of the number of seats in the auditorium.

4 **Application** An animal shelter has 4 beagles available for adoption. There are 481 other dogs for adoption that are not beagles. About what percentage of the dogs are beagles?

A. 8% **B.** 0.8% **C.** 0.08% **D.** 0.008%

$\square + \square = \square$ ← Add.

$\frac{\square}{\square} = \frac{\square}{\square}$ ← Write the fraction.

$= \square$ ← Use a calculator.

$= \square$ ← Write as a percent and round.

About $\square$ of the dogs are beagles. The correct answer is choice $\square$.

CA Standards Check

3. You plan to run $2\frac{4}{5}$ times the distance you ran yesterday. Write this number as a percent.

4. Idaho has 2 members in the U.S. House of Representatives. There are a total of 435 representatives. What percent of the representatives are from Idaho? Round to the nearest hundredth of a percent.

Name ______________________ Class ______________ Date ______________

Lesson 6-3

Finding a Percent of a Number

Lesson Objective	California Content Standards
To use a percent to find part of a whole	NS 1.4, MR 3.2

Examples

1 Finding a Percent of a Number Find 80% of 460.

Method 1 Write the percent as a fraction.

$80\% = \frac{\square}{\square}$ ← **Write 80% as a fraction in simplest terms.**

$\frac{\square}{\square} \cdot 460 = \square$ ← **Multiply.**

Method 2 Write the percent as a decimal.

$80\% = \square$ ← **Write 80% as a decimal.**

$\square \cdot 460 = \square$ ← **Multiply.**

80% of 460 is $\square$.

2 Using Mental Math Find 49% of 300.

What You Think

49% is 50% − $\square$%

50% of 300 is $\square$ · 300, or $\square$.

1% of 300 is $\square$ · 300, or $\square$.

$\square - \square = \square$, so 49% of 300 is $\square$.

Why It Works

$49\% \text{ of } 300 = \square \cdot 300$ ← **Write 49% as a decimal.**

$= (0.50 - 0.01) \cdot 300$ ← **Substitute 0.50 − 0.01 for 0.49.**

$= (0.50 \cdot 300) - (0.01 \cdot 300)$ ← **Use the $\square$ Property.**

$= \square - \square$ ← **Multiply.**

$= \square$ ← **Subtract.**

Example

③ Estimating a Percent Estimate each answer.

a. 76% of 405

76% · 405 ← **Write an expression.**

↓ ↓

$\frac{3}{4}$ · ______ = ______ ← **Use ______ numbers such as $\frac{3}{4}$ and ______.**

76% of 405 is about ______.

b. 12% of 5,575

12% · 5,575 ← **Write an expression.**

↓ ↓

$\frac{1}{10}$ · ______ = ______ ← **Use ______ numbers such as $\frac{1}{10}$ and ______.**

12% of 5,575 is about ______.

CA Standards Check

1. Find each answer.

a. 75% of 140 **b.** 13% of 200 **c.** 10% of 680

2. Use mental math to find 40% of 2,400.

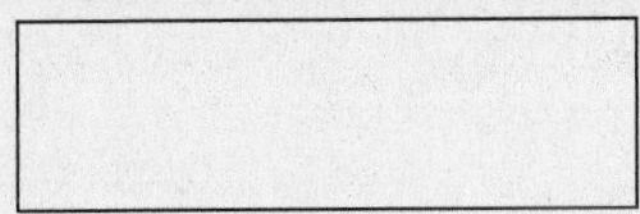

3. Estimate each answer.

a. 24% of 238 **b.** 19% of 473 **c.** 82% of 747

Name ______________________ Class ______________________ Date ______________________

Lesson 6-4

Solving Percent Problems Using Proportions

Lesson Objective	California Content Standards
To find the percent and the whole using proportions	NS 1.0, NS 1.3

Take Note

Percents and Proportions

Finding a Percent

What percent of 25 is 5?

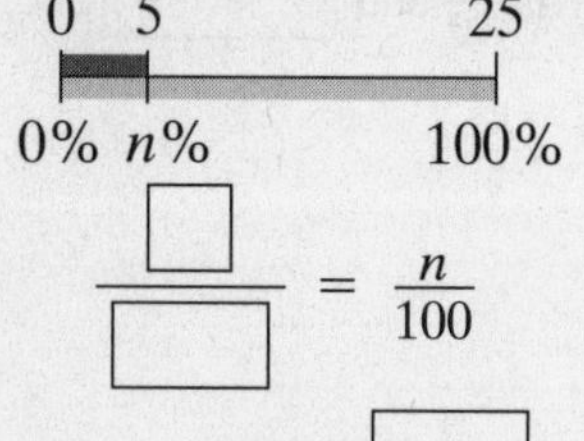

$\frac{\square}{\square} = \frac{n}{100}$

$n = \square$

$\square$ of 25 is 5.

Finding a Part

What is 20% of 25?

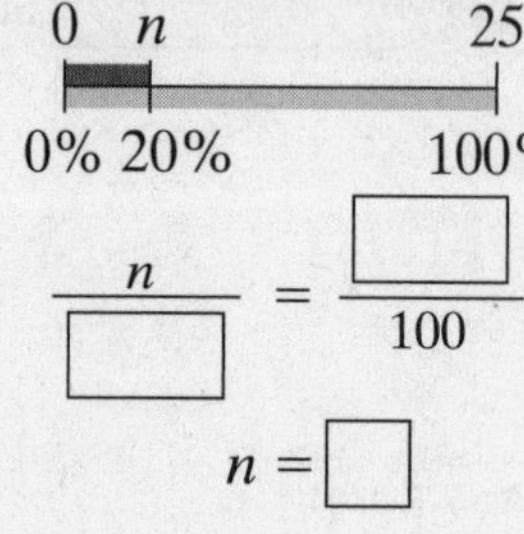

$\frac{n}{\square} = \frac{\square}{100}$

$n = \square$

$\square$ is 20% of 25.

Finding a Whole

20% of what is 5?

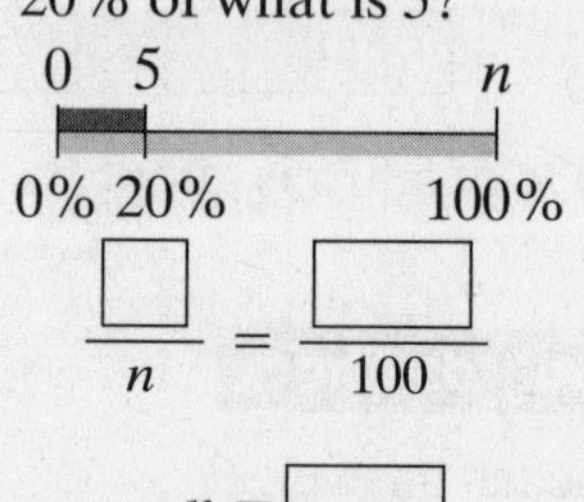

$\frac{\square}{n} = \frac{\square}{100}$

$n = \square$

$\square$ of 25 is 5.

Example

1 Finding a Percent What percent of 150 is 45?

You can write a proportion to find the percent.

$\frac{45}{\square} = \frac{n}{\square}$ ← **Write a proportion.**

$\square n = 45(\square)$ ← **Write cross products.**

$\frac{150n}{\square} = \frac{45(100)}{\square}$ ← **Divide each side by** $\square$.

$n = \square$ ← **Simplify.**

45 is $\square$% of 150.

CA Standards Check

1. a. What percent of 92 is 23? **b.** 36 is what percent of 125?

Name ______________________ Class ____________ Date ____________

Examples

2 Finding a Part 24% of 25 is what number?

$\frac{n}{\square} = \frac{\square}{100}$ ← **Write a proportion.**

$\frac{n}{\square} = \frac{\square}{25}$ ← **Simplify the fraction.**

$n = \square$ ← **Simplify.**

$\square$ is 24% of 25.

3 Finding the Whole Use a proportion to answer the question: 117 is 45% of what number?

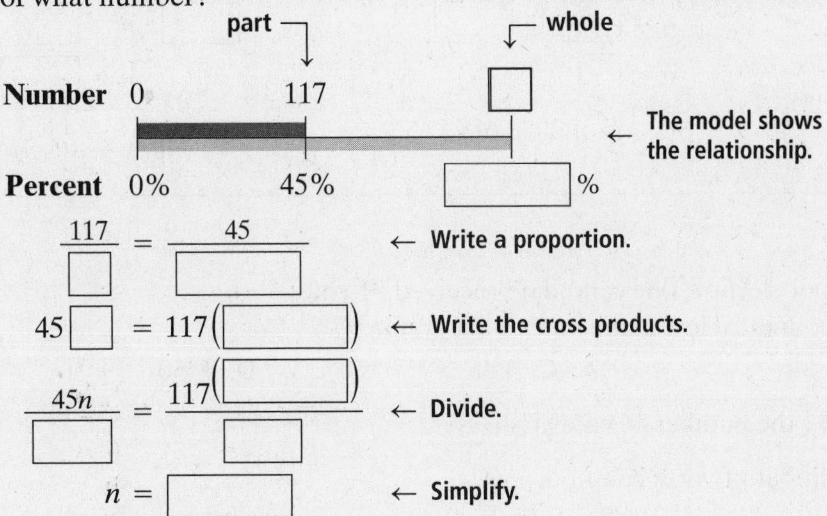

117 is 45% of $\square$.

CA Standards Check

2. a. 85% of 20 is what number?

b. An animal shelter has 80 animals; 60% of them are cats. How many cats are in the shelter?

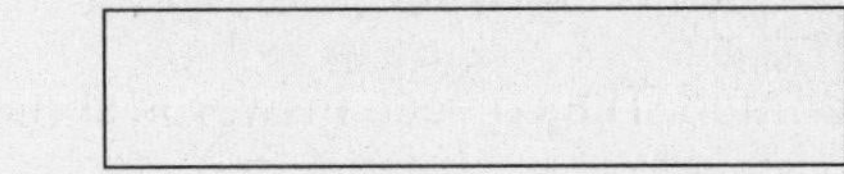

3. a. 70% of what number is 42?

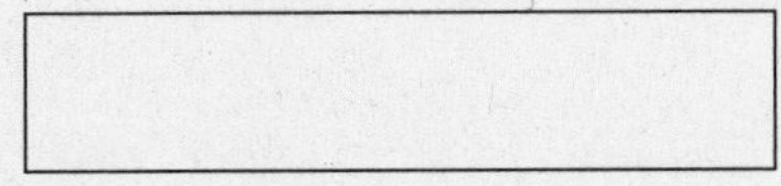

b. Dara finished 18 math problems. This was 60% of the problems her math teacher assigned for homework. How many problems did Dara's teacher assign?

Name ______________________ Class ______________ Date ______________

Lesson 6-5

Solving Percent Problems Using Equations

Lesson Objective	California Content Standards
To write and solve percent equations	NS 1.4

Take Note

Percents and Equations

Finding a Percent
What percent of 25 is 5?
$n \cdot$ ☐ $=$ ☐
$n =$ ☐
5 is ☐ of 25.

Finding a Part
What is 20% of 25?
$n =$ ☐ $\cdot$ ☐
$n =$ ☐
☐ is of 20% of 25.

Finding a Whole
20% of what is 5?
☐ $\cdot\, n =$ ☐
$n =$ ☐
20% of ☐ is 5.

Examples

❶ **Finding a Whole** In a school election, one candidate received 81 votes. This was 18% of the votes counted. How many votes were counted?

A. 45 **B.** 145 **C.** 450 **D.** 1450

Words 18% of the number of votes is 81.

Let n = the number of votes counted.

Equation ☐ $\cdot$ ☐ $=$ ☐

☐ $\cdot$ ☐ $=$ ☐ ← **Write the equation.**

$\frac{0.18n}{☐} = \frac{81}{☐}$ ← **Divide each side by** ☐.

$n =$ ☐ ← **Simplify.**

☐ votes were counted. The correct answer is choice ☐.

❷ **Finding a Part** What number is 32% of 40?

Words A number is 32% of 40.

Let ☐ = the number.

Equation ☐ $=$ ☐ $\cdot$ ☐

$=$ ☐ ← **Simplify.**

Name ________________ Class ________________ Date ________________

❸ Finding a Percent Of the 257 sandwiches sold at a delicatessen one day, 45 were turkey sandwiches. What percent of the sandwiches were turkey?

Estimate About 50 of 250 sandwiches were turkey.

$\frac{\square}{\square} = \frac{\square}{\square} = \square\%$

$\square \cdot \square = \square$ ← Write an equation. Let p = the percent of sandwiches that are turkey.

$\frac{257p}{\square} = \frac{45}{\square}$ ← Divide each side by $\square$.

$p \approx \square$ ← Use a calculator.

$p \approx \square\%$ ← Write the decimal as a percent.

Check for Reasonableness $\square$% is close to the estimate $\square$%.

CA Standards Check

1. A plane flies with 54% of its seats empty. If 81 seats are empty, what is the total number of seats on the plane?

2. 27% of 60 is what number?

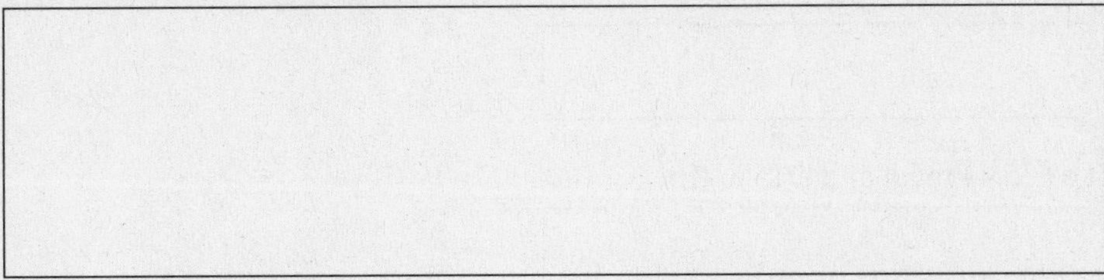

3. It rained 75 days last year. About what percent of the year was rainy?

Name ______________________ Class ______________________ Date ______________________

Lesson 6-6

Tips and Discounts

Lesson Objective	California Content Standards
To find tips and discounts	NS 1.4

Vocabulary

A discount is ______________________

Examples

1 Finding a Tip You and your mother have your hair cut at a hair salon. The bill is $78.00 for both of you. How much would a 20% tip be?

$0.20 \cdot 78 \approx$ ☐ ← **Find the tip. Round to the nearest cent.**

The tip would be ☐.

2 Adding the Tip to the Bill Your Book Club has lunch at an outdoor café. The bill is $118.21. Find the total cost of the meal and a 15% tip.

$0.15 \cdot 118.21 =$ ☐ ← **Find the tip. Round to the nearest cent.**

$118.21 + 17.73 =$ ☐ ← **Add the tip to the cost of the meal.**

The total cost of the meal and the tip is ☐.

CA Standards Check

1. Find a 15% tip for a taxi ride that costs $12.50.

☐

2. Find the total cost of a $35.44 meal and a 15% tip.

☐

Name ______________________ Class ______________ Date ______________

Examples

3 Finding the Discount A tent that regularly costs $74.99 is discounted by 35%. How much will the discount be?

☐ · 74.99 = ☐ ← **Write 35% as a** ☐ **and multiply.**

The discount will be ☐.

4 Finding the Cost After Discount A dictionary normally costs $54.95. There is a 33% discount. How much will the dictionary cost after the discount?

Step 1 Find the amount of the discount.

☐ · 54.95 = ☐ ← **Write** ☐ **as a decimal and multiply.**

Step 2 Subtract the amount of the discount from the original price.

54.95 − 18.13 = ☐ ← **Subtract.**

After the discount, the dictionary will cost ☐.

CA Standards Check

3. Find the amount of each discount.

a. a 12% discount on a book that costs $7.99

b. a 20% discount on a DVD that costs $22.49

4. A dress costs $35. There is a 15% discount. How much will the dress cost after the discount?

Name ________________ Class ________________ Date ________________

Lesson 6-7

Interest

Lesson Objective	**California Content Standards**
To find interest	NS 1.4

Vocabulary

Interest is ________________

____

Principal is ________________

The balance of an account is ________________

Examples

1 Finding Interest Find the simple interest you pay on $1,250 borrowed at an annual interest rate of 6%.

$I = pr$ ← **Write the formula.**

$I = (\square)(\square)$ ← **Substitute. Use** ☐ for ☐.

$= \square$ ← **Simplify.**

The interest is ☐.

2 Finding the Balance You have $667 in an account that earns an annual interest rate of 5.7%. Find the balance at the end of one year.

$B = p(1 + r)$ ← **Use the formula for balance.**

$= \square(1 + \square)$ ← **Substitute** ☐ **for** ***p*****, and** ☐ **for** ***r*****.**

$= 667(1.057)$ ← **Simplify.**

$= \square$ ← **Multiply.**

At the end of the year, the balance will be ☐.

Name ______________________ Class ______________ Date ______________

3 **Working Backward With Interest** Olivia has \$888.33 in her bank account after making a single deposit one year ago. The account has earned 3.3% annual interest. Find the principal that Olivia started with.

$B = p(1 + r)$ ← **Write the formula.**

$\square = p(1 + \square)$ ← **Substitute** $\square$ **for** B**, and** $\square$ **for** r**.**

$888.33 = p(1.033)$ ← **Simplify.**

$\square = \square$ ← **Divide each side by** $\square$**.**

The principal was $\square$.

CA Standards Check

1. How much interest is earned on \$150 deposited in a bank account at a 2% annual interest rate?

2. Find the balance in an account that had a principal of \$950 and earned interest at an annual rate of 4.2%.

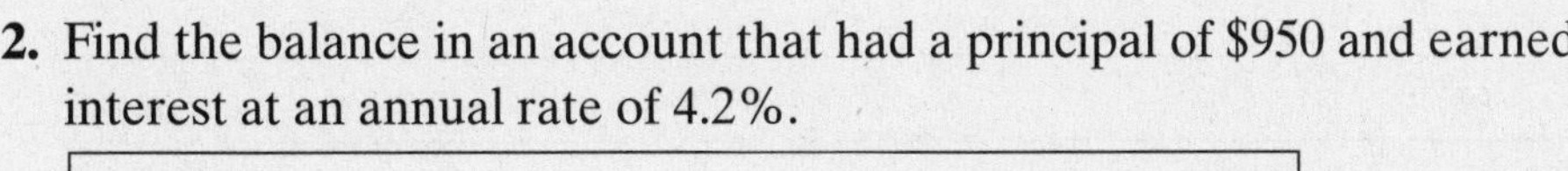

3. After one year Cody owes \$689 on a loan. The bank charged 6% interest. What was the original amount Cody borrowed?

Name ______________________ Class ______________________ Date ______________________

Lesson 7-1

Lines and Planes

Lesson Objective	**California Content Standards**
To identify segments, rays, and lines	MG 2.0

Vocabulary

A point ____

A line is ____

A ray is ____

A segment is ____

A plane is ____

Intersecting lines are ____

Parallel lines are ____

Skew lines are ____

Example

1 Naming Segments, Rays, and Lines Use the points in each diagram to name the figure shown.

a. 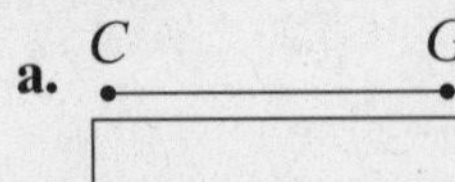

b. 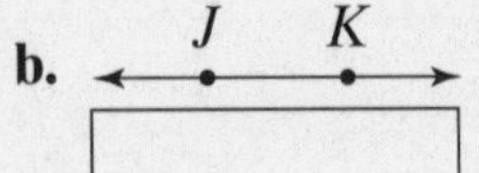

c. A B

CA Standards Check

1. Use the points to name the figure shown.

a. 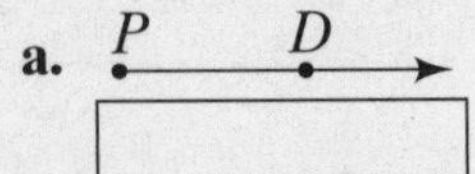

b. R S

c. A V

Name ______________________ Class ______________ Date ______________

Example

❷ Intersecting, Parallel, and Skew Name all the segments that fit the given description.

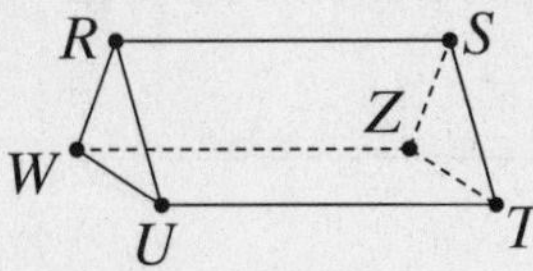

a. parallel to $\overline{UT}$

[ ] and [ ] are parallel to $\overline{UT}$.

b. intersect $\overline{RU}$

[ ], [ ], [ ], and [ ] intersect $\overline{RU}$.

c. skew to $\overline{RS}$

[ ] and [ ] are skew to $\overline{RS}$.

CA Standards Check

2. Name the segments in the diagram that fit each description.

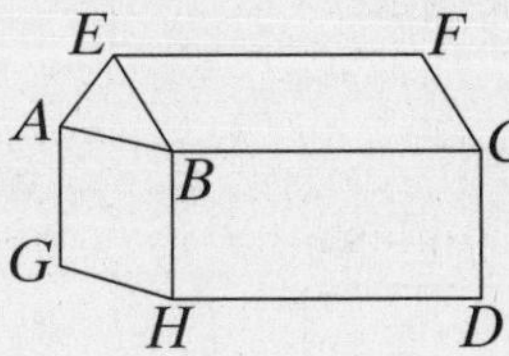

a. parallel to $\overline{BC}$

b. intersect $\overline{BH}$

c. skew to $\overline{AG}$

Name ______________________ Class ______________ Date ______________

Lesson 7-2

Identifying and Classifying Angles

Lesson Objective	**California Content Standards**
To classify angles and to work with pairs of angles	MG 2.0, MG 2.1, MG 2.2

Vocabulary

An angle is ____

A vertex is ____

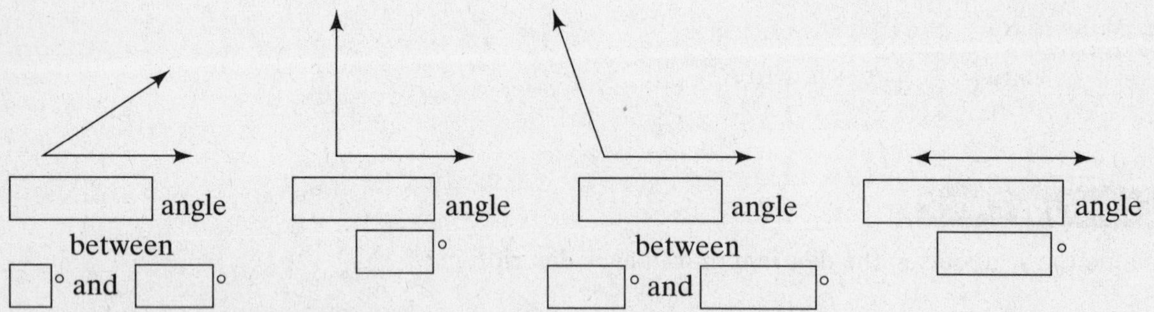

If the sum of the measure of two angles is 90°, the angles are ________.
If the sum is 180°, the angles are ________.

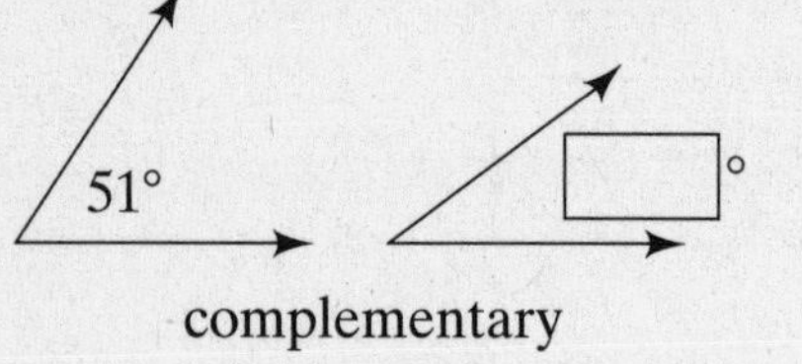

65°
°
supplementary

Adjacent angles are ____

Circle an angle adjacent to ∠1.

1 2 3 4

Vertical angles are ____

Circle the vertical angle to ∠1.

1 2 3 4

Congruent angles are ____

Name ______________________ Class ______________ Date ______________

Examples

1 Identifying Angles Identify the acute angles, obtuse angles, and straight angles in the figure.

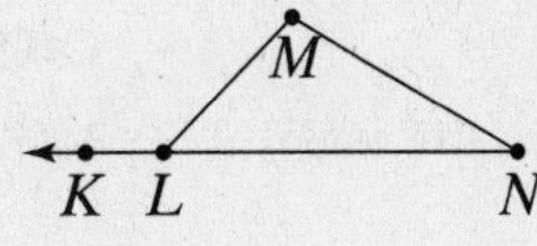

acute angles: 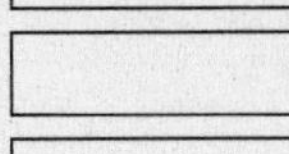 and ______

obtuse angles: ______ and ______

straight angle: ______

2 Finding Angle Measures Find the measures of $\angle 1$, $\angle 2$, and $\angle 4$, for $m\angle 3 = 32°$.

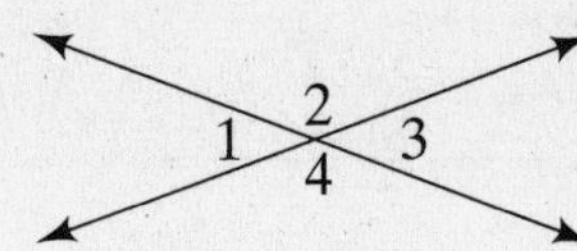

$m\angle 2 + 32° =$ ______ ← **$\angle 2$ and $\angle 3$ are ______.**

$m\angle 2 + 32° - 32° = 180° - 32°$ ← **Subtract 32° from each side.**

$m\angle 2 =$ ______ ← **Simplify.**

$m\angle 1 =$ ______ ← **$\angle 1$ and $\angle 3$ are ______ angles.**

$m\angle 4 =$ ______ ← **$\angle 2$ and $\angle 4$ are ______ angles.**

CA Standards Check

1. Classify $\angle AFE$ as *acute*, *right*, *obtuse*, or *straight*.

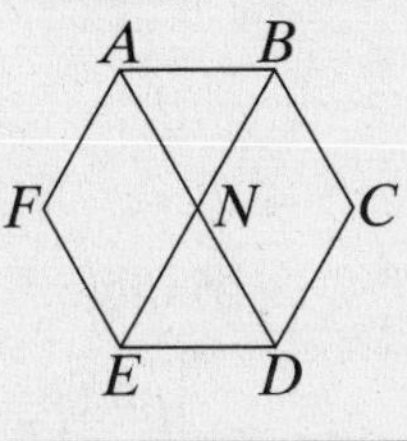

______

2. Find the measure of the complement of $\angle 3$ in Example 2.

3. In the diagram at the right, $m\angle 8 = 72°$. Find the measures of $\angle 5$, $\angle 6$, and $\angle 7$.

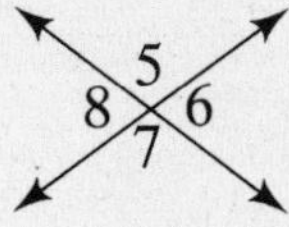

______

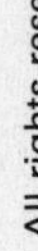

Name ______________________ Class ______________ Date ______________

Lesson 7-3

Triangles

Lesson Objective	California Content Standards
To classify triangles and to find the angle measures of triangles	MG 2.2

Take Note

Angle Sum of a Triangle

The sum of the measures of the angles of a triangle is ____.

Congruent sides are ____

scalene triangle

____ congruent sides

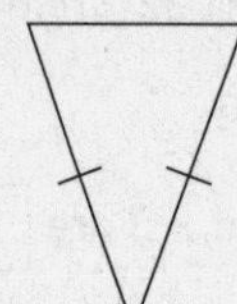

isosceles triangle

____ congruent sides

equilateral triangle

____ congruent sides

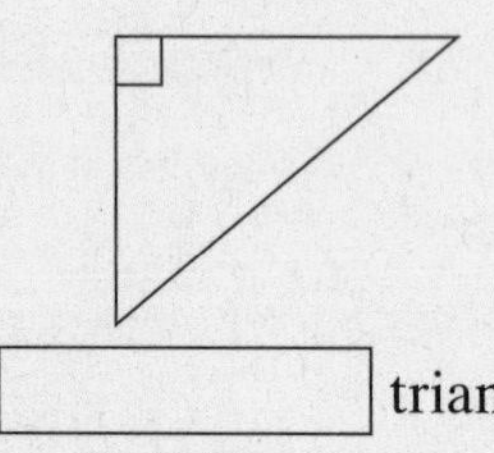

____ triangle

one ____ angle

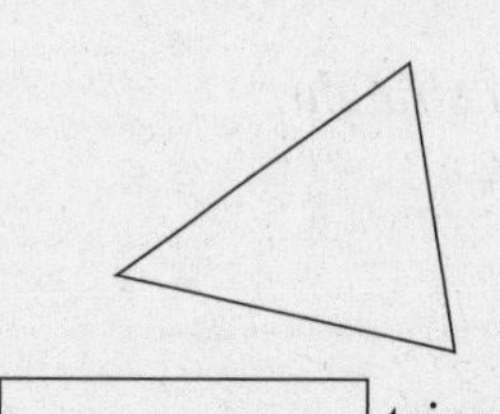

____ triangle

____ angles

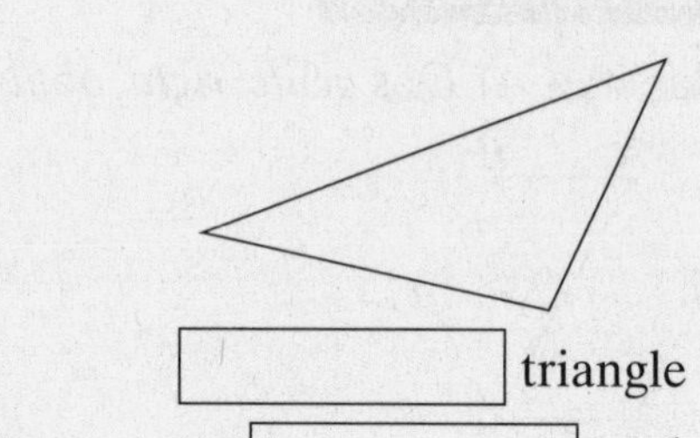

____ triangle

one ____ angle

Examples

1 Classifying Triangles by Sides Classify each triangle by its sides.

a. 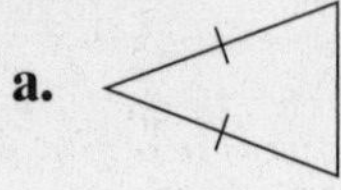 There are two congruent sides, so the triangle is ____.

b.  There are no congruent sides, so the triangle is ____.

Name ______________________ Class ______________ Date ______________

❷ Classifying Triangles by Angles Classify each triangle by its angle measures.

a.

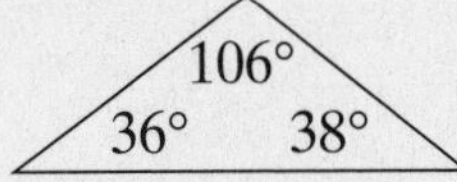

The triangle has [ ] obtuse angle, so it is an [ ] triangle.

b.

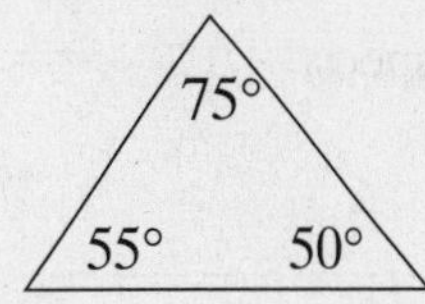

The triangle has [ ] acute angles, so it is an [ ] triangle.

❸ Finding an Angle Measure Find the value of x in the triangle.

$x + 78° + 56° = \square$

$x + \square = \square$

$x + \square - \square = \square - \square$

$x = \square$

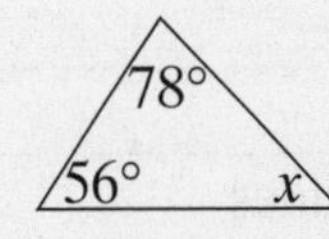

CA Standards Check

1. Classify $\triangle BCD$ by its sides.

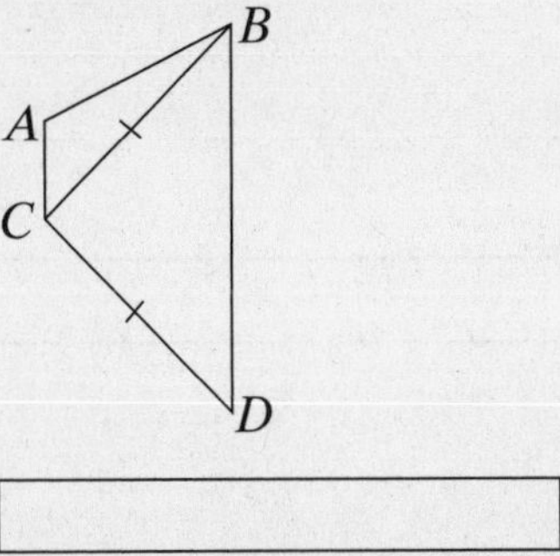

2. Classify the triangle by its angle measures.

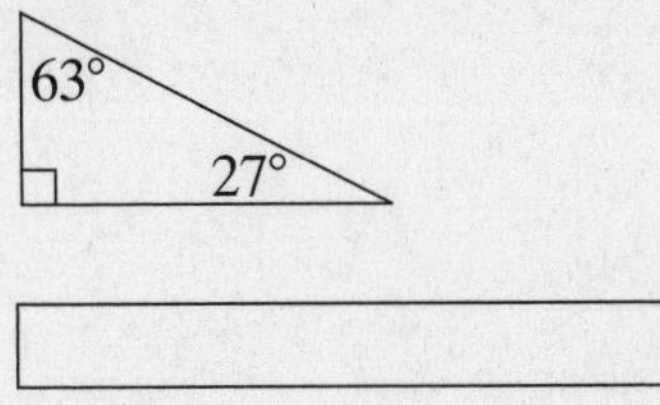

3. Find the value of x in the triangle.

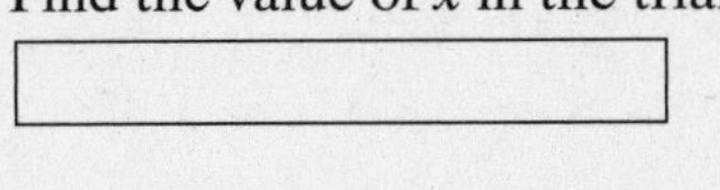

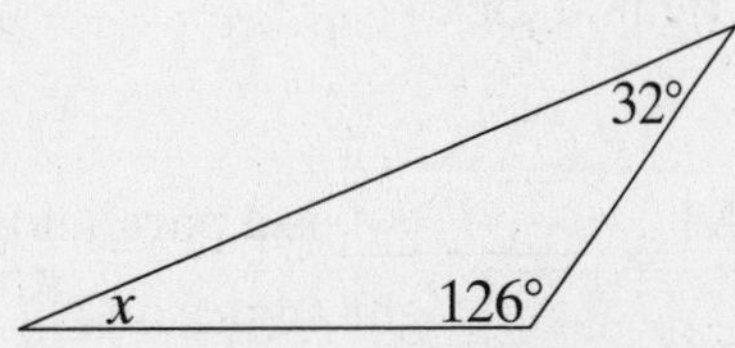

Name ______________________ Class ______________ Date ______________

Lesson 7-4

Quadrilaterals and Other Polygons

Lesson Objective	California Content Standards
To classify polygons and special quadrilaterals	MG 2.0, MG 2.3

Vocabulary

A polygon is ______________________________

____

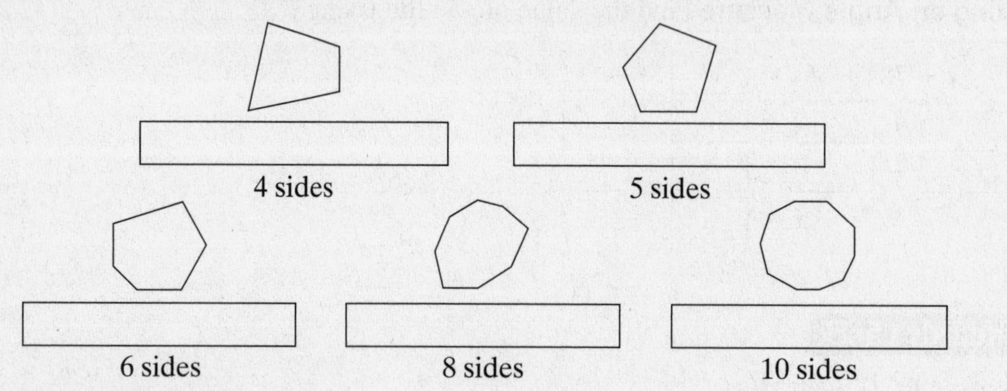

A regular polygon is ______________________________

____

An irregular polygon is ______________________________

____

A [ ] is a quadrilateral with exactly [ ] pair of parallel sides.

A [ ] is a quadrilateral with [ ] pairs of opposite sides parallel.

There are three special types of parallelograms.

A [ ] is a parallelogram with [ ] right angles.

A [ ] is a parallelogram with [ ] congruent sides.

A [ ] is a parallelogram with [ ] right angles and [ ] congruent sides.

Name ______________ Class ______________ Date ______________

Examples

1 Identifying Regular Polygons Identify the polygon and classify it as *regular* or *irregular*.

The figure has ☐ sides. Not all sides are congruent.

The ______ is ______.

2 Classifying Polygons Use the best names to identify the polygons in the design.

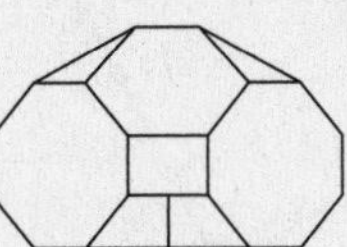

The outside polygon is a ______. Inside the decagon are ______, ______, ______, a ______ and a ______.

3 Using Dot Paper Draw a regular parallelogram.

A ______ is a regular parallelogram.

CA Standards Check

1. Identify each polygon and classify it as *regular* or *irregular*.

   a. 7.3 cm, 2 cm, 2 cm, 2 cm, 135°, 2 cm, 2 cm, 2 cm, 7.3 cm

   b. 5, 60°, 5, 60°, 60°, 5

   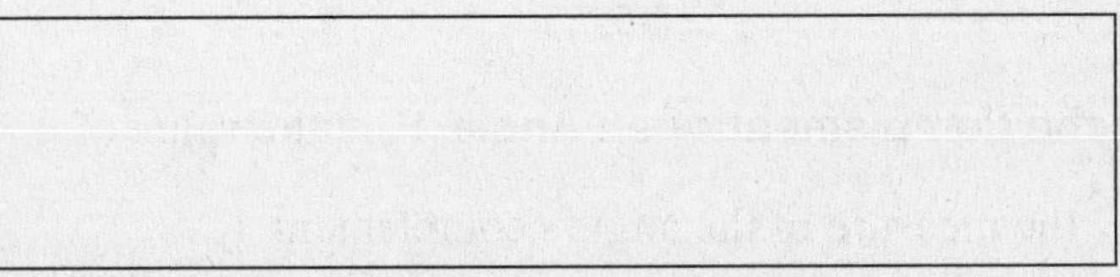

   c. **Reasoning** How would you find the perimeter of a regular polygon? Explain.

   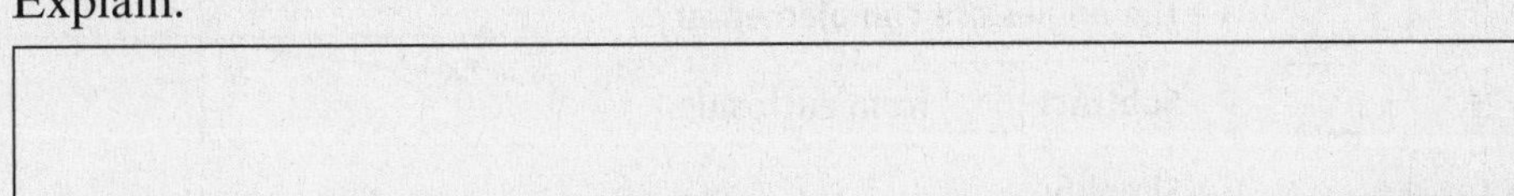

2. Use the best names to identify the polygons in the pattern.

3. Use dot paper to draw a trapezoid with a pair of congruent opposite sides.

Name ______________________ Class ______________ Date ____________

Lesson 7-5

Using the Properties of Angles

Lesson Objective	California Content Standards
To find missing angle measures	MG 2.1, MG 2.2

Examples

1 Using Supplementary Angles Use the diagram at the right. Lines AB and CD are parallel. What is the measure of angle 1?

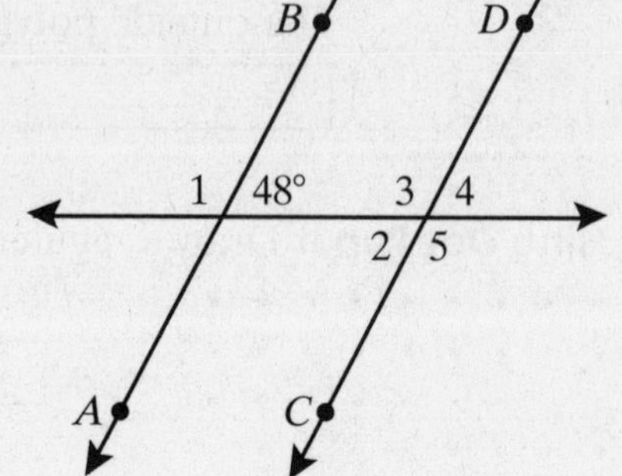

The straight angle has a measure of 180°. Since $\angle 1$ and the angle 48° are supplementary, you can write an equation.

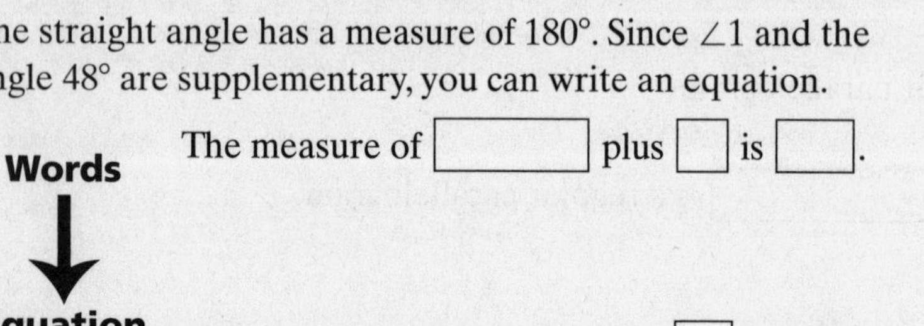

Words The measure of ______ plus ____ is ____.

Equation $m\angle 1 \quad + \quad \square = 180°$

$m\angle 1 + 48 - \square = 180 - \square$ ← **Subtract** ____ **from each side.**

$m\angle 1 = \square$ ← **Simplify.**

The measure of angle 1 is ______.

2 Using the Complement of an Angle Find the value of n.

Let n = the measure of the angle's complement.

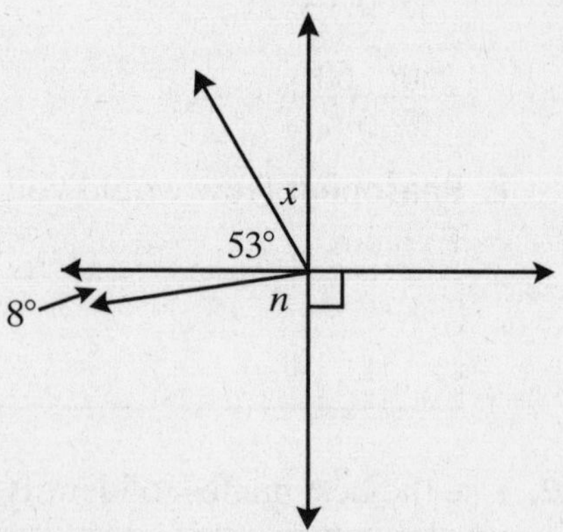

$n + \square = \square$ ← **The angles are complementary.**

$n + \square - \square = 90° - \square$ ← **Subtract** ____ **from each side.**

$n = \square$ ← **Simplify.**

Name ______________________ Class ______________ Date ______________

❸ Using the Angles of a Triangle Find the measure of $\angle CBD$. $\overline{BC}$ and $\overline{CD}$ are congruent.

Since $\angle BCD$ and $\angle XCY$ are vertical angles, their measures are equal. So $m\angle BCD = \square$.

Since $\overline{BC}$ and $\overline{CD}$ are congruent, the measures of $\angle CBD$ and $\square$ are equal.

Write an equation to find the measure of $\angle CBD$.

$m\angle CBD + m\angle BDC + 30 = \square$ ← **The sum of the measures of the angles of a triangle is $\square$.**

$x + x + \square = 180$ ← **Substitute x for both $m\angle CBD$ and $m\angle BDC$, since they are equal.**

$2x + \square = 180$ ← **Simplify.**

$2x + 30 - \square = 180 - \square$ ← **Subtract $\square$ from each side.**

$2x = \square$ ← **Simplify.**

$2x \div \square = 150 \div \square$ ← **Divide each side by 2.**

$x = \square$ ← **Simplify.**

The measure of $\angle CBD$ is $\square$.

CA Standards Check

1. Use the diagram in Example 1. What is the measure of angle 2?

2. Use the diagram in Example 2. Find the value of z.

3. Use the diagram at the right. Find each angle measure.

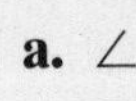

a. $\angle 3$ b. $\angle 4$ c. $\angle 5$

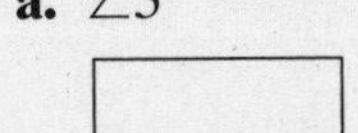 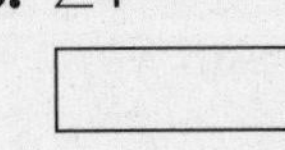 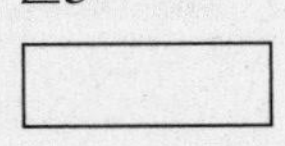

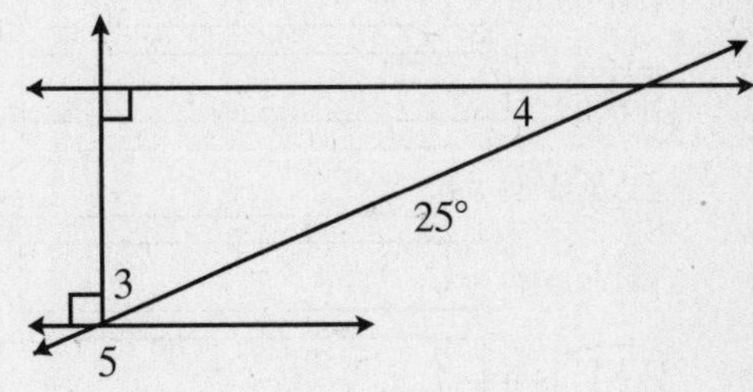

Name ____________________ Class ____________ Date ____________

Lesson 7-6

Circles

Lesson Objective	**California Content Standards**
To identify parts of a circle	Prepares for MG 1.1, AF 3.2

Vocabulary

A circle is ______________________________

A radius is ______________________________

A diameter is ______________________________

A central angle is ______________________________

A chord is ______________________________

An arc is ______________________________

A semicircle is ______________________________

$\overline{ST}$ is a ____________.

$\overline{VW}$ is a ____________.

$\overline{WX}$ is a ____________.

$\angle STW$ is a ____________.

$\widehat{SV}$ is an ____________.

$\widehat{WSV}$ is a ____________.

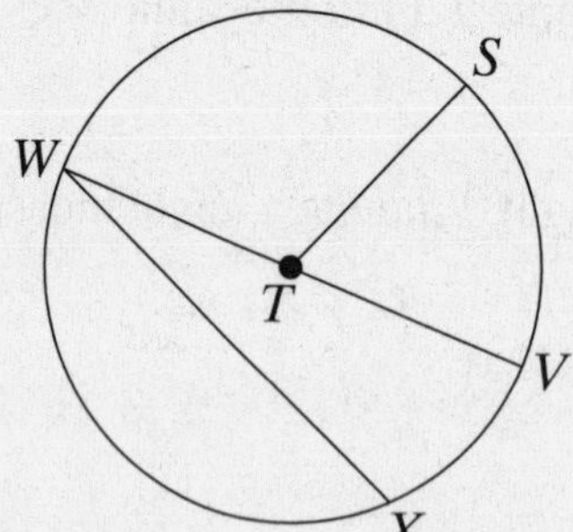

Name ______________________ Class ______________ Date ______________

Examples

Use circle *F* for Examples 1–3.

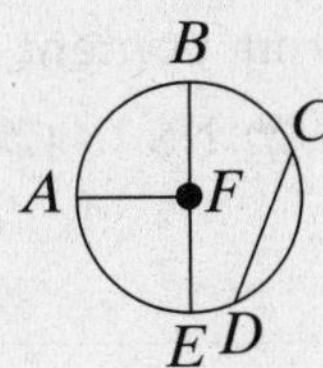

❶ **Naming Parts Inside a Circle** Name all the radii, diameters, and chords shown for circle *F*.

radii: ☐, ☐, and ☐

diameter: ☐

chords: ☐ and ☐

❷ **Naming Arcs** Name three of the arcs in circle *F*.

☐

❸ **Naming Arcs** Name two different arcs between points *C* and *D*.

The shorter arc is ☐.

The longer arc is ☐.

CA Standards Check

1. Name all the central angles shown in circle *O*.

2. Name three arcs in circle *F* not mentioned in your answers to Example 2.

☐

3. Name two different arcs between points *A* and *D* in circle *F*.

☐

Name ______________________ Class ______________ Date ______________

Lesson 7-7

Circle Graphs

Lesson Objective	California Content Standards
To analyze and construct circle graphs	NS 1.3, NS 1.4

Vocabulary

A circle graph is ____

____

Examples

1 Analyzing a Circle Graph Use the circle graph at the right to find how many of the days, to the nearest day, were cloudy.

November Weather (30 days)

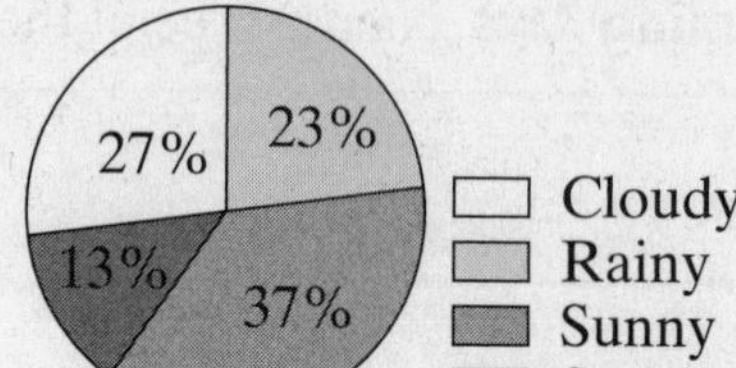

☐ of 30 days = ☐ · 30 = ☐

☐ days were cloudy.

2 Constructing a Circle Graph Use the information in the table to make a circle graph.

Size of U.S. Households (2000)

No. of People in Household	Number (in thousands)
1	26,724
2	34,666
3	17,152
4	15,309
5 or more	10,854

Step 1 Add to find the total number of households.

26,724 + 34,666 + 17,152 + 15,309 + 10,854 = ☐ (in thousands)

Step 2 For each central angle, set up a proportion to find the angle measure. Use a calculator. Round to the nearest tenth of a degree.

$\frac{\square}{104{,}705} = \frac{a}{360^\circ}$ $a \approx$ ☐

$\frac{\square}{104{,}705} = \frac{b}{360^\circ}$ $b \approx$ ☐

$\frac{\square}{104{,}705} = \frac{c}{360^\circ}$ $c \approx$ ☐

$\frac{\square}{104{,}705} = \frac{d}{360^\circ}$ $d \approx$ ☐

$\frac{\square}{104{,}705} = \frac{f}{360^\circ}$ $f \approx$ ☐

Name ______________________ Class ______________ Date ______________

Step 3 Use the circle below. Draw the central angles using the measures found in Step 2. Label each section. Include a title and a key.

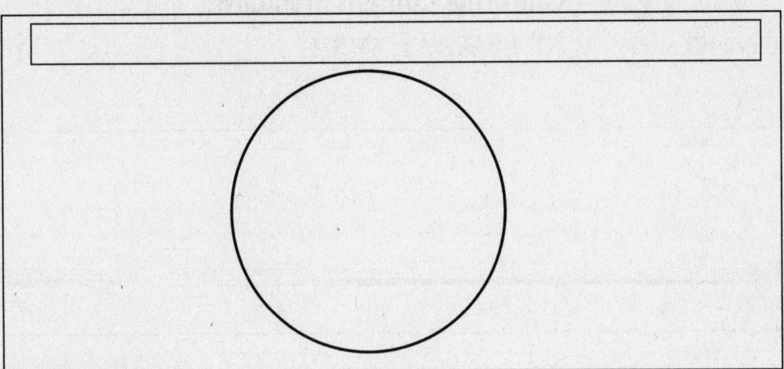

CA Standards Check

1. According to the circle graph in Example 1, approximately how many days were sunny?

2. Favorite Season

Season	Percent
Summer	40%
Spring	11%
Winter	4%
Fall	45%

a. Find the measure of the central angle that you would draw to represent summer.

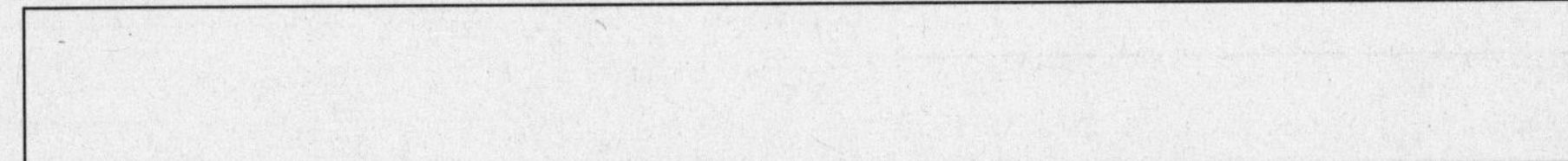

b. Use the information in the table to make a circle graph.

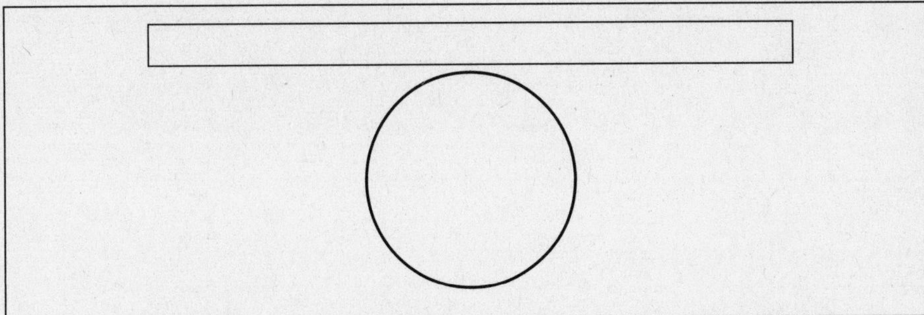

Name ______________________ Class ______________ Date ______________

Lesson 8-1

Perimeter and Area of a Rectangle

Lesson Objective	California Content Standards
To use formulas for the perimeter and area of a rectangle	AF 1.0, AF 3.1, AF 3.2

Vocabulary

The perimeter of a figure is ______________________

The area of a figure is ______________________

Examples

1 Writing Perimeter Formulas Write an equation for the perimeter of the rectangle at the right.

$P = 2l + 2w$ ← **Use the formula for perimeter.**

$P = 2(\square) + \square$ ← **Substitute 53 for *l*.**

$P = \square + \square$ ← **Multiply.**

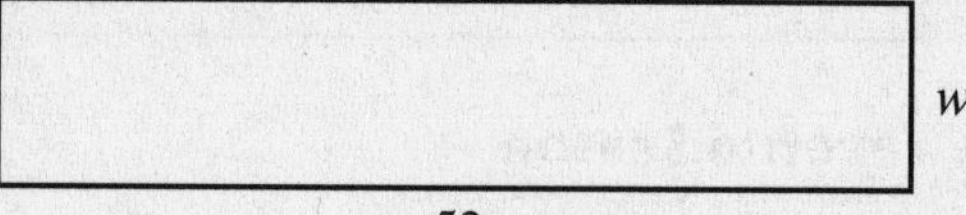

CA Standards Check

1. a. Use the equation $P = 106 + 2w$ to find the perimeter of the rectangle in Example 1 if its width is 9 cm.

[ ]

b. A rectangle has a width of 10 feet. Write an equation for the perimeter of the rectangle.

[ ]

Name ______________________ Class ______________ Date ______________

Example

❷ Writing Area Formulas The figure at the right is made up of a square within a square. Write an expression for the area of the shaded region.

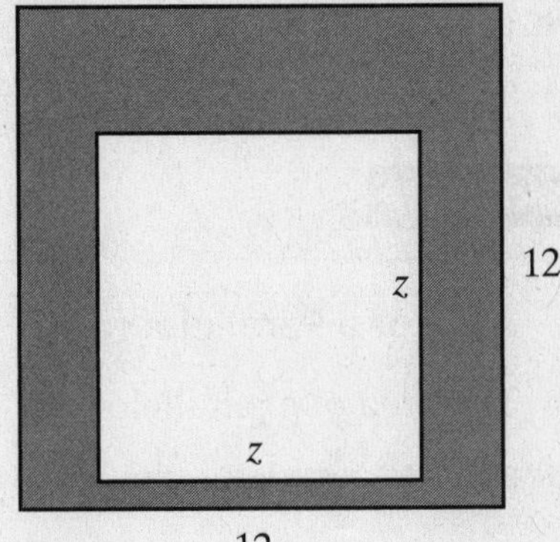

Write an expression for the area of each square.

Outer square: $12 \cdot 12 = 144$

Inner square: $\square \cdot \square = \square$

area of the shaded region	=	area of the outer square	−	area of the inner square
	=	$\square$	−	$\square$

The expression for the area of the shaded region is $\square$.

CA Standards Check

2. a. In Example 2, suppose $z = 9$. Evaluate $144 - z^2$ to find the area of the shaded region.

$\square$

b. Write an expression for the area of the shaded region in the figure at the right.

$\square$

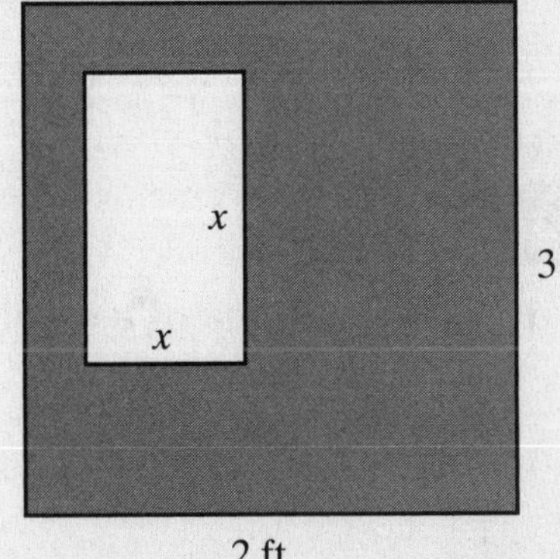

Name ______________________ Class ______________ Date ______________

Lesson 8-2

Perimeter and Area of a Parallelogram

Lesson Objective	California Content Standards
To find the perimeter and area of a parallelogram	AF 3.1, AF 3.2

Take Note

Area of a Parallelogram

The area of a parallelogram is equal to the product of any [ ] b and the corresponding [ ] h.

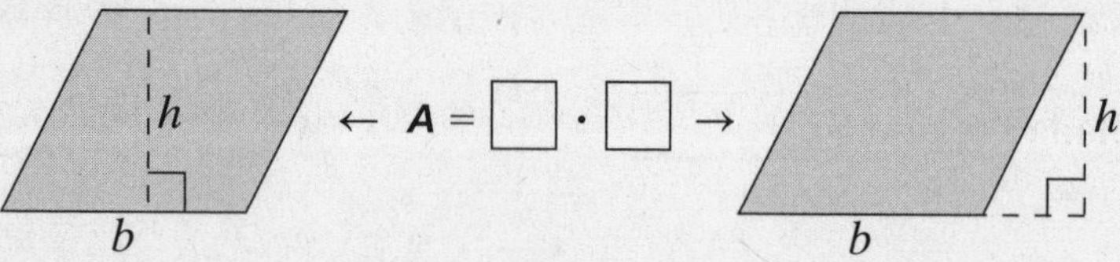

The height of a parallelogram is ______________________________

____

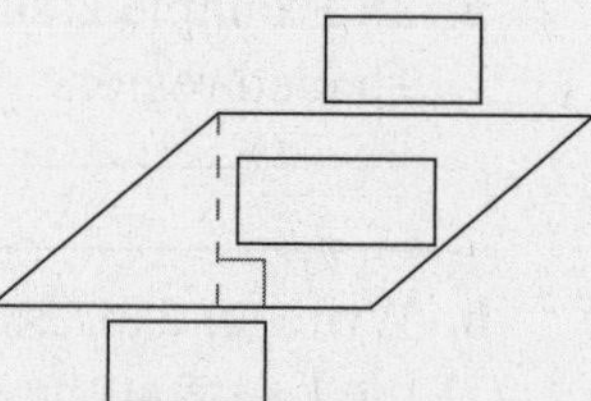

Examples

1 Finding the Area of a Parallelogram Find the area of the parallelogram.

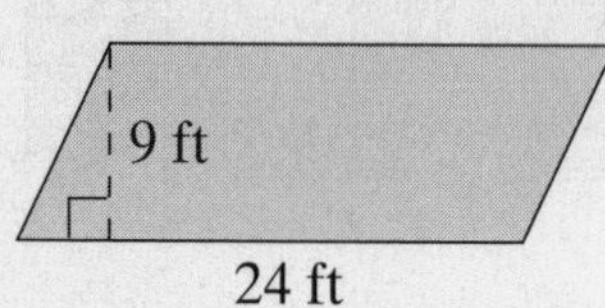

A = [ ][ ] ← **Use the area formula.**

= ([ ])([ ]) ← **Substitute.**

= [ ] ← **Simplify.**

The area is [ ] ft^2.

CA Standards Check

1. Find the area of the parallelogram.

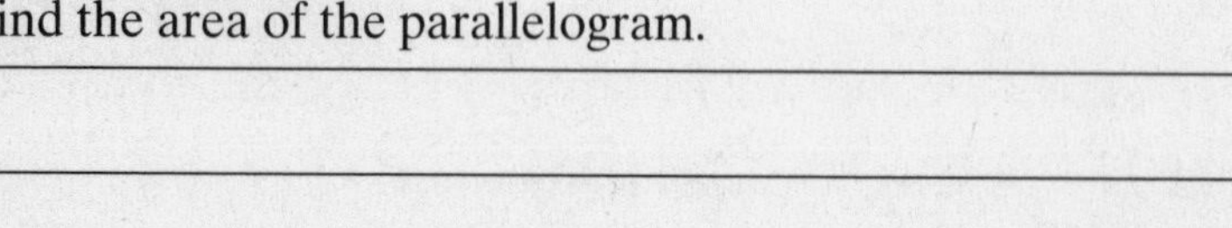

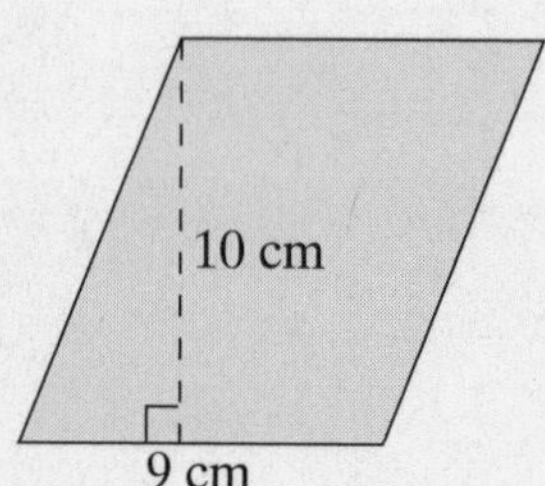

Name ____________________ Class ____________ Date ____________

Example

❷ Perimeter of a Parallelogram Find the perimeter of the parallelogram at the right.

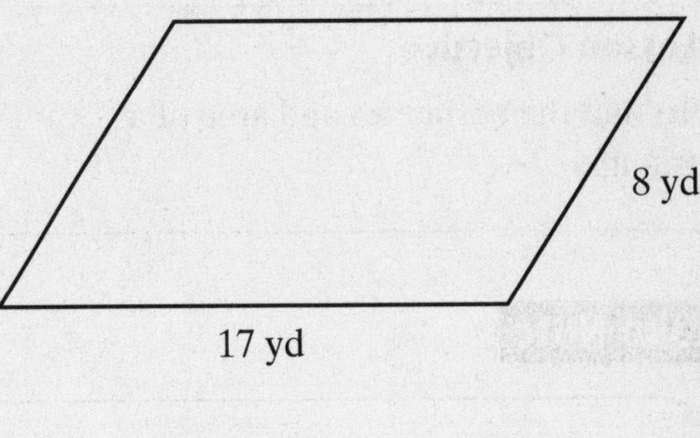

$P = \square + \square$ ← **The perimeter is the** ☐ **of the bases and the sides.**

$P = \square + \square$ ← **Multiply.**

$P = \square$ ← **Add.**

The perimeter is ☐ yards.

CA Standards Check

2. a. Find the perimeter of the parallelogram at the right.

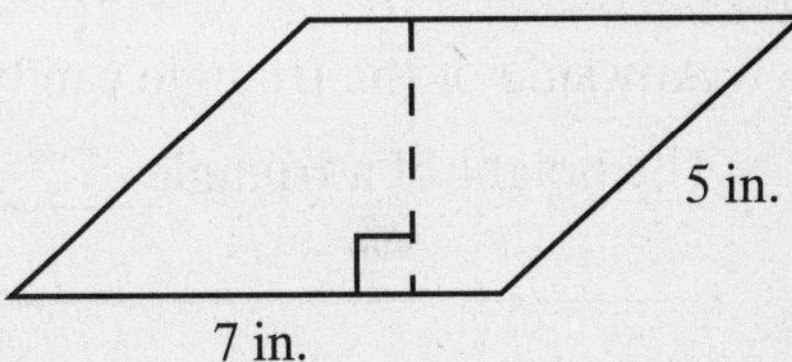

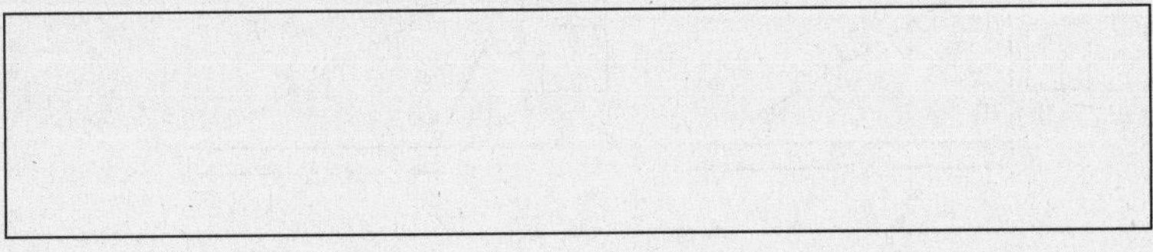

b. Reasoning The perimeter of a parallelogram is 45 inches. What would the perimeter be if the length of the bases and the sides were doubled? Explain.

Name ______________________ Class ______________ Date ______________

Lesson 8-3

Perimeter and Area of a Triangle

Lesson Objective	California Content Standards
To find the perimeter and area of a triangle	AF 3.1

Take Note

Area of a Triangle

The area of a triangle is equal to half the product of any [______] b and the corresponding [______] h.

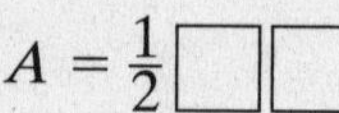

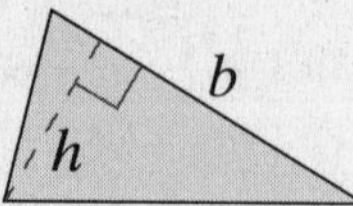

Any side of the triangle can be considered the ______________________

The height of a triangle ______________________

____

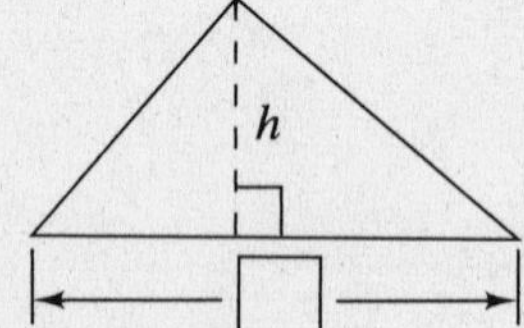

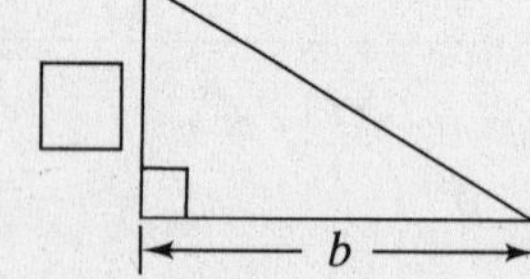

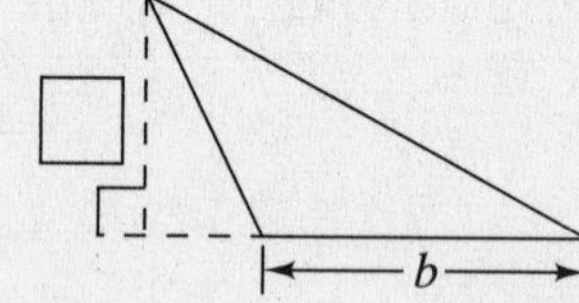

Example

1 **Finding the Perimeter of a Triangle** A school is creating a triangular playground with the dimensions shown. How many yards of fencing are needed to fence the playground?

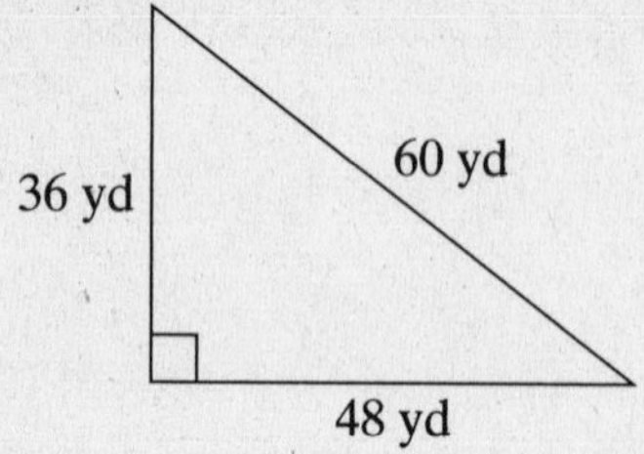

P = [______] [ ] 48 [ ] 60 ← **Find the perimeter.**

= [______] ← **Simplify.**

The school needs [______] yards of fencing to fence the playground.

Example

❷ Finding the Area of a Triangle Find the area of each triangle.

a.

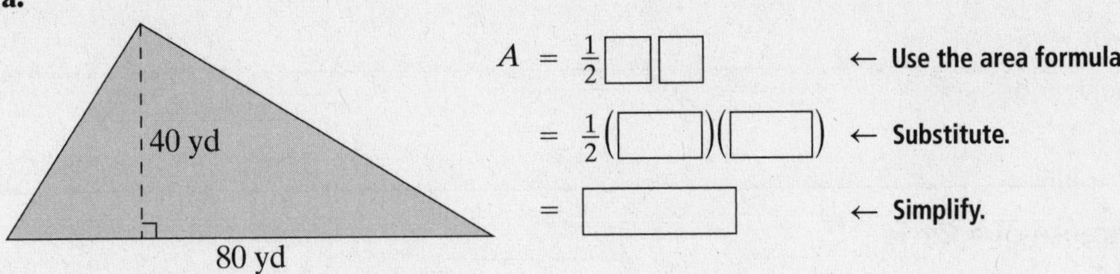

The area is ______ yd^2.

b. The triangle has side lengths of 16.2 cm, 15.4 cm, and 2.4 cm. Draw the height going to the base of length 2.4 cm. The height is 15 cm.

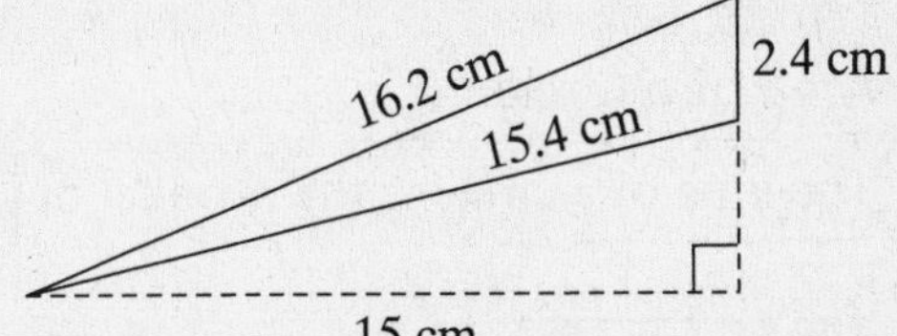

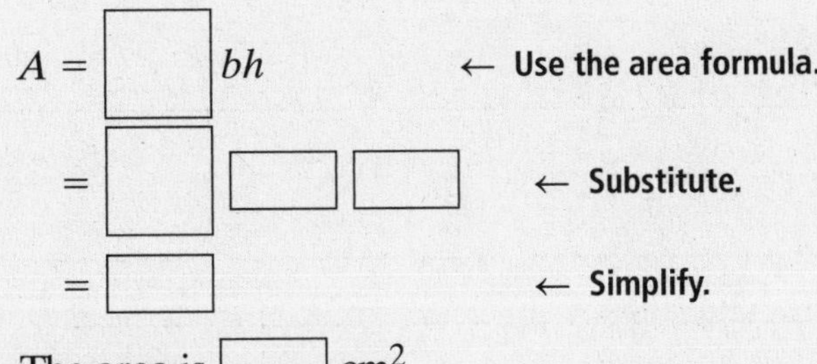

The area is ______ cm^2.

CA Standards Check

1. Find the perimeter of a triangle with sides 5 cm, 6 cm, and 8 cm.

2. Find the area of each triangle.

a.

26.8 m 12 m 19 m

36 m

b.

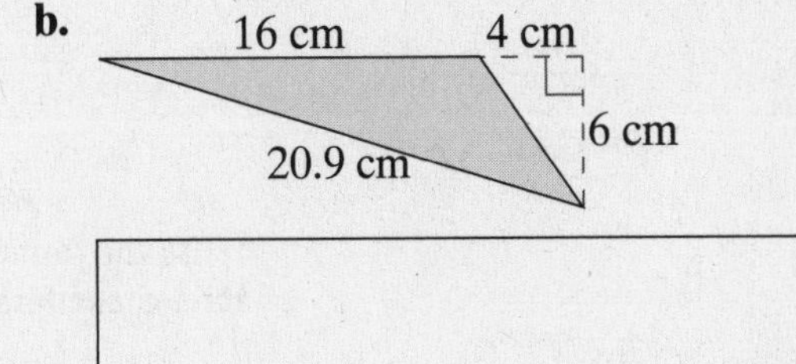

Lesson 8-4

Circumference and Area of a Circle

Lesson Objective	California Content Standards
To find the circumference and area of a circle	MG 1.1 (key), MG 1.2

Take Note

Circumference of a Circle

The circumference of a circle is ☐ times the ☐ d.

$$C = \pi d = 2\pi r$$

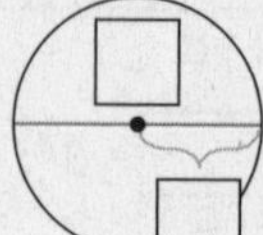

Area of a Circle

The area of a circle is the product of ☐ and the square of the ☐ r.

$$A = \pi r^2$$

Circumference is ________________________________

____

Pi (π) is ________________________________

____

Examples

1 Finding the Circumference of a Circle Find the circumference of each circle. Round to the nearest tenth.

a. Use 3.14 for π.

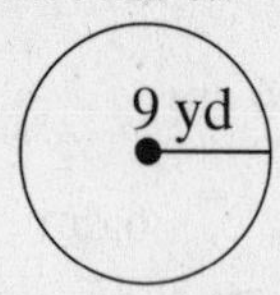

b. Use $\frac{22}{7}$ for π.

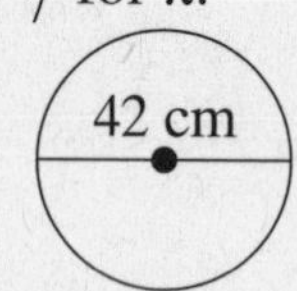

← **Use the formula for a circumference.** →

← **Substitute.** →

a. C = ☐

= 2(3.14)(☐)

= ☐

The circumference is about ☐ yd.

b. C = ☐

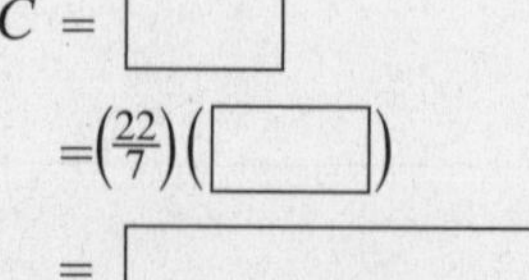

$= \left(\frac{22}{7}\right)$(☐)

= ☐

The circumference is about ☐ cm.

Name ______________________ Class ______________ Date ______________

❷ Finding the Area of a Circle A pizza has a diameter of 28 cm. What is the area of the pizza? Round to the nearest tenth.

$r = \dfrac{\square}{2} = \square$ ← **The radius is half of the diameter.**

$A = \square$ ← **Use the formula for the area of a circle.**

$= \pi(\square)^2$ ← **Substitute $\square$ for the radius.**

$\approx \square$ ← **Use a calculator.**

$\approx \square$ ← **Round to the nearest tenth.**

The area of the pizza is about $\square$ cm^2.

CA Standards Check

1. Find the circumference of the circle. Round to the nearest tenth.

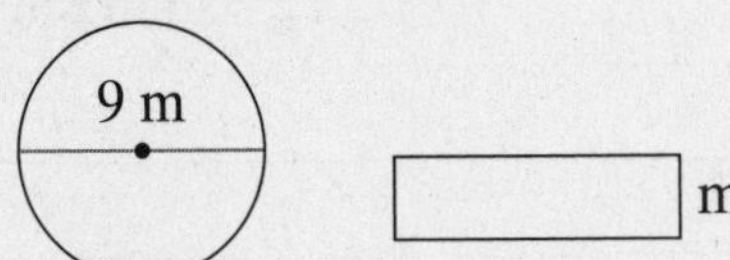

$\square$ m

2. Find the area of the circle. Round to the nearest square unit.

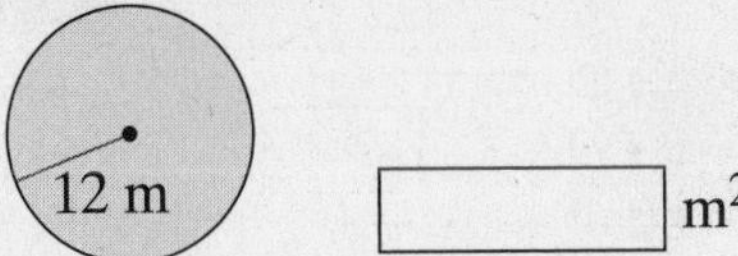

$\square$ m^2

Name ____________ Class ____________ Date ____________

Lesson 8-5

Three-Dimensional Figures

Lesson Objective	California Content Standards
To identify and draw three-dimensional figures	MG 1.0, prepares for MG 1.3

Vocabulary

A three-dimensional figure is ____________

A face is ____________

An edge is ____________

A prism is ____________

Prism

The bases of a prism are ____________

The height of a prism is ____________

A cube is ____________

A [ ] has two congruent parallel [ ] that are [ ].

The height of a cylinder is ____________

A [ ] has [ ] faces that meet at one point, a [ ], and a base that is a [ ].

A [ ] has one circular [ ] and one [ ].

A [ ] is the set of all points in space that are the same distance from a [ ] point.

Name _______________ Class _______________ Date _______________

Examples

❶ **Naming Figures** Name the geometric figure.

The figure is a ☐.

❷ **Drawing Three-Dimensional Figures** Draw a pentagonal prism.

Step 1 Draw a ☐.

Step 2 Draw a second

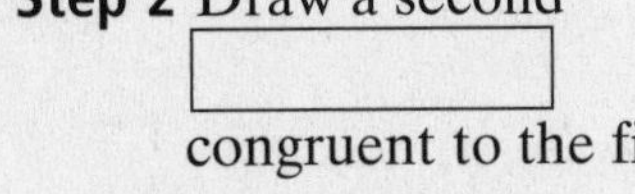

congruent to the first.

Step 3 Connect the vertices. Use

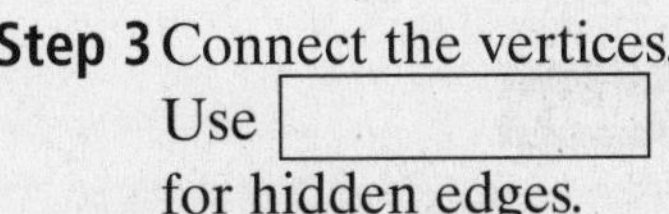

for hidden edges.

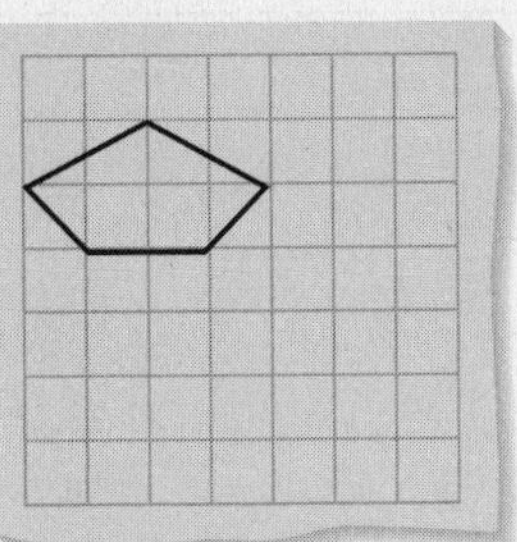

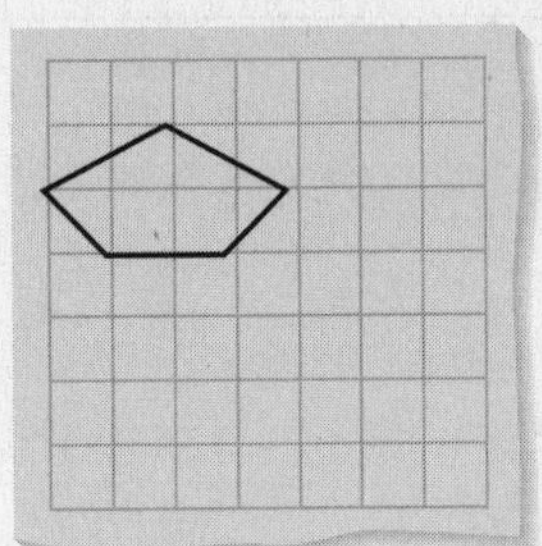

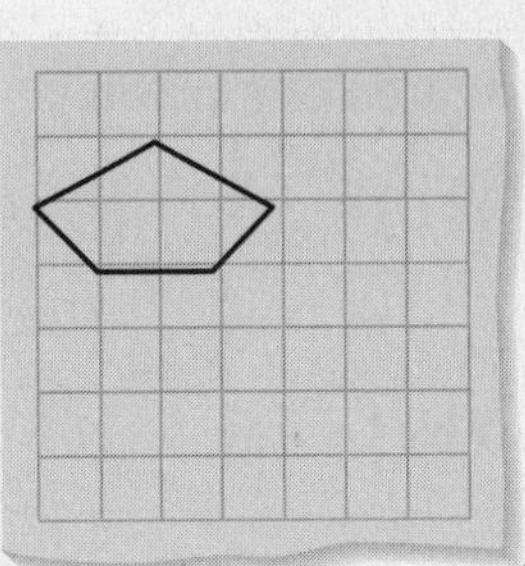

CA Standards Check

1. Name each figure.

a.

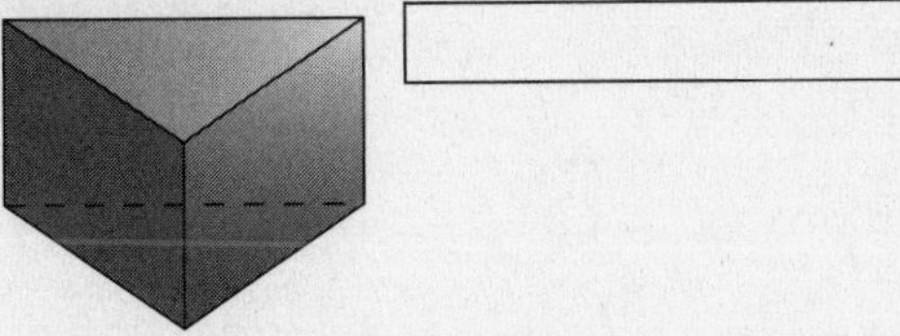

b.

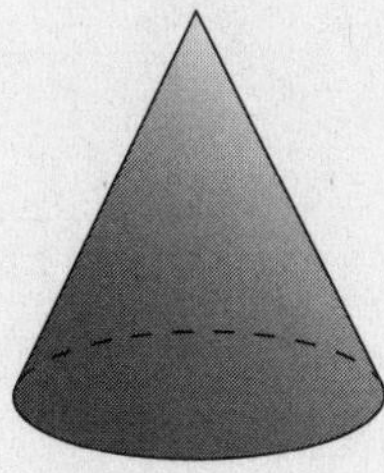

2. Use the grid to draw a triangular prism.

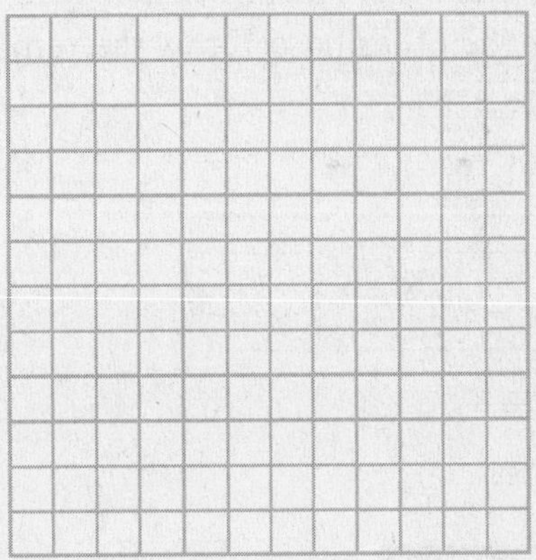

Name ______________________ Class ______________ Date ______________

Lesson 8-6

Surface Areas of Prisms and Cylinders

Lesson Objective	**California Content Standards**
To draw nets and find surface areas of three-dimensional figures	MG 1.0

Vocabulary

A net is ____

The surface area of a prism is ______________________________

Example

1 Drawing a Net Draw a net for the cube.

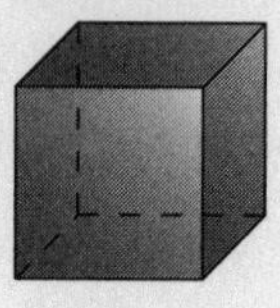

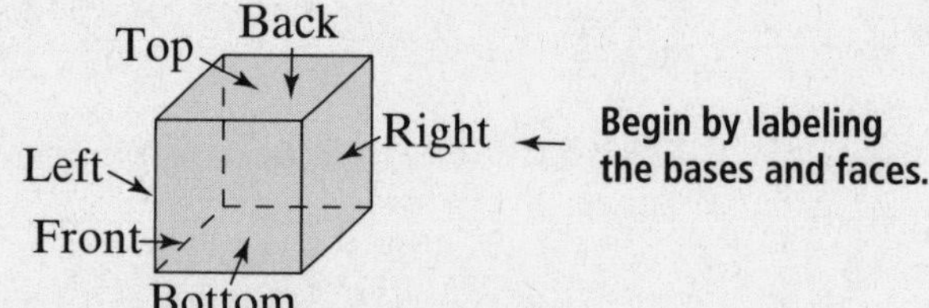

First, draw one base. Then draw one face that connects both bases.
Next, draw the other base. Draw the remaining faces.

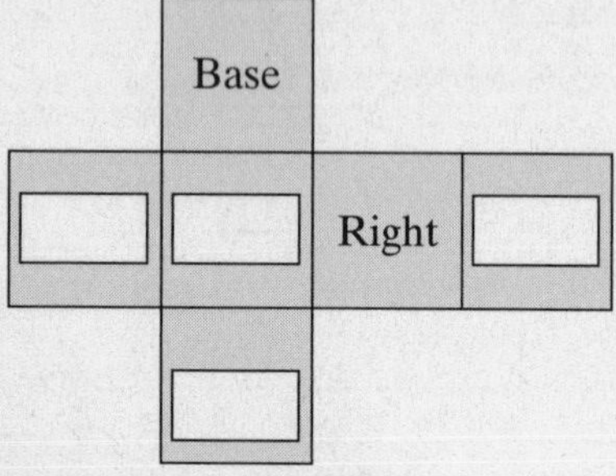

CA Standards Check

1. Draw a different net for the cube in Example 1.

Examples

❷ Finding the Surface Area of a Prism Find the surface area of the triangular prism.

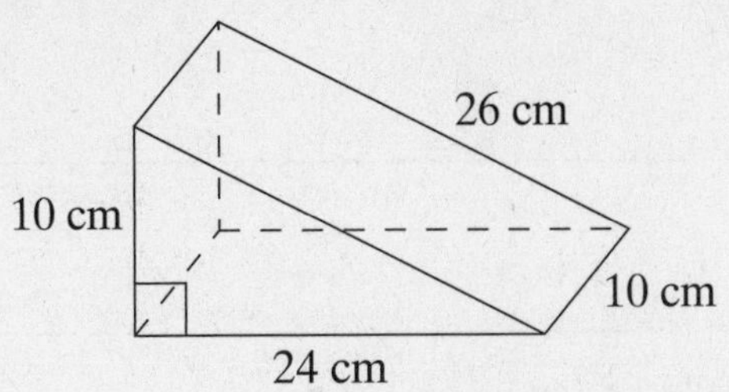

First draw a net for the prism.

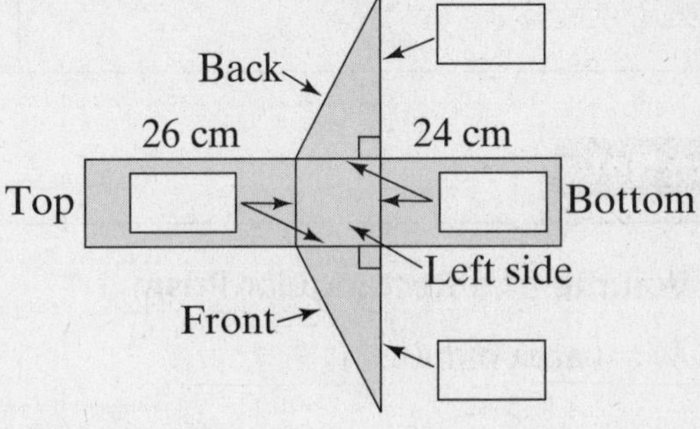

Then find the total area of the five faces.

top	bottom	left side	front	back	
$10(\square)$ +	$10(\square)$ +	$10(\square)$ +	$\frac{1}{2}(\square)(\square)$ +	$\frac{1}{2}(\square)(\square)$	= $\square$

The surface area of the triangular prism is $\square$ cm^2.

❸ Finding the Surface Area of a Cylinder Find the surface area of the cylinder. Round to the nearest tenth.

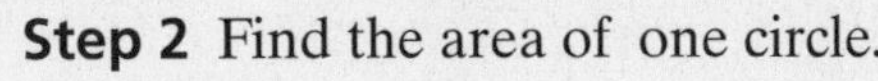

Step 1 Draw a net.

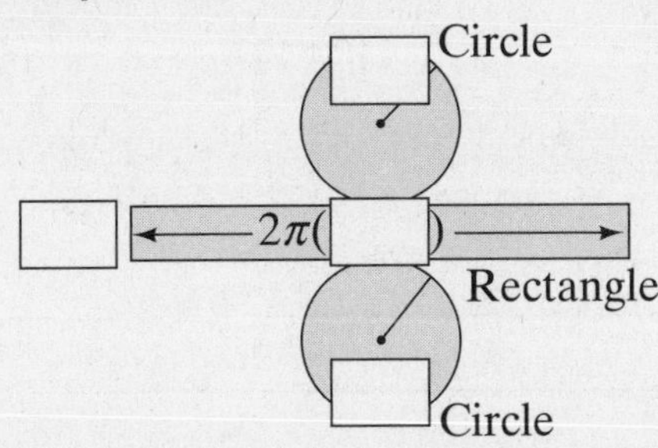

Step 2 Find the area of one circle.

$$A = \pi r^2$$
$$= \pi(\square)^2$$
$$= \pi(\square)$$
$$\approx \square$$

Step 3 Find the area of the rectangle.

$(2\pi r)\square = 2\pi(3)(\square) = \square\pi \approx \square$

Step 4 Add the areas of the two circles and the rectangle.

Surface Area = $\square + \square + \square = \square$

The surface area of the cylinder is about $\square$ cm^2.

CA Standards Check

2. Find the surface area of the rectangular prism.

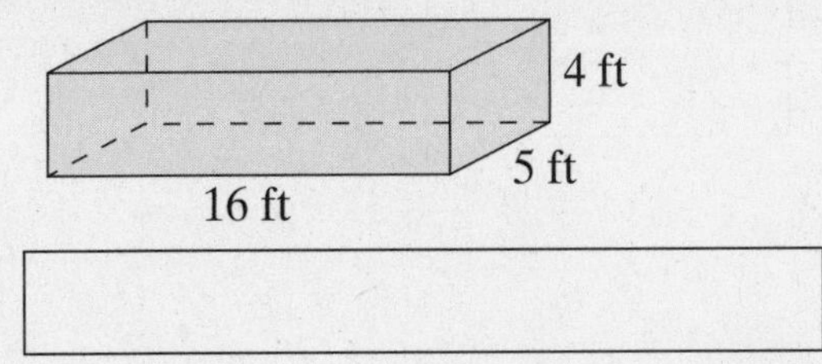

3. What is the surface area of the cylinder? Round to the nearest tenth.

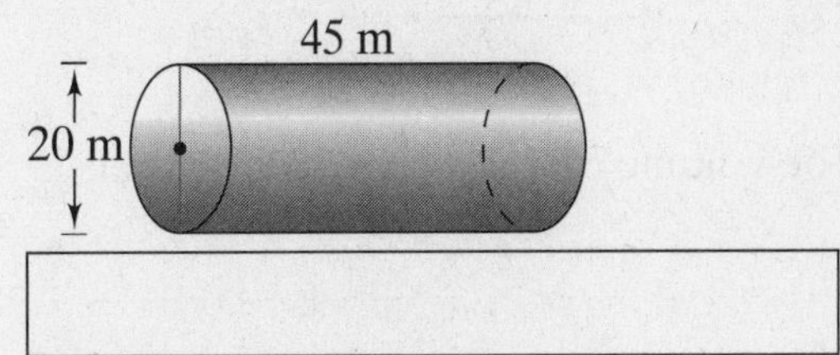

Name ______________________ Class ______________ Date ______________

Lesson 8-7

Volumes of Prisms and Cylinders

Lesson Objective	California Content Standards
To find the volume of prisms and cylinders	MG 1.3, MR 2.1

Take Note

Volume of a Rectangular Prism

V = area of base · ______

$= Bh$

$=$ ______

Volume of a Triangular Prism

V = area of base · height

$= Bh$

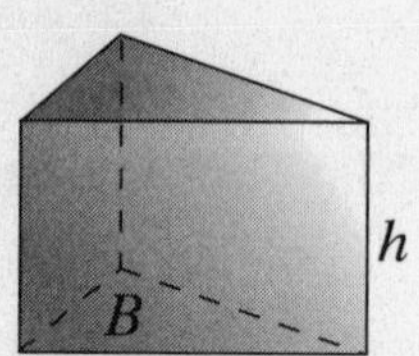

Volume of a Cylinder

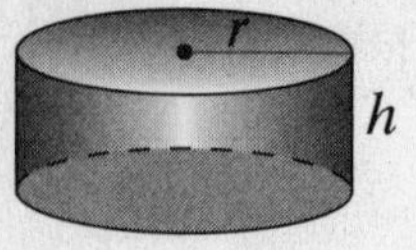

The volume of a three-dimensional figure is ______________________________

____

A cubic unit is ______________________________

Examples

1 Finding the Volume of a Rectangular Prism Find the volume of the rectangular prism.

$V =$ ______ ← **Use the formula.**

$=$ (____)(____)(____) ← **Substitute.**

$=$ ______ ← **Multiply.**

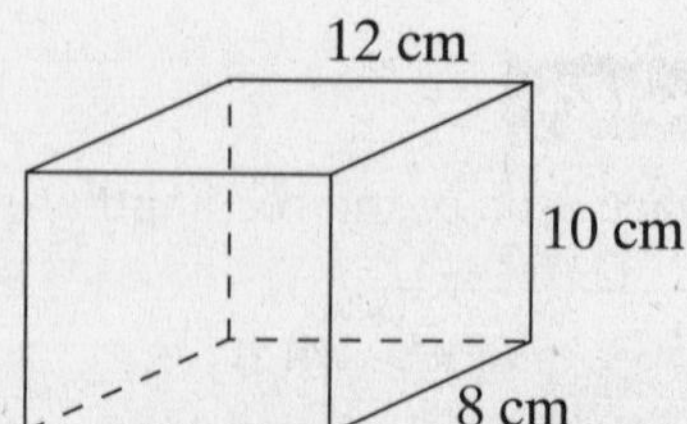

The volume of the rectangular prism is ______ cm^3.

Name ______________________ Class ______________ Date ______________

❷ Finding the Volume of a Triangular Prism Find the volume of the triangular prism.

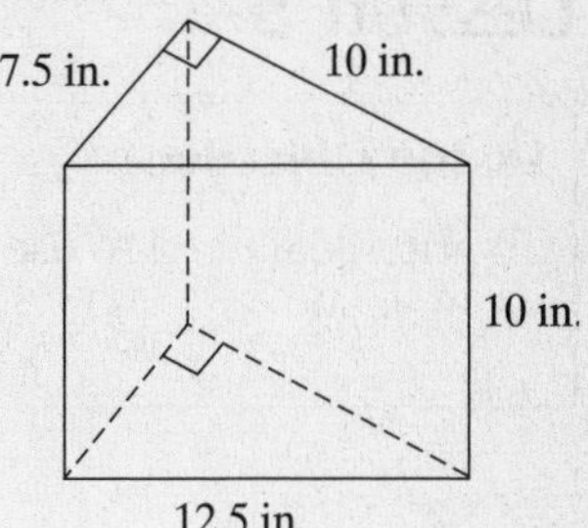

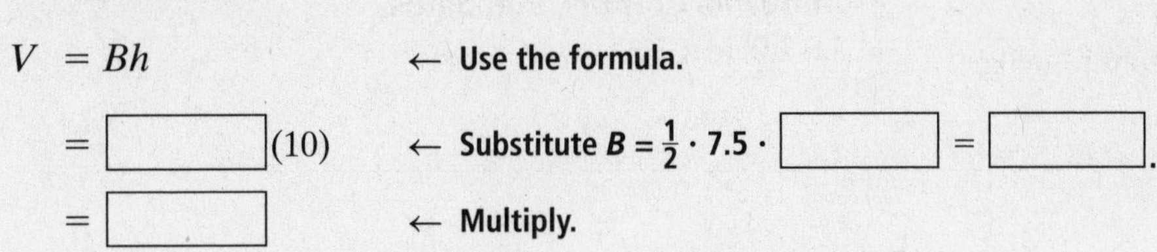

$V = Bh$ ← **Use the formula.**

$= \square(10)$ ← **Substitute $B = \frac{1}{2} \cdot 7.5 \cdot \square = \square$.**

$= \square$ ← **Multiply.**

The volume of the triangular prism is ☐ cubic inches.

❸ Finding the Volume of a Cylinder Estimate the volume of the cylindrical glass. Then find the volume to the nearest cubic unit.

Estimate

$V = \square$ ← **Use the formula.**

$\approx (\square)(\square)^2(\square)$ ← **Use 3 to estimate π.**

$\approx \square \square = \square$ ← **Use 30 to estimate 27.**

18 cm

6 cm

The estimated volume is ☐ cm^3.

Calculate: $V = \pi(\square)^2(\square) \approx \square$. ← **Use a calculator.**

The calculated volume is about ☐ cm^3. ← **Round to the nearest whole number.**

CA Standards Check

1. If the height of the prism in Example 1 is doubled, what is the volume?

2. If the height of the prism in Example 2 is doubled, what is the volume?

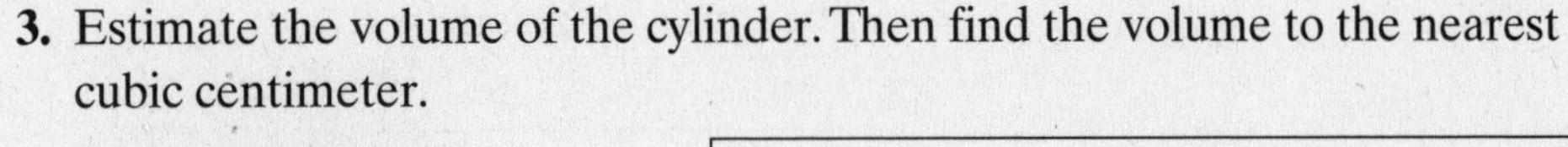

3. Estimate the volume of the cylinder. Then find the volume to the nearest cubic centimeter.

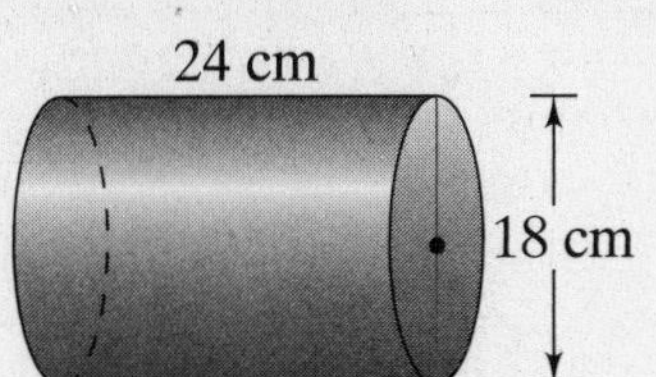

Name ____________ Class ____________ Date ____________

Lesson 9-1

Patterns and Graphs

Lesson Objective	California Content Standards
To graph data and to use graphs to make predictions	AF 2.0, MR 2.3

Example

1 Graphing Data Graph the data in the table.

The pattern in the first column of data suggests a horizontal interval of 20. Graphs that have from 6 to 10 intervals are easy to read. The greatest value in the second column is 50. Divide 50 by a factor from 6 to 10.

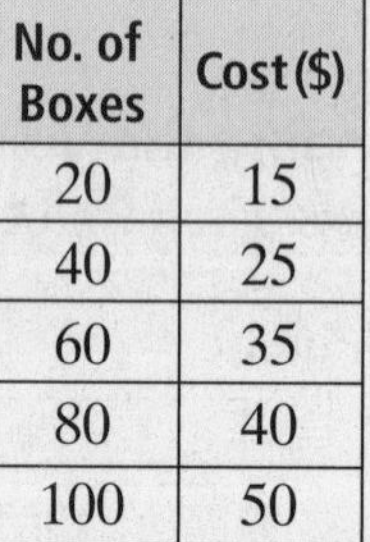

No. of Boxes	Cost ($)
20	15
40	25
60	35
80	40
100	50

Choose ☐, since 50 is divisible by ☐.

50 ÷ ☐ = ☐ ← **Divide the greatest amount by a compatible number.**

Use ☐ intervals of 5 for the vertical scale.

Use points to represent the data.

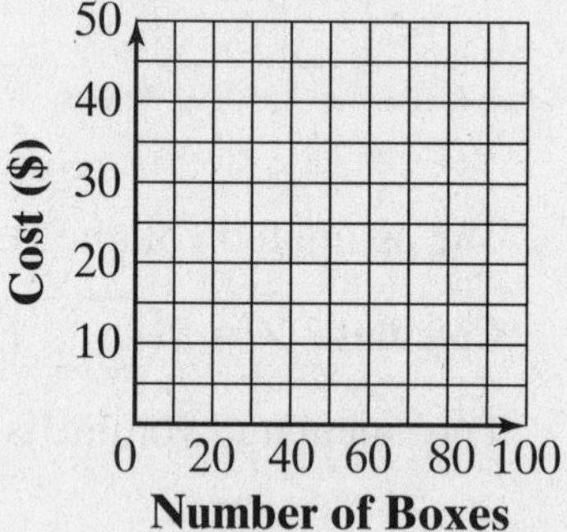

CA Standards Check

1. Graph the data in the table below.

Amount of Yogurt (c)	Price ($)
50	26
100	49
150	72
200	95

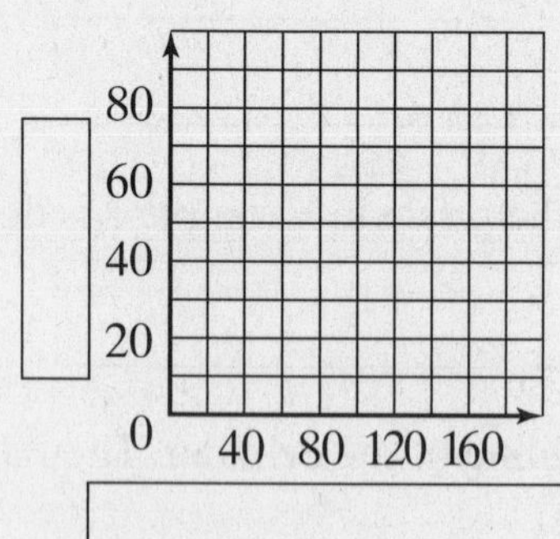

Name ______________________ Class ______________ Date ______________

Examples

❷ Estimating on a Graph The graph shows the cost of renting a bowling lane for an hour. Which is the best estimate for the cost of the rental for 7 people?

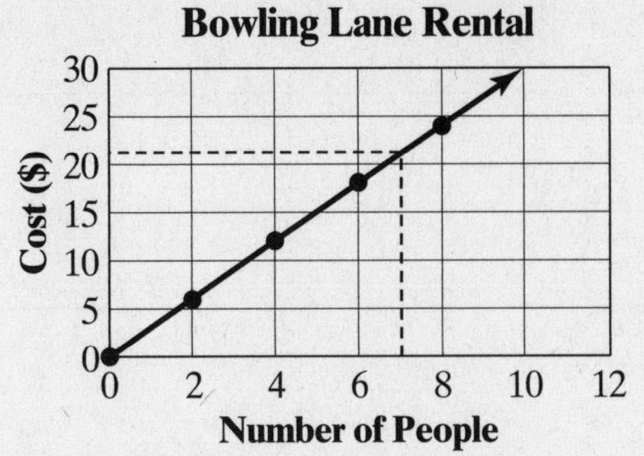

← Draw lines to locate the value on the [ ] axis that corresponds to 7 on the [ ] axis.

← The cost of the rental for 7 people is more than [ ] but less than [ ]. Estimate the cost as [ ].

The cost of a rental for 7 people is about [ ].

❸ Making a Prediction Estimate the cost of 600 gallons of water.

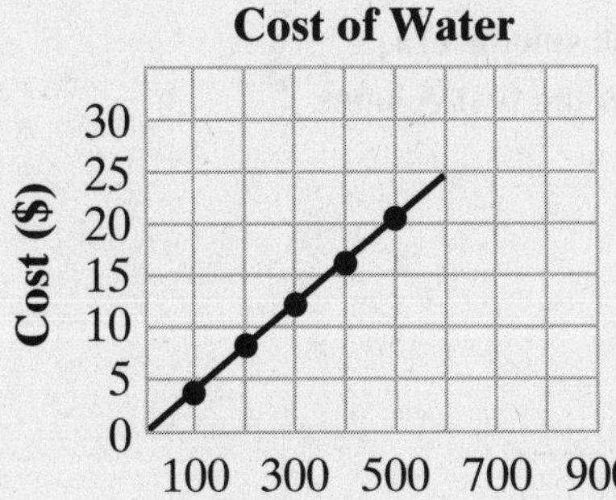

← Extend the graph beyond 500 gallons.

← For 600 gallons, the cost is slightly less than $25. Estimate the answer.

The cost of 600 gallons is about [ ].

CA Standards Check

2. Use the graph in Example 2 to estimate the cost of the rental for 5 people.

[ ]

3. Use the graph in Example 3 to estimate the cost of 800 gallons of water.

[ ]

Name ________________ Class ____________ Date ____________

Lesson 9-2

Patterns and Tables

Lesson Objective	California Content Standards
To use tables to represent and describe patterns	AF 3.0, MR 3.1

Vocabulary

A sequence is ____

Examples

❶ **Representing a Pattern** Use the table below to find the number of horseshoes for 15 horses.

Number of Horses	Number of Horseshoes	
1	4	= 1 × ☐
3	12	= 3 × ☐
5		= 5 × ☐
9		= 9 × ☐

← **The values in the second column are ☐ times the values in the first column.**

To find the number of horseshoes for 15 horses, multiply 15 by ☐.

The number of horseshoes for 15 horses is ☐.

❷ **Finding the Value of a Term** Which sequence follows the rule $-4z + 12$, where z represents the position of a term in a sequence?

A. 16, 4, −8, −20, −32 **B.** −12, −8, −4, 0, 4

C. 12, 8, 4, 0, −4 **D.** 24, 12, 0, −12, −24

Position	$-4z + 12$	Value of Term
0		12
	$-4(1) + 12$	
		−4

← **Substitute 0, 1, 2, 3, and 4 for *z*.**

The correct answer is choice ☐.

3 Using a Table With a Sequence Write an expression to describe the sequence 2, 4, 6, 8, 10, . . . Then, find the 10th term in the sequence.

2	4	6	8	10	...
↑	↑	↑	↑	↑	
Position 1	**Position 2**	**Position 3**	**Position 4**	**Position 5**	**and so on.**

Make a table that pairs the position of each term in the sequence with its value.

Position	1	2	3	4	5	. . .	n
Value of Term	2	☐	6	☐	10	. . .	☐

← **The value of each term is ☐ times its position.**

Let n = the term number. You can write the expression $n \cdot 2$, or ☐.

$n \cdot 2 = 10 \cdot 2 =$ ☐ ← **Substitute 10 for n to find the 10th term.**

CA Standards Check

1. The table shows the number of miles a car can travel using different amounts of gasoline. Complete the table. Find the distance the car can travel using 15 gallons of gasoline.

Gas (gal)	Miles Driven
1	18.1
2	36.2
3	54.3
4	☐
5	☐

2. Use the rule $2n + 3$, where n represents the position of a term in a sequence. Find the first four terms in the sequence.

3. Write an expression to describe the sequence −8, −7, −6, −5, ... Find the 10th term in the sequence.

Name ______________________ Class ______________ Date ______________

Lesson 9-3

Function Rules

Lesson Objective	California Content Standards
To write and evaluate functions	NS 2.3, AF 2.3, MR 3.0

Vocabulary

A function is ____

____

Examples

1 Writing a Function Rule Suppose you can bicycle at an average speed of 10 mi/h. Write a function rule that describes the relationship between time and the distance you travel.

You can ***make a table*** to solve this problem.

Input: time (h)	1	2	3	4
Output: distance (mi)	10	20		

distance in miles = 10 · time in hours ← **Write the function rule in words.**

☐ = 10☐ ← **Use variables *d* for distance and *t* for time.**

2 Using Tables to Analyze Functions Write a rule for the function represented by the table.

x	*y*
0	−2
1	2
2	6
3	10
4	14

When $x = 0$, $y = -2$.

Each *y* equals ☐ times *x*, plus ☐.

The function rule is ______.

CA Standards Check

1. Write a function rule for the relationship between the time and the distance you travel at an average speed of 62 mi/h.

Example

❸ Evaluating Functions Use the function $y = 2x - 3$. Find y when $x = -1, 0, 2$, and 3. Then make a table for the function.

$y = 2(-1) - 3 =$ ☐ ← **Substitute −1, 0, 2, and 3 for *x*.**

$y = 2(0) - 3 =$ ☐

$y = 2(2) - 3 =$ ☐

$y = 2(3) - 3 =$ ☐

List the values in a table. →

x	$y = 2x - 3$
−1	
0	
2	
3	

CA Standards Check

2. Write a rule for the function represented by the table below.

x	0	1	2	3
y	1	5	9	13

☐

3. Use the function rule $y = 2x - 4$. Find y for $x = 0, 1, 2$, and 3. Then make a table for the function.

☐ = ☐(☐) − ☐ = ☐

☐ = ☐(☐) − ☐ = ☐

☐ = ☐(☐) − ☐ = ☐

☐ = ☐(☐) − ☐ = ☐

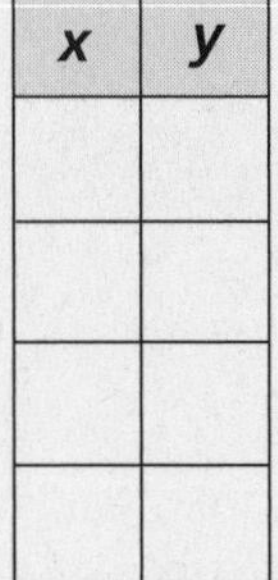

x	y

Lesson 9-4

Using Tables, Rules, and Graphs

Lesson Objective	California Content Standards
To find solutions to applications problems using tables, rules, and graphs	NS 2.0, AF 1.0, AF 2.2

Example

1 Graphing Using a Table The table shows the relationship between gallons (input) and quarts (output). The rule $y = 4x$, where x represents the number of gallons, and y represents the number of quarts. Graph the relationship represented by the table. Graph gallons on the horizontal axis and quarts on the vertical axis. Draw a line through the points.

Gallons	Quarts
1	4
2	8
3	☐
4	☐

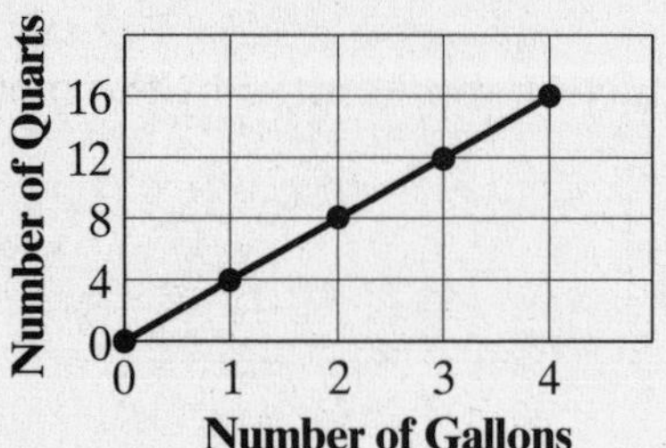

CA Standards Check

1. Graph each function.

a.

Input x	Output y
0	3
1	5
2	7
3	9

b.

Input x	Output y
5	3.5
10	7
15	10.5
20	14

Name ______________ Class ______________ Date ______________

Example

❷ Graphing Using a Function Rule After one week, a 1-in. seedling grows to 3 inches. The second week, its height is 5 in., and the third week its height is 7 in. Write and graph a rule to find the height of the plant in week 4.

Step 1 Write a rule.

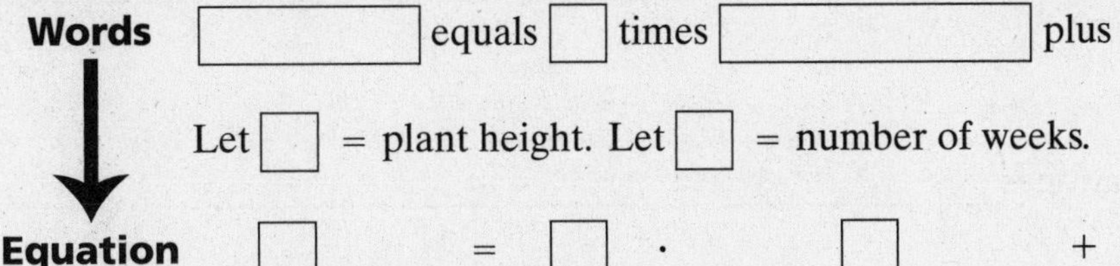

Step 2 Make a table of values. Graph the function.

Number of Weeks	Process	Plant Height (in.)
1	1 · ☐ + 1	3
2	2 · ☐ + 1	5
3	3 · ☐ + 1	7
4	4 · ☐ + 1	☐

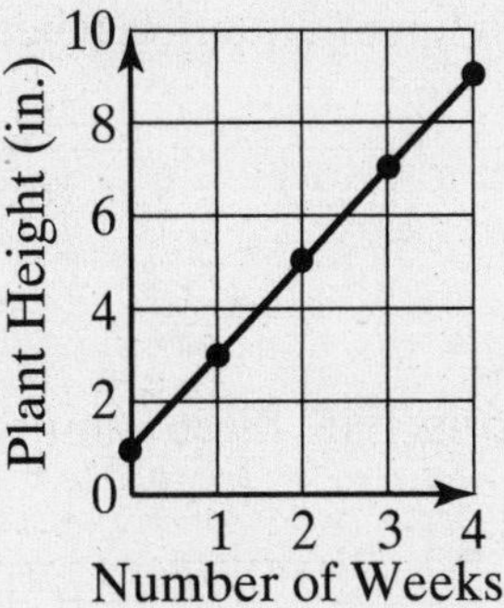

The height of the plant in week 4 is ☐

CA Standards Check

2. A bus travels 60 miles per hour. Write and graph a rule to find the number of miles the bus can travel in 4.5 hours.

Number of Hours	Process	Distance (mi)

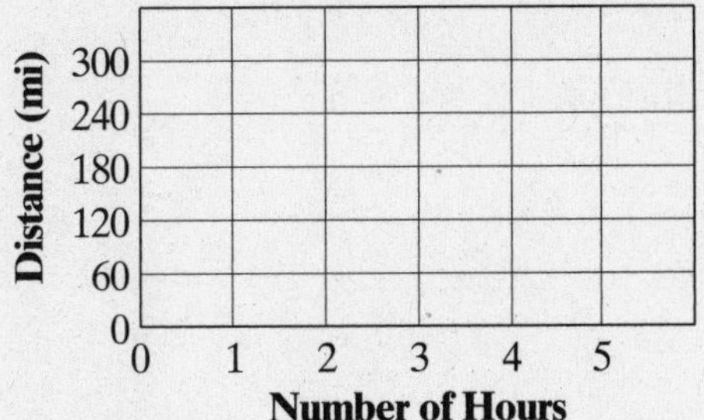

Name ______________________ Class ______________ Date ______________

Lesson 9-5

Graphing Linear Equations

Lesson Objective	**California Content Standards**
To find solutions of linear equations and to graph linear equations	AF 1.0

Vocabulary

A solution of a linear equation is ______________________________

A graph of an equation is ______________________________

____

An equation is a linear equation when ______________________________

____

Examples

❶ **Finding Solutions** Find three solutions of $y = x - 5$. Organize your solutions in a table.

x	$x - 5$	y	Solution (x, y)
5	☐ − 5		
6	☐ − 5		
0	☐ − 5		

❷ **Graphing to Test Solutions** Graph the equation $y = x - 5$. Is $(3, -4)$ a solution to the equation?

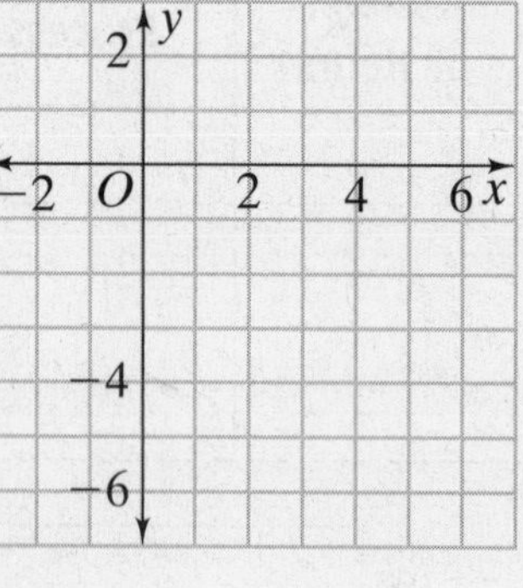

Step 1 Plot the three ordered-pair solutions from Example 1.

Step 2 Draw a line through the points.

Step 3 Test $(3, -4)$ by plotting the point in the same coordinate plane. Look to see if the point lies on the line of the graph of the equation.

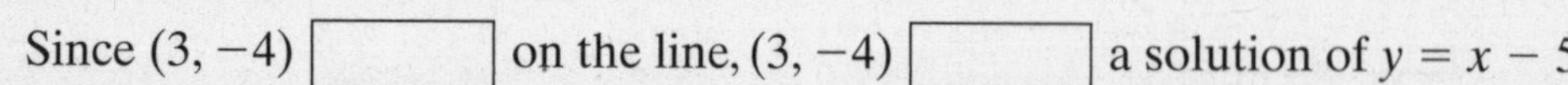

Since $(3, -4)$ ☐ on the line, $(3, -4)$ ☐ a solution of $y = x - 5$.

Example

❸ Graphing a Linear Equation Graph the linear equation $y = x - 1$.

Step 1 Make a table of solutions. Use zero as well as positive and negative values for x.

x	$x - 1$	y	(x, y)
−4	$\square - 1$		
−2	$\square - 1$		
0	$\square - 1$		
1	$\square - 1$		
3	$\square - 1$		

Step 2 Graph the points. Draw a line through the points.

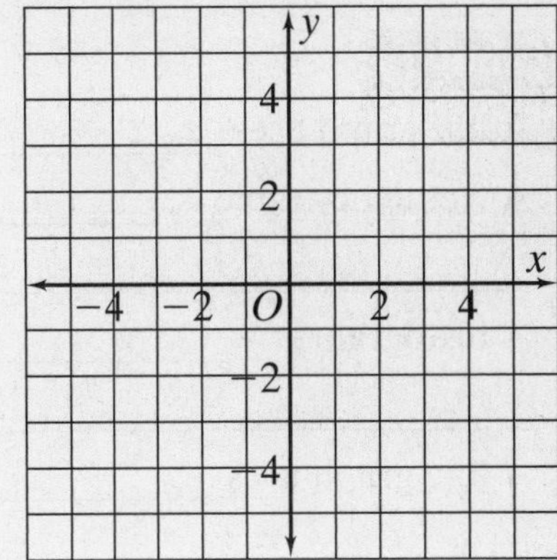

CA Standards Check

1. Find three solutions of each equation. Use $x = -2, x = 0$, and $x = 2$.

   a. $y = x + 8$

   b. $y = x - 1$

   c. $y = -2x$

2. Tell whether $(7, 12)$ is a solution of $y = 3x - 1$.

3. Graph each linear equation.

   a. $y = x + 4$

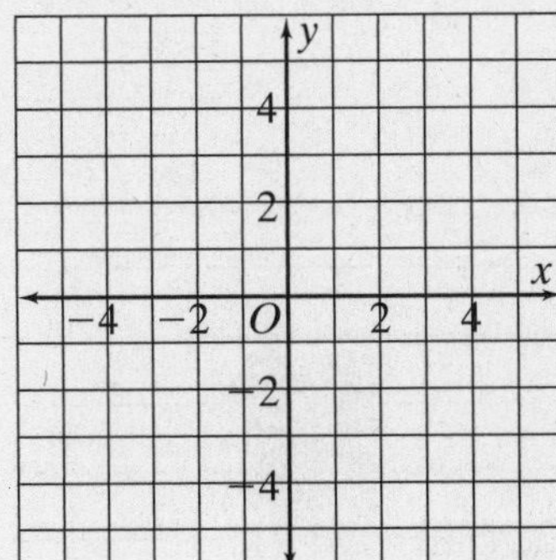

   b. $y = \frac{1}{2}x$

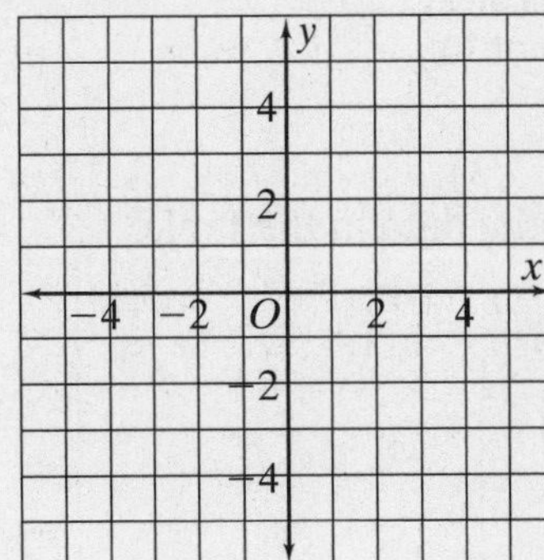

   c. $y = -x$

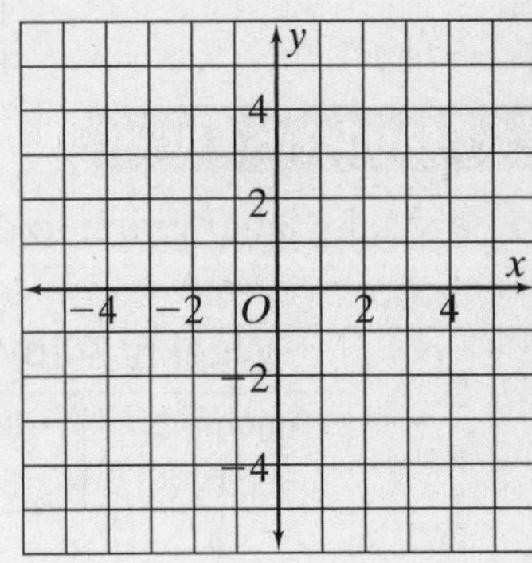

Name ______________________ Class ______________ Date ______________

Lesson 10-1

Making Data Displays

Lesson Objective	**California Content Standards**
To make data displays	Prepares for SDAP 2.3

Vocabulary

A bar graph uses ______________________

A frequency table is ______________________

____

A histogram is ______________________

____

A line graph uses ______________________

Example

1 Making a Bar Graph Make a bar graph to display the data in the table.

Students With Employer Jobs

Age	Number of Students
14	33
15	60
16	74

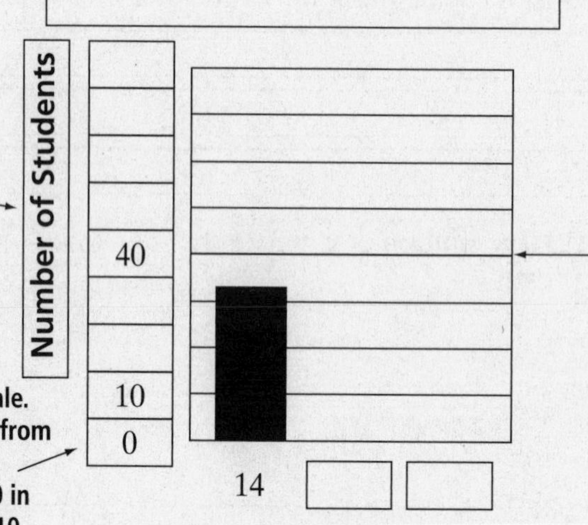

CA Standards Check

1. a. Make a bar graph to display the data in the table.

Weekly Allowance

Amount of Money ($)	Number of Students
4	10
5	21
6	34
8	12
10	6

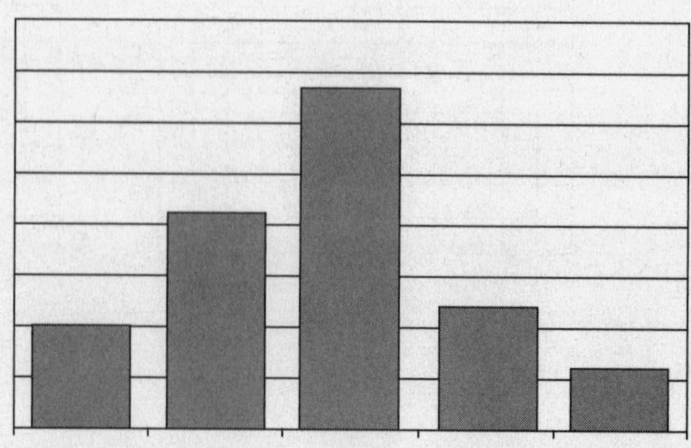

Examples

❷ Making a Histogram The data below show the number of hours spent on the Internet each week.

1 3 5 7 8 20 16 17 4 2 7 6 12 18 9 15 19 20 11 2 10 6 11 1 8 13 3
19 14 20 11 17 5 12 18 17 9 7 16 5 11 8

Make a frequency table and a histogram of the data. Use the equal-sized intervals 1–4, 5–8, 9–12, 13–16, and 17–20.

Hours Spent on the Internet

Hours	Frequency
1–4	𝍸 ‖
5–8	𝍸 𝍸 |
9–12	𝍸 |||
13–16	𝍸
17–20	𝍸 𝍸

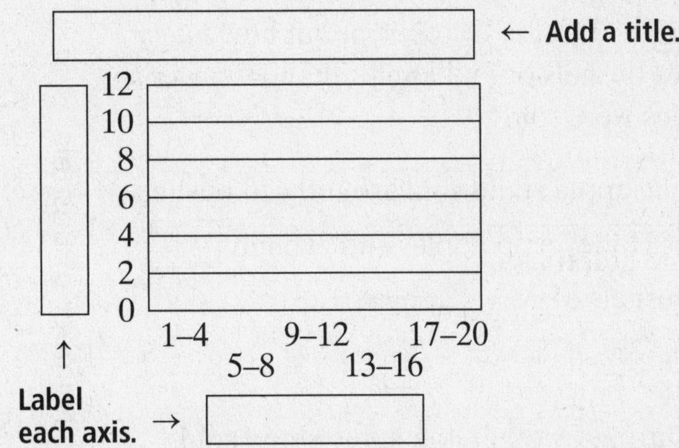

❸ Making a Line Graph Use the data in the table to make a line graph.

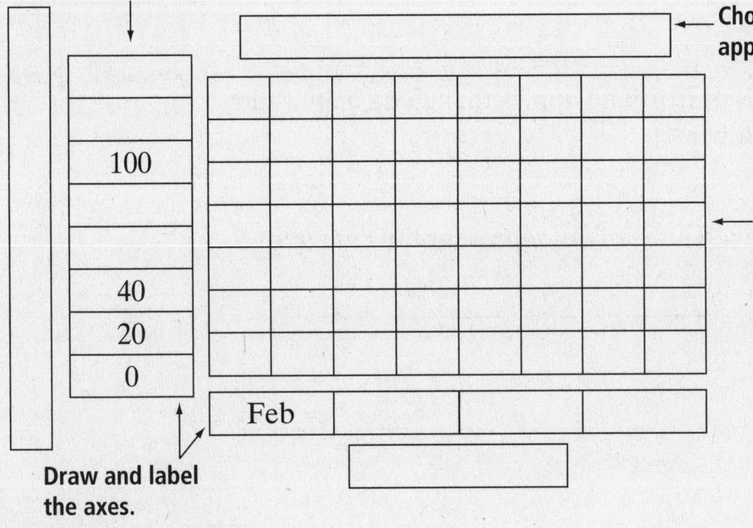

Running Shoes Sold

Month	Pairs Sold
February	54
March	86
April	121
May	115

CA Standards Check

2. Make a histogram of the ages of employees at a retail store:
28 20 44 72 65 40 59 29 22 36 28 61 30
27 33 55 48 24 28 32

3. Make a line graph of the data in the table.

Ticket Sales

Week	1	2	3	4
Tickets Sold	22	35	33	46

Lesson 10-2

Analyzing Data Displays

Lesson Objective	**California Content Standards**
To analyze data displays	SDAP 2.3, SDAP 2.5

Example

1 Analyzing Bar Graphs Use the bar graph at the right. During October, about how many fewer bushels of Fuji apples than Honeycrisp apples were sold?

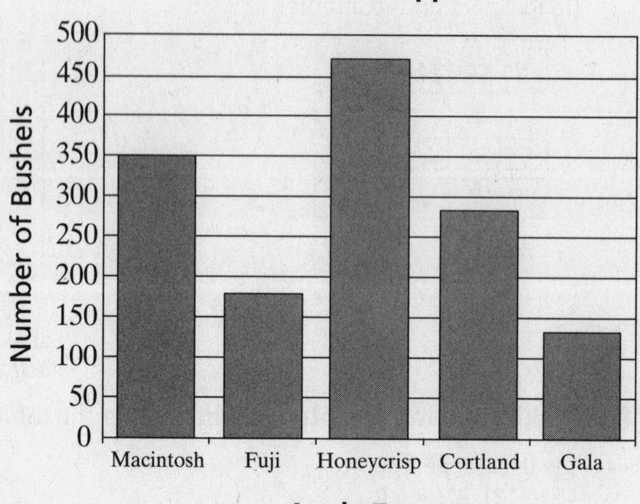

The apple stand sold around 470 bushels of Honeycrisp apples and around ☐ bushels of ☐ apples.

☐ − ☐ = ☐

During October, the apple stand sold about ☐ fewer bushels of Fuji apples than Honeycrisp apples.

CA Standards Check

1. a. About how many more bushels of Cortland apples than Gala apples did the apple stand sell during October?

☐

b. Reasoning Why is a bar graph a better way to represent the data above than a line graph?

☐

Examples

❷ **Analyzing Histograms** Use the histogram to the right. In the pottery class, how many students made fewer than 12 pieces of pottery?

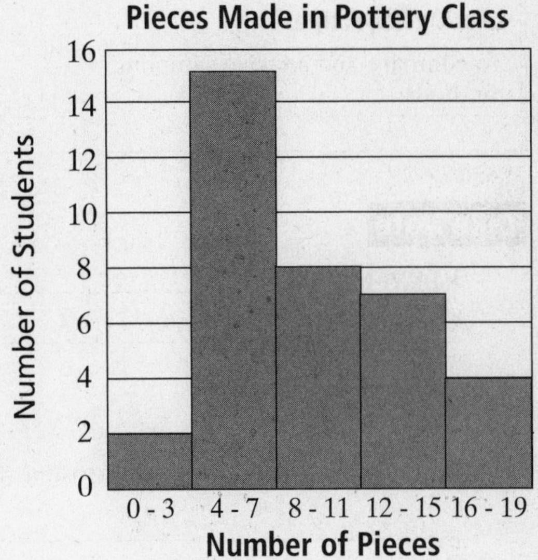

Students represented by the first [ ] intervals, 0–3, [ ], and [ ], made fewer than 12 pieces of pottery. So 2 + 15 + 8 = 25.

[ ] students made fewer than 12 pieces.

❸ **Analyzing Line Graphs** Use the line graph to the right. During which years did the annual amount of rainfall decrease?

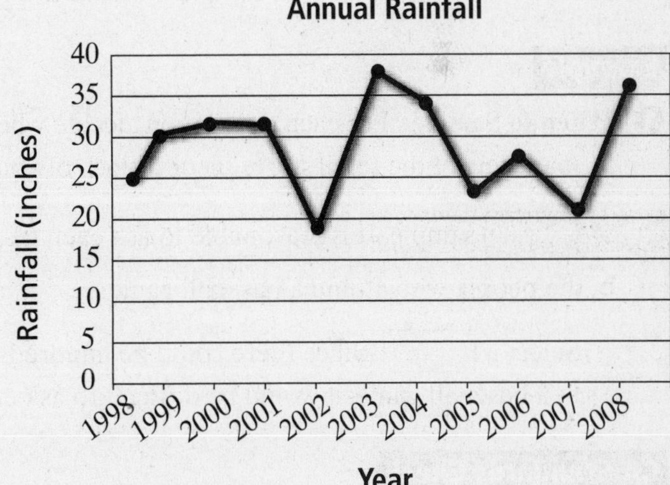

Rainfall decreased in 2002, 2004, 2005, and 2007.

CA Standards Check

2. a. In Example 2, how many students are represented by the histogram?

[ ]

3. a. In Example 3, which two years had the highest amounts of rainfall?

[ ]

b. What is the range of the data?

[ ]

Name ______________________ Class ____________ Date ____________

Lesson 10-3

Sampling

Lesson Objective	California Content Standards
To compare and analyze sampling methods	SDAP 2.1, SDAP 2.2, SDAP 2.4

Take Note

A population is ______________________

A sample is ______________________

Sampling Methods

Random Sampling Choose a sample so that ______________________

____

Systematic Sampling A sample is selected ______________________

Convenience Sampling A sample is selected ______________________

Example

1 When to Sample For each population, decide when to survey each member or to take a sample.

a. managers of the retail stores on one block of your downtown shopping area

[ ] sample. It is reasonable to ask each manager.

b. the people who attend a baseball game

Select a [ ]. Since there could be hundreds or thousands of people at a baseball game, it would be difficult to ask each of them.

CA Standards Check

1. Suppose you want to find the median height of the adults in your town. Would you select a sample or ask each adult? Explain.

Name ______________________ Class ______________ Date ______________

Examples

❷ Identifying Sampling Methods For each situation, decide which sampling method is used.

a. Tickets with stubs numbered from 1 to 1,000 were sold to 1,000 people. Mix the ticket stubs and select 25 numbers.

[ ] **Sampling:** Every ticket holder has an [ ] of being selected.

b. Select every 8th person who enters a theatre performance in an auditorium.

[ ] **Sampling:** The method follows a [ ].

c. Select every customer at the post office.

[ ] **Sampling:** The selected members are [ ].

❸ Understanding Samples You survey moviegoers at a 15-screen cinema complex to find out what types of movies they like to see. Decide which method below best represents the population. Explain.

a. You survey moviegoers exiting a foreign-language film.

People exiting a foreign-language film [ ] represent the general movie-going population.

b. You survey people in line to buy tickets at the box office.

By surveying people in the ticket line, you give all moviegoers [ ] chance of being surveyed. This sample is [ ] likely to represent the general movie-going population.

CA Standards Check

2. Suppose you sample every 10th person who walks into the library. Which method of sampling is this?

[ ]

3. You survey a store's customers. You ask why they chose the store. Which sample is more likely to be random? Explain.

a. You survey 20 people at the entrance from 5:00 P.M. to 8:00 P.M.

[ ]

b. You survey 20 people at the entrance throughout the day.

[ ]

Name ____________________ Class ____________________ Date ____________

Lesson 10-4

Surveys and Samples

Lesson Objective	**California Content Standards**
To identify biased survey questions	SDAP 2.0, SDAP 2.3, SDAP 2.4

Vocabulary

A biased question is ______________________________

____

Example

1 Identifying Biased Questions Is each question *fair* or *biased*? Explain.

a. "Which is a brighter color: pink or green?"
This question is ______. The choices are presented equally.

b. "Is an electric pink shirt brighter than a green shirt?"
This question is ______. It implies that pink is brighter, thus influencing the responses.

CA Standards Check

1. Is each question *fair* or *biased*? Explain.

a. Which pizza topping do you like best?

b. Do you prefer greasy meat or healthy vegetables on your pizza?

Name ______ Class ______ Date ______

Example

2 Analyzing Survey Results A department store published the graph to the right to summarize the results of a survey they conducted.

The survey was conducted near a display of organic cotton clothing. Customers were asked the following question:

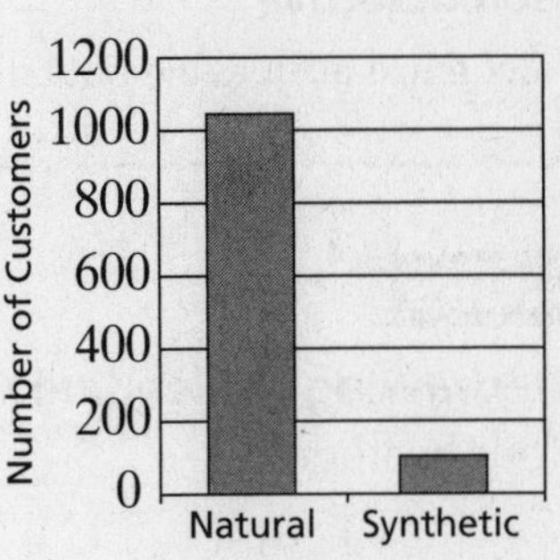

Do you think that soft, luxurious fabrics made from natural fibers are more comfortable than fabrics made from synthetic fibers?

Identify the sources of bias in the question and in the sampling method.

a. This question is ______. It implies that natural fibers are soft and luxurious and that synthetic fibers are not.

b. The sample ______ represent the general population. Shoppers looking at a display of organic cotton clothing are more likely to prefer natural fibers.

CA Standards Check

2. a. Rewrite the survey question from Example 2 so that it is not biased.

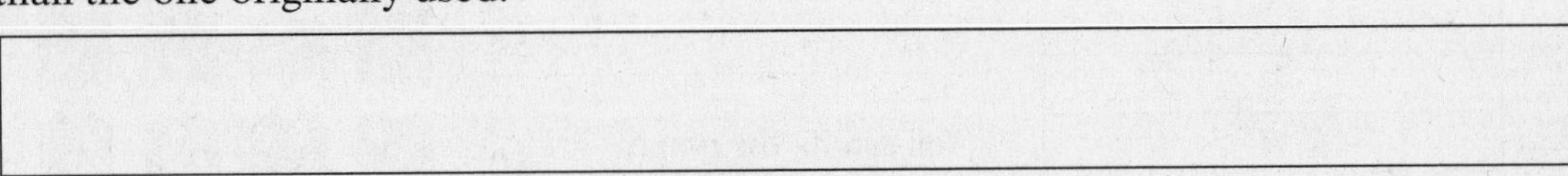

b. Open-Ended Describe a sampling method that would be less biased than the one originally used.

Name ______________________ Class ______________ Date ______________

Lesson 10-5

Using Graphs to Persuade

Lesson Objective	**California Content Standards**
To recognize misleading data displays	SDAP 2.3, supports SDAP 2.5, MR 3.0

Examples

1 Redrawing Misleading Graphs The graph shows the weekly earnings of four brothers.

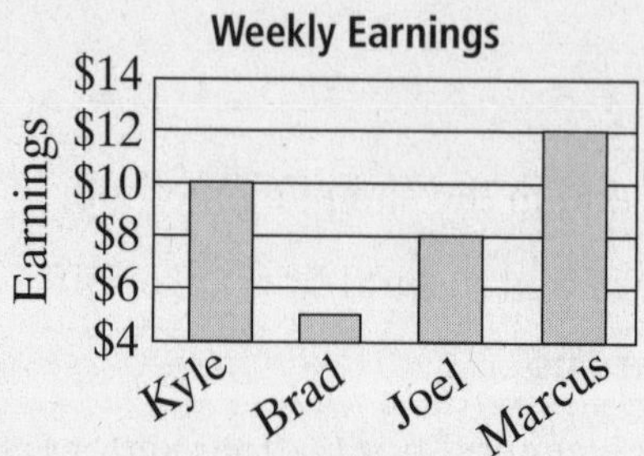

Redraw the graph so it is not misleading.

Method 1

Start the vertical scale at 0. Draw the bars to match the data.

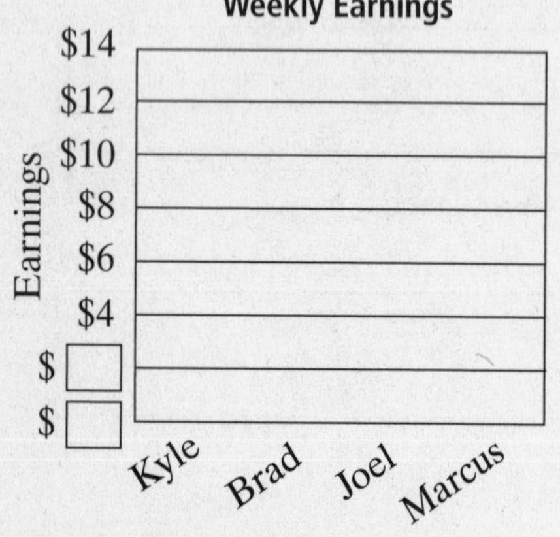

← **You can fix the graph by drawing it so that the vertical scale starts at ____.**

Method 2

Use a break in the vertical scale.

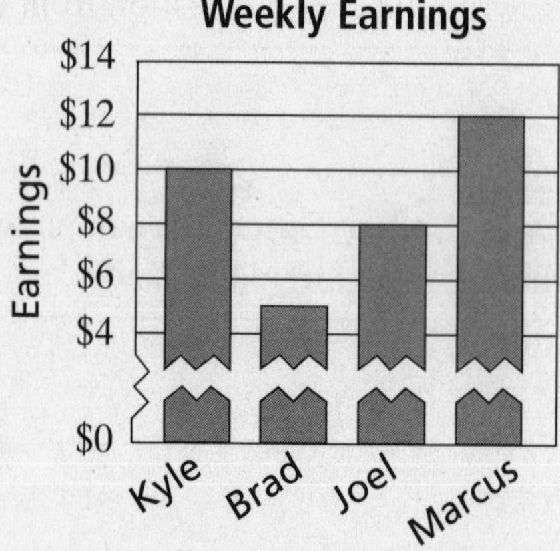

CA Standards Check

1. When is a break in a vertical scale especially useful?

Name ______________________ Class ______________ Date ______________

Examples

2 Misleading Intervals A television station presented this graph to its advertisers to show how viewership has increased. Explain why the graph is misleading.

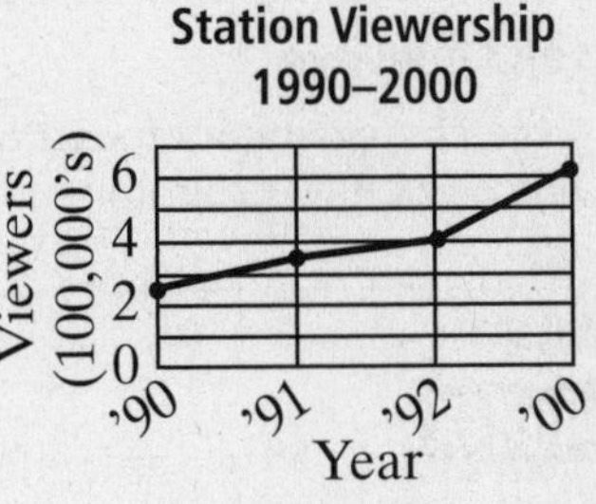

The intervals on the horizontal axis are ______.

The number of viewers increases ______ in the first 2 years and then another ______ over the next 8 years.

CA Standards Check

2. a. Redraw the graph in Example 2. Use equal intervals on both axes.

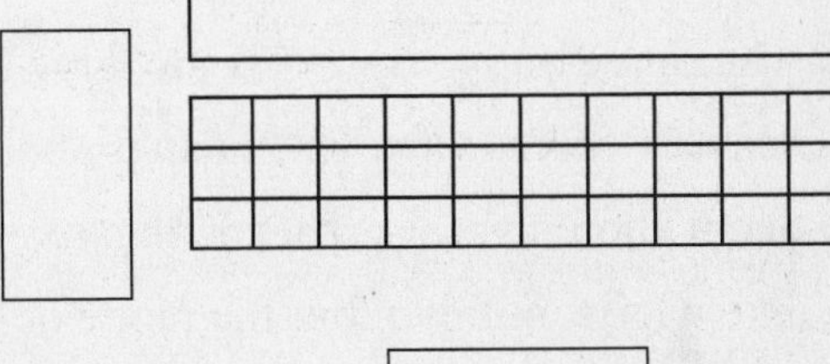

b. Why is the graph at the right misleading?

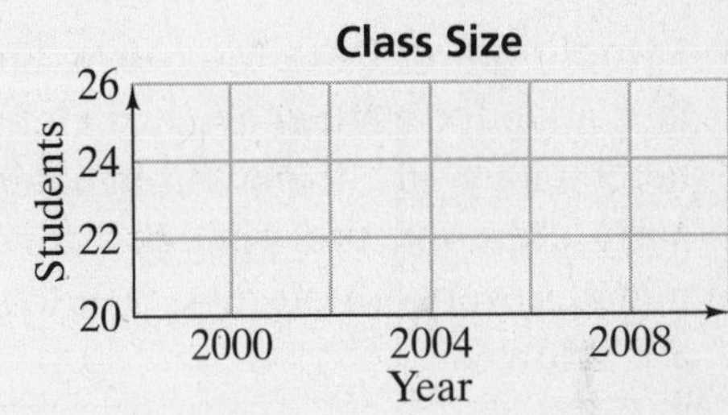

c. Redraw the graph so it does not mislead.

Name ______________________ Class ______________ Date ______________

Lesson 10-6

Using Data to Persuade

Lesson Objective	**California Content Standards**
How the choice of data measures can influence the interpretation of data sets	SDAP 1.2, SDAP 1.4, SDAP 2.5

Examples

1 Misleading Use of Data Measures The number of points scored by different players on a basketball team are listed below. Julio scored 7 points. Which measure of data makes Julio's performance seem the most impressive?

0 2 25 4 2 7 6

A. mean **B.** median **C.** mode **D.** range

The range of ______ is too large and only shows how much the players' scores vary. The mean is about ______ and makes 7 points seem about average. The median score of ______ makes 7 points seem like a large number, but the mode of ______ makes scoring 7 points seem even more impressive. The correct answer is choice ______.

2 Sampling and Data Measures Suppose a citizens' group wants another lane added to a street at a main intersection. The traffic is so heavy that it takes a long time to get through the intersection's traffic light. During the early afternoon, the group performs a traffic count by timing how many minutes every 8th car must wait to get through the traffic light. The results are below.

2 3 4 2 2 2 1 2 3 4 2 2 3 4 2 1 3 4 2 2 3

mean = 2.52 median = 2

This data will not convince the transportation department to add another lane. So, the citizens' group decides to include more data. Describe a sample that would help them influence the transportation department.

Perform the traffic count at the morning and afternoon rush hours, as well as several other times during the day and evening. This sample would more fairly represent the population. By including the higher values from the rush hours, the ______ and ______ are likely to ______.

Name ______________________ Class ______________ Date ______________

Example

3 Advertising The sign at the right is advertising for an auto dealership. Below it are the data for the cars at the dealership. Is the ad misleading?

Model	Quantity	Price ($)
Pico	2	9,999
Toro	7	13,999
Enviro	9	15,999
Urban	4	22,999

Only ☐ of the 22 cars offered are under $10,000, and only by ☐. There are many more over that amount, so the ad ☐ misleading.

CA Standards Check

1. Which value in the data in Example 1 is an outlier?

2. **Reasoning** In Example 2, will it be easier to raise the mean or the median? Explain.

3. How could you change the ad in Example 3 to better reflect the data?

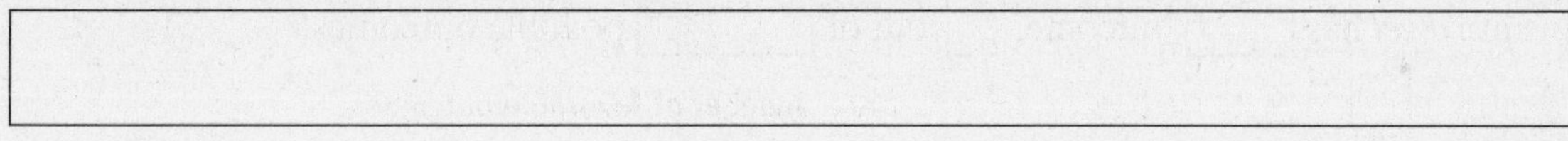

Name ______________________ Class ______________ Date ______________

Lesson 11-1

Probability

Lesson Objective	**California Content Standards**
To find the probability and the complement of an event	SDAP 3.3

Take Note

Theoretical Probability

$$\text{theoretical probability} = P(\text{event}) = \frac{\text{number of } \underline{\qquad} \text{ outcomes}}{\text{total number of } \underline{\qquad} \text{ outcomes}}$$

An outcome is ______________________________

An event is ______________________________

The complement of an event is ______________________________

____

Example

1 Finding Probability You select a letter at random from the letters F, G, H, and I. Find the probability of selecting a vowel. Express the probability as a fraction, a decimal, and a percent.

The event *vowel* has ____ outcome, ____, out of ____ possible outcomes.

$P(\text{vowel}) = \frac{\square}{\square}$ ← **number of favorable outcomes** / ← **total number of possible outcomes**

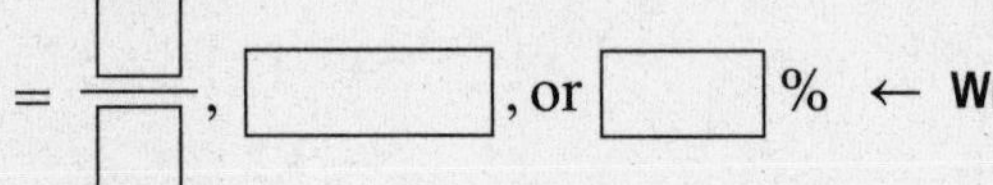

$= \frac{\square}{\square}$, ____, or ____ % ← **Write as a fraction, a decimal, and a percent.**

CA Standards Check

1. Find $P(\text{consonant})$ as a fraction for the letters in Example 1.

Name ___ Class ___ Date ___

Example

❷ Finding Probabilities from 0 to 1 A jar contains 1 blue marble, 3 green marbles, 3 yellow marbles, and 4 red marbles. You randomly select a marble from the jar. Find each probability.

a. *P*(red)

There are ___ possible outcomes. Since there are ___ red marbles, there are ___ favorable outcomes.

P(red) $\frac{\square}{\square}$ ← **number of favorable outcomes** / ← **total number of possible outcomes**

b. *P*(orange)

The event *orange* has ___ favorable outcomes.

P(orange) $\frac{\square}{\square}$, or ___ ← **number of favorable outcomes** / ← **total number of possible outcomes**

c. *P*(not orange)

P(not orange) + *P*(orange) = ___ ← **The sum of the probabilities of an event and its complement is 1.**

$\frac{\square}{\square}$ + ___ = ___ ← **Substitute ___ for *P*(orange).**

P(not orange) = ___ ← **Simplify.**

CA Standards Check

2. You roll a standard number cube once. Find each probability.

a. *P*(multiple of 3)

b. *P*(not multiple of 2)

c. *P*(9)

Name ____________________ Class ____________________ Date ____________________

Lesson 11-2

Experimental Probability

Lesson Objective	California Content Standards
To find experimental probability and to use simulations	SDAP 3.0, SDAP 3.2

Take Note

Experimental Probability

$$P(\text{event}) = \frac{\text{number of times an event occurs}}{\text{total number of trials}}$$

Experimental probability is ____

____

Examples

1 Finding Experimental Probability A manufacturer of computer parts checks 100 parts each day. On Monday, two of the checked parts are defective.

a. What is the experimental probability that a part is defective?

$P(\text{defective part}) = \frac{\square}{\square}$ ← **number of defective parts** / ← **total number of parts checked**

$= \frac{\square}{\square}$ ← **Simplify.**

The experimental probability is $\frac{\square}{\square}$.

b. Predict the number of defective parts in Monday's total production of 1,250 parts.

Let x represent the predicted number of defective parts.

defective → $\frac{1}{\square} = \frac{x}{\square}$ ← **defective** / ← **total** ← **Write a proportion.**
total →

$\square = x$ ← **Solve the proportion.**

You can predict that $\square$ parts out of 1,250 parts are defective.

❷ Simulating an Event A dog breeder knows that it is equally likely that a puppy will be male or female. Use a simulation to find the experimental probability that, in a litter of four puppies, all four will be male.

Simulate the problem by tossing four coins at the same time. Let "heads" represent a female and "tails" represent a male. A sample of 16 tosses is shown below.

Trial	Male	Female
1	✓✓	✓✓
2	✓	✓✓✓
3	✓✓✓✓	
4	✓✓	✓✓
5	✓✓✓	✓
6	✓✓	✓✓
7	✓	✓✓✓
8	✓✓	✓✓

Trial	Male	Female
9	✓✓	✓✓
10	✓✓✓	✓
11	✓✓	✓✓
12	✓	✓✓✓
13	✓✓	✓✓
14		✓✓✓✓
15	✓✓	✓✓
16	✓✓✓	✓

$P(\text{exactly four males}) = \frac{\square}{\square}$ ← **number of times four tails occurs** / ← **total number of trials**

The experimental probability that, in a litter of four puppies, all four will be male is ☐.

CA Standards Check

1. In 60 coin tosses, 25 are tails. Find the experimental probability.

☐

2. Use the data in Example 1. Predict the number of defective computer parts in a batch of 3,500.

☐

3. Use the data in Example 2. What is the experimental probability that exactly three of the four puppies are male?

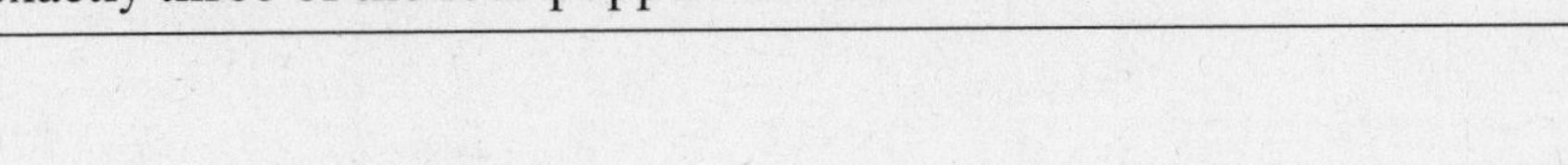

Name ______________________ Class ______________ Date ______________

Lesson 11-3

Sample Spaces

Lesson Objective	California Content Standards
To make and use sample spaces and to use the counting principle	SDAP 3.1, MR 2.5

Take Note

The Counting Principle

Suppose there are *m* ways of making one choice and *n* ways of making a second choice. There are ☐ · ☐ ways to make the first choice followed by the second choice.

Example If you can choose a shirt in 5 sizes and 7 colors, then you can choose ☐ · ☐, or ☐, shirts.

A sample space is ____

____

Example

1 Finding a Sample Space

a. A spinner is divided into five equal sections labeled A–E. Make a table to show the sample space for spinning the spinner twice. Write the outcomes as ordered pairs.

☐

b. Find the probability of spinning at least one D.

There are ☐ outcomes with at least one D. There are ☐ possible outcomes. So, the probability of spinning at least one D is $\frac{\square}{\square}$.

CA Standards Check

1. Give the sample space for tossing two coins. Find the probability of getting two heads. ☐

Name ________________ Class ________________ Date ________________

Examples

❷ **Using a Tree Diagram** Suppose you plan to travel either west or northwest. You can go by train, bus, or car.

a. Draw a tree diagram to show the sample space for your journey.

Train	West	Train, ☐
	Northwest	☐, Northwest
Bus	West	Bus, ☐
	Northwest	☐, Northwest
Car	West	Car, ☐
	Northwest	☐, Northwest

← There are ☐ possible outcomes.

b. What is the probability that a random selection will result in a bus trip west?

There is ☐ favorable outcome (bus, ☐) out of ☐ possible outcomes. The probability is ☐.

❸ **Using the Counting Principle** How many kinds of coin purses are available if the purses come in small or large sizes, and colors red, blue, yellow, and black?

Size	Color
small	red
large	blue
	yellow
	black

Size number of choices · **Color** number of choices

☐ · ☐ = ☐

There are ☐ different kinds of coin purses available.

CA Standards Check

2. a. Suppose that an airplane is added as another travel choice in Example 2. Draw a tree diagram to show the sample space.

b. Find the probability of selecting an airplane at random for your journey.

3. A manager at the Deli Counter decides to add chicken to the list of meat choices. How many different sandwiches are now available?

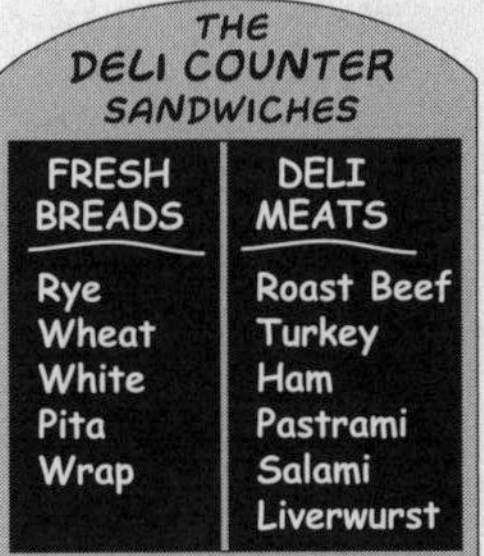

Name ______________________ Class ______________ Date ______________

Lesson 11-4

Compound Events

Lesson Objective	**California Content Standards**
To find the probability of independent and dependent events	SDAP 3.4, SDAP 3.5

Take Note

Probability of Independent Events

If A and B are independent events,
then $P(A, \text{then } B) =$ ______ · ______.

Probability of Dependent Events

If event B depends on event A, then
$P(A, \text{then } B) =$ ______ · ______.

A compound event ______________________

Two events are independent if ______________________

____

Two events are dependent if ______________________

____

Examples

1 Probability of Independent Events A spinner has equal sections labeled 1 through 10. Suppose you spin twice. Find $P(2, \text{then } 5)$.

The two events are independent. There are ______ possibilities on each spin.

$P(2, \text{then } 5) = P(2) \times$ ______ ← **Spinning 2 is the first event. Spinning 5 is the second event.**

$= \frac{1}{10} \times \frac{\square}{\square} = \frac{\square}{\square}$ ← **Substitute $\frac{\square}{\square}$ for $P(2)$ and $P(5)$. Then multiply.**

The probability that you will spin a 2 and then a 5 is ______.

Name ______________________ Class ______________ Date ______________

② Probability of Dependent Events You select two cards at random from the lettered cards shown below. The two cards do not show vowels. Without replacing the two cards, you select a third card. Find the probability that your third card has a vowel.

P R O B A B I L I T Y

There are ☐ remaining after you select the first two cards.

$P(\text{vowel}) = \frac{\square}{\square}$ ← **number of remaining cards with vowels** / ← **total number of remaining cards**

The probability of selecting a vowel for the third card is ☐.

③ Probability of Dependent Events A bag contains 3 red marbles, 4 white marbles, and 1 blue marble. You draw one marble. Without replacing it, you draw a second marble. What is the probability that you draw red and then white?

The two events are dependent. After the first selection, there are ☐ marbles to choose from.

$P(\text{red, then white}) = P(\text{red}) \times \square$ ← **Use the formula for dependent events.**

$= \frac{3}{8} \times \frac{\square}{\square}$ ← **Substitute.**

$= \frac{\square}{\square} = \frac{\square}{\square}$ ← **Multiply. Then simplify.**

The probability of choosing red and then white is ☐.

CA Standards Check

1. You and a friend play a game twice. Assume that the probability of winning is $\frac{1}{2}$. Find P(win, then lose).

2. Use the cards in Example 2. You select a B card at random. Without replacing the B card, you select a second card. Find P(Y).

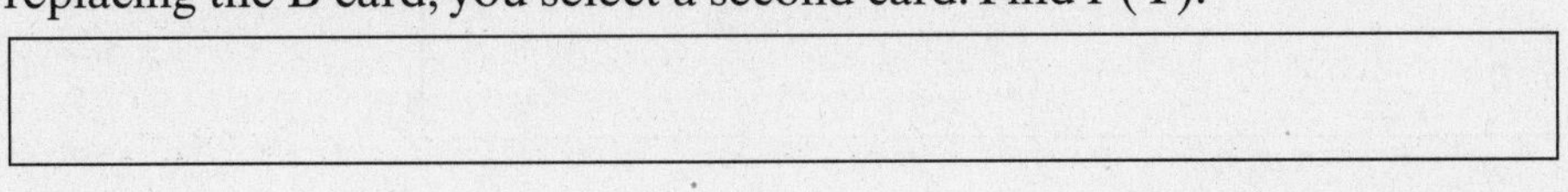

3. Suppose two sets of 26 cards lettered A–Z are put in a bucket. You select a card. Without replacing the first card, you select a second one. Find P(J, then J).

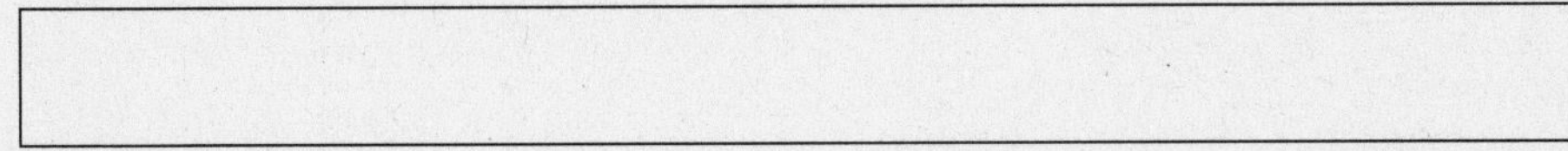

Name ______________________ Class ______________ Date ______________

Lesson 11-5

Disjoint Events

Lesson Objective	**California Content Standards**
To find probabilities of disjoint events	SDAP 3.0, SDAP 3.3, SDAP 3.4

Take Note

Probability of *A* or *B*

If A and B are disjoint, then

$P(A \text{ or } B) = \square + \square$

Two events are disjoint events when ______________________.

Example

1 Disjoint Events Suppose 10 cards numbered 0 through 9 are placed in a hat. Are the events below disjoint? Explain.

a. selecting an odd number and selecting a number greater than 6

b. selecting a 3 and selecting an even number

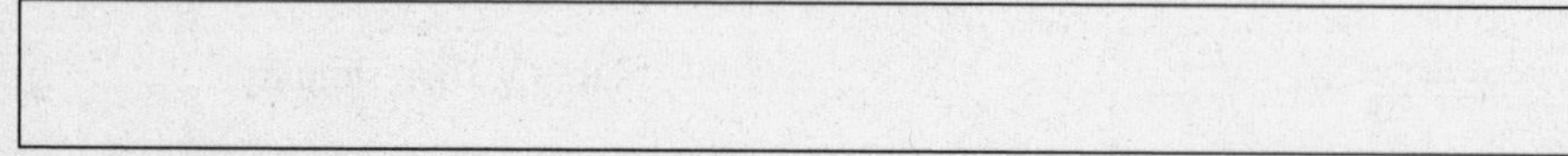

CA Standards Check

1. Are the events disjoint? Explain.

a. rolling an even number and rolling a prime number on a number cube

b. rolling an even number and rolling a number less than 2 on a number cube

Name ____________________ Class ____________ Date ____________

Example

2 Finding P(*A* or *B*) Suppose a bag contains 5 orange marbles, 4 purple marbles, 3 green marbles, and 3 yellow marbles. If you select one marble at random, what is the probability that the marble is purple or green?

Since one marble cannot be both purple and green at the same time, the events are disjoint.

$P(\text{purple or green}) = P(\square) + P(\square)$ ← Write an equation.

$= \dfrac{\square}{\square} + \dfrac{\square}{\text{15 marbles}}$ ← Substitute.

$= \dfrac{\square}{\square} + \dfrac{\square}{15} = \dfrac{\square}{\square}$ ← Simplify.

The probability that you select a purple or a green marble is ☐, or about ☐%.

CA Standards Check

2. Use the bag of marbles above.

 a. What is the probability that you select an orange marble or a green marble?

 b. What is the probability that you select a marble that is yellow, orange, or green?

Name ______________ Class ______________ Date ______________

Practice 1-1

Using Estimation Strategies

Use rounding to estimate the nearest half-dollar.

1. $4.85 + 1.47 ______

2. $6.79 − 3.95 ______

3. $14.19 + 5.59 ______

4. $25.43 − 21.20 ______

Use front-end estimation to estimate each sum.

5. 4.76 + 6.15 ______

6. 1.409 + 3.512 ______

7. 2.479 + 6.518 ______

8. 3.17 + 2.72 ______

9. 9.87 + 2.16 ______

10. 5.89 + 7.21 ______

Use compatible numbers to estimate each quotient.

11. 76.32 ÷ 24.98 ______

12. 42.693 ÷ 4.7 ______

13. 54.36 ÷ 11.001 ______

Use any estimation strategy to calculate. Tell which strategy you used.

14. $66.93 + $72.18 + $69.18 + $71.94 + $65.75 ______

15. 93.26 − 69.78 ______

16. 51.12 · 87.906 ______

17. 457.03 + 592.8 ______

18. 702 ÷ 61 ______

19. 12.87 + 14.31 + 15.09 ______

20. 536 ÷ 41 ______

Find each estimate.

21. A rare truffle once sold for $13.20 for a 0.44 oz can. Approximately how much would 1 lb of this truffle cost? ______

22. The length of the longest loaf of bread measured 1,405 ft $1\frac{3}{4}$ in. It was cut into slices $\frac{1}{2}$ in. thick. How many slices were there? ______

Name ______________________ Class ______________ Date ______________

1-1 • Guided Problem Solving

GPS Exercise 30:

Travel On vacation, you wish to send eight postcards to friends at home. The cards cost $.59 each. Eight postcard stamps cost about $2 total. About how much will it cost to buy and mail the cards?

Understand

1. Circle the information you will need to solve the problem.
2. What are you being asked to do?

 ____

 ____

3. Before you estimate the total cost, what do you have to estimate first?

 ____

Plan and Carry Out

4. Round $.59 to the nearest tenth. ______________
5. Use the answer to Step 4 to estimate the product $8 \cdot 0.59$.

 ____

6. About how much are eight postcard stamps?

 ____

7. About how much will it cost to buy and mail the cards?

 ____

Check

8. Is your estimate reasonable? Multiply 8 by 0.59 and then add 2.

 ____

 ____

Solve Another Problem

9. Paul stops by the market to buy his lunch. The market is selling bananas for $.22 each and sandwiches for $3.95. About how much does Paul spend if he buys a sandwich and 4 bananas?

Name ______________________ Class ______________ Date ______________

Practice 1-2

Adding and Subtracting Decimals

Identify each property shown.

1. (8.7 + 6.3) + 3.7 = 8.7 + (6.3 + 3.7) ______________
2. 9.06 + 0 = 9.06 ______________
3. 4.06 + 8.92 = 8.92 + 4.06 ______________
4. 0 + 7.13 = 7.13 + 0 ______________

Find each sum.

5. 4.6 + 8.79 ______________
6. 14.8 + 29.07 ______________
7. 20.16 + 15.703 ______________
8. 36.12 + 5.793 ______________
9. 8.9 + 2.14 + 7.1 ______________
10. 3.6 + 5.27 + 8.93 ______________
11. 107.5 + 6 ______________
12. 15.26 + 13.29 + 38.96 ______________
13. 46.21 + 53.942 ______________

Find each difference.

14. 8.7 − 2.03 ______________
15. 53.86 − 4.02 ______________
16. 14.59 − 8.3 ______________
17. 42.75 − 26.36 ______________
18. 53.86 − 16.47 ______________
19. 56.89 − 48.91 ______________
20. 5.06 − 3.297 ______________
21. 3.4 − 2.768 ______________
22. 5.002 − 4.3 ______________

Use the advertisement at the right. Find each cost.

23. 1 egg ______________
24. toast ______________
25. fruit ______________
26. milk ______________
27. 1 egg and milk ______________
28. 1 egg and fruit ______________

2 eggs, toast, fruit, milk	$2.75
1 egg, toast, fruit, milk	$2.20
toast, milk	$0.90
toast, fruit, milk	$1.65
1 egg, toast	$0.95

1-2 • Guided Problem Solving

GPS Exercise 32:

You decide to save some money. In week 1 you save $4.20, in week 2 you save $3.85, and in week 3 you save $2.50. Estimate your total savings. Then find the exact amount you saved.

Understand

1. Circle the information you will need to solve the problem.
2. What are you being asked to do?

   ____

3. Which operation will you use to solve the problem? _______________
4. Which estimation strategy will you use? Explain. _______________

   ____

Plan and Carry Out

5. What is the sum of the front-end digits? _______________
6. What is the sum of the cents to the nearest dollar? _______________
7. Use your answers to Steps 5 and 6 to estimate your total savings.

   ____

8. Now find the exact amount you saved. _______________

Check

9. Is your estimate reasonable? _______________
10. Is your estimate in Step 7 close to your exact amount in Step 8?

    ____

Solve Another Problem

11. You go to the school store to buy a ruler, some pencils, and some notebook paper. Rulers cost $.39 each, a pack of 72 pencils costs $3.59, and a pack of notebook paper costs $2.19. About how much will your purchase cost?

    ____

Name ____________________ Class ____________ Date ____________

Practice 1-3 Multiplying and Dividing Decimals

Find each product.

1. 28 · 6

2. 7.3 · 0.9

3. 58 · 2.1

4. 15(187)

5. 6.6 · 25

6. (1.8)(0.7)

7. 0.91 · 2.7

8. 4.6(3.9)

9. 17.3 · 15.23

10. 847 ÷ 0.01

11. 0.3 ÷ 0.1

12. 32.6 ÷ 0.01

13. $2.1\overline{)12.6}$

14. 29.75 ÷ 0.7

15. 37 ÷ 0.2

16. 1.414 ÷ 1.4

17. $0.78\overline{)0.16614}$

18. 0.154 ÷ 5.5

Annex zeros to find each quotient.

19. 1.3 ÷ 0.8

20. $2.4\overline{)5.4}$

21. 79.04 ÷ 9.5

22. 36.78 ÷ 2.4

23. $\frac{58.5}{10.4}$

24. $1.2\overline{)38.7}$

Solve.

25. Each trip on a ride at the carnival costs $1.25. If Tara goes on 4 rides, how much will it cost her?

26. Postage stamps cost $0.37 each. How much does a book of 50 stamps cost?

27. Alicia paid $1.32 for a bag of pinto beans. The beans cost $.55 per lb. How much did the bag of pinto beans weigh?

28. Nina and 3 friends ate lunch at a cafe. They decided to split the bill evenly. The total bill was $17.84. How much was each person's share?

Name ______________________ Class ______________ Date ______________

1-3 • Guided Problem Solving

GPS Exercise 39:

After digging up lilac bushes in the garden, a landscape architect uses sod to cover the ground. The sod costs $2.25/yd. She pays $31.50. How much sod does she buy?

Understand

1. Circle the information you will need to solve the problem.
2. What are you being asked to do?

   ____

   ____

3. Which operation must you perform to determine the answer?

   ____

Plan and Carry Out

4. How much money does the landscape architect spend?

   ____

5. How much is each yard of sod?

   ____

6. What is $31.50 ÷ $2.25/yd?

   ____

Check

7. Calculate $2.25/yd · 14 yd. Does your answer equal the total amount of money spent?

   ____

Solve Another Problem

8. Marissa created a platform for the set of the school play. She used boards that are each 3.15 in. wide. If the platform is 37.8 inches wide, how many boards did Marissa use?

   ____

Practice 1-4

Measuring in Metric Units

Choose a reasonable estimate.

1. Length of a calculator	18 m	18 cm	18 mm
2. Length of a football field	100 km	100 m	100 cm
3. Thickness of a paperback book	25 km	25 m	25 mm
4. Capacity of a bottle of shampoo	250 mL	250 L	250 kL

Complete each statement. You may find a number line helpful.

5. 0.7 km = __________ m
6. __________ L = 40 mL
7. 83 m = __________ mm
8. 9,500 m = __________ km
9. 8 g = __________ kg
10. __________ m = 800 km

Change each measurement to the given unit.

11. 43 km 14 m to kilometers ______________________
12. 84 m 15 cm to centimeters ______________________
13. 9 kg 421 g to kilograms ______________________
14. 14 L 7 mL to liters ______________________

Write the metric unit that makes each statement true.

15. 9.85 kg = 9,850 __________
16. 87.43 m = 8,743 __________
17. 10,542 mL = 10.542 __________
18. 8.42 mm = 0.842 __________
19. 2,347 m = 2.347 __________
20. 0.356 m = 356 __________

Solve.

21. The capacity of a beaker is 150 mL. How many beakers can be filled from a 4 L container?

____

22. Vitamin C comes in pills with a strength of 500 mg. How many pills would you need to take if you want a dosage of one gram?

____

23. Your science teacher mixes the contents of two beakers containing 2.5 L and 800 mL of a liquid. What is the combined amount?

____

24. A teaspoon of common table salt contains about 2,000 mg of sodium. How many grams of sodium is this?

____

Name ______________________ Class ______________ Date ______________

1-4 • Guided Problem Solving

Exercise 28:

The capacity of a coffee mug is 350 mL. How many coffee mugs can you fill from a 2 L container?

Understand

1. Circle the information you will need to solve the problem.

2. What are you being asked to do?

 ____

 ____

3. How many milliliters are there in one liter?

 ____

Plan and Carry Out

4. How many liters does the container hold?

 ____

5. Do you multiply or divide to change liters into milliliters?

 ____

6. How many milliliters are there in 2 L?

 ____

7. Do you multiply or divide to find how many coffee mugs can be filled?

 ____

8. How many coffee mugs can be filled from a 2 L container?

 ____

Check

9. Is the total capacity of the coffee mugs filled less than or equal to 2,000 mL? Does your answer make sense?

 ____

Solve Another Problem

10. Lily drinks 0.5 L of water during her exercise routine. If her aerobics instructor tells her that she should be drinking at least 300 mL of water, is Lily drinking enough? Explain.

 ____

Name ______________________ Class ______________ Date ____________

Practice 1-5

Comparing and Ordering Integers

Name the integer represented by each point on the number line.

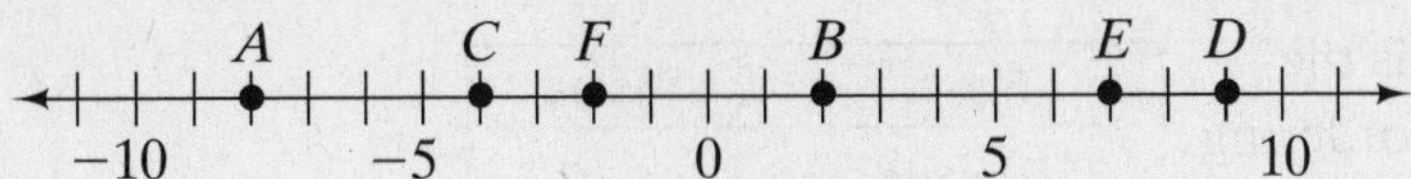

1. *A* ____ 2. *B* ____ 3. *C* ____ 4. *D* ____ 5. *E* ____ 6. *F* ____

Compare. Use <, >, or =.

7. −8 ☐ 8
8. 4 ☐ −4
9. |5| ☐ |−5|
10. −8 ☐ 0
11. −6 ☐ −2
12. −1 ☐ −3
13. |−4| ☐ 0
14. |−3| ☐ 2

Graph each integer and its opposite on the number line.

15. −9

−8 −6 −4 −2 0 2 4 6 8

16. 5

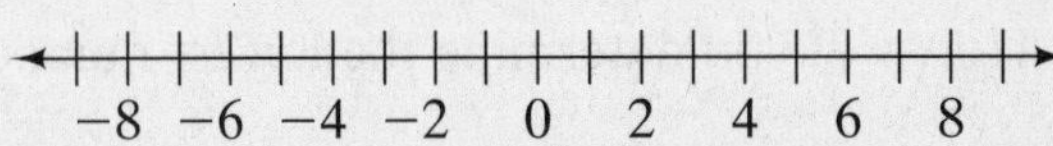

17. 8

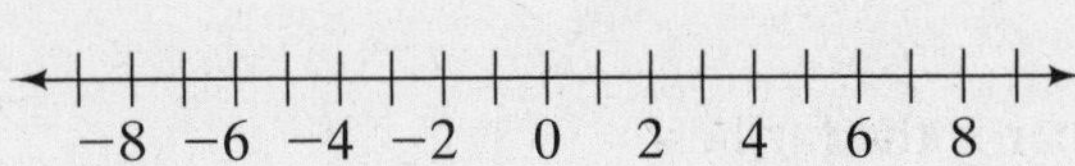

18. −2

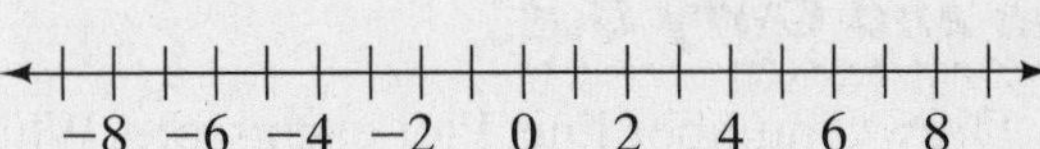

Find each absolute value.

19. |2| ________
20. |−3| ________
21. |−38| ________
22. |−2 + 5| ________
23. |−44| ________
24. |5 + 2| ________
25. |−16| ________
26. |3 − 7| ________

Write an integer to represent each situation.

27. a gain of 5 yards ________
28. a debt of $5 ________
29. a temperature of 100°F ________
30. 135 feet below sea level ________

Name ______________________ Class ______________ Date ______________

1-5 • Guided Problem Solving

GPS Exercise 44:

In golf, the person with the lowest score is the winner. Rank the players at the right by ordering their scores from lowest to highest.

Player	Score
T. Woods	−12
V. Singh	−4
E. Els	+10
P. Mickelson	−3
R. Goosen	−5

Understand

1. Who wins in a golf game?

____

2. How will you determine the lowest number?

____

Plan and Carry Out

3. Draw a number line. Plot each score. Which number is the farthest to the left of zero on the number line?

____

4. What is the order of all five numbers? ______________

5. Rank the players from lowest score to highest score.

____

____

Check

6. Is the person with the highest score last? Is the person with the lowest score first?

____

Solve Another Problem

7. Anne had the following golf scores this week: −6, +5, −4, +13, −2, +4, +6, −11. Which was her best score? Which was her worst score?

____

Name ______________________ Class ______________ Date ______________

Practice 1-6

Adding and Subtracting Integers

Find each sum.

1. $-2 + (-3)$ ______
2. $8 - 7 + 4$ ______
3. $8 + (-5)$ ______
4. $15 + (-3)$ ______
5. $-16 + 8$ ______
6. $7 + (-10)$ ______
7. $-9 + (-5)$ ______
8. $-12 + 14$ ______

Find each difference. You may find a number line helpful.

9. $9 - 26$ ______
10. $-4 - 15$ ______
11. $21 - (-7)$ ______
12. $27 - (-16)$ ______
13. $-16 - (-43)$ ______
14. $47 - 19$ ______
15. $-156 - 98$ ______
16. $-192 - 47$ ______
17. $0 - (-51)$ ______
18. $-63 - 89$ ______
19. $-12 - (-21)$ ______
20. $92 - (-16)$ ______

Find the value of each expression.

21. $3 + 8 + (-4)$ ______
22. $2 + |-3| + (-3)$ ______
23. $9 + 7 - 6$ ______
24. $56 + (-4) + (-58)$ ______
25. $-4 - 3 + (-2)$ ______
26. $|-8| - 15 + (-8)$ ______

Use >, <, or = to complete each statement.

27. $-9 - (-11)$ ☐ 0
28. $-17 + 20$ ☐ 0
29. $11 - (-4)$ ☐ 0
30. $28 - 19$ ☐ 0
31. $52 + (-65)$ ☐ 0
32. $-28 - (-28)$ ☐ 0

Solve.

33. The highest and lowest temperatures ever recorded in Africa are 136°F and −11°F. The highest temperature was recorded in Libya, and the lowest temperature was recorded in Morocco. What is the difference in these temperature extremes?

______

34. The highest and lowest temperatures ever recorded in South America are 120°F and −27°F. Both the highest and lowest temperatures were recorded in Argentina. What is the difference in these temperature extremes?

______

Name ______________________ Class ______________ Date ______________

1-6 • Guided Problem Solving

GPS Exercise 28:

The highest temperature ever recorded in the United States was 134°F, measured at Death Valley, California. The coldest temperature, −80°F, was recorded at Prospect Creek, Alaska. What is the difference between these temperatures?

Understand

1. Circle the information you will need to solve the problem.
2. What are you being asked to do?

   ____

3. Which word tells you what operation to perform?

   ____

Plan and Carry Out

4. Write a subtraction expression for the problem.

   ____

5. Subtracting a negative number is the same as adding what type of number?

   ____

6. Write an addition expression that is the same as the expression you wrote in Step 4.

   ____

7. What is the difference between these temperatures?

   ____

Check

8. What is 134°F − 214°F?

   ____

Solve Another Problem

9. At 6:00 A.M. the temperature was 25°F. At 9:00 P.M. the temperature was −13°F. What was the difference in the temperature?

   ____

Name ____________________ Class ____________ Date ____________

Practice 1-7

Multiplying and Dividing Integers

Complete each statement. Then write two examples to illustrate each relationship.

1. positive ÷ positive = ?
2. negative · positive = ?
3. positive · positive = ?
4. negative ÷ negative = ?
5. negative ÷ positive = ?
6. positive · positive = ?
7. positive ÷ negative = ?
8. negative · negative = ?

Estimate each product or quotient.

9. $-72 \cdot 57$
10. $-92 \cdot (-41)$
11. $-476 \div 90$
12. $-83 \cdot 52$
13. $538 \div (-63)$
14. $-803 \cdot (-106)$
15. $49 \cdot 61$
16. $479 \div (-61)$

Find each product or quotient.

17. $\frac{-36}{9}$
18. $\frac{-52}{-4}$
19. $(-5) \cdot (-20)$
20. $\frac{-63}{-9}$
21. $(-15) \cdot (2)$
22. $\frac{22}{-2}$
23. $(13) \cdot (-6)$
24. $\frac{-100}{-5}$
25. $(-60) \cdot (-3)$
26. $\frac{-240}{30}$
27. $(43) \cdot (-8)$
28. $\frac{-169}{-13}$

Name ______________________ Class ______________ Date ______________

1-7 • Guided Problem Solving

GPS Exercise 34:

A scuba diver is 180 ft below sea level and rises to the surface at a rate of 30 ft/min. How long will the diver take to reach the surface?

Understand

1. Circle the information you will need to solve the problem.
2. What are you being asked to do?

____

____

Plan and Carry Out

3. Will you multiply or divide to solve this problem?

____

4. How far below sea level is the diver?

____

5. How fast is the diver rising?

____

6. How long will the diver take to reach the surface?

____

Check

7. What is 30 ft/min · 6 min? Does your answer equal the original distance below sea level?

____

Solve Another Problem

8. A rock climber climbs down into the Grand Canyon at a rate of 2 ft/min. How long will it take him to climb down 50 ft?

____

Name ______________________ Class ______________ Date ______________

Practice 1-8

Order of Operations and the Distributive Property

Find the value of each expression.

1. $(8 + 2) \cdot 9$ ________
2. $5 - 1 \div 4$ ________
3. $(6 + 3) \div 18$ ________
4. $80 - 6 \cdot 7$ ________
5. $4 \cdot 6 + 3$ ________
6. $4 \cdot (6 + 3)$ ________
7. $35 - 6 \cdot 5$ ________
8. $9 \div 3 + 6$ ________

Find the missing numbers. Then simplify.

9. $5(9 + 6) = 5(\underline{\ ?\ }) + 5(\underline{\ ?\ })$ ________
10. $4(9.7 - 8.1) = \underline{\ ?\ }(9.7) - \underline{\ ?\ }(8.1)$ ________
11. $\underline{\ ?\ }(3.8) = 9(4) - 9(\underline{\ ?\ })$ ________
12. $\underline{\ ?\ }(17.1 + 12.6) = 6(17.1) + 6(12.6)$ ________

Use the Distributive Property to find each product.

13. $3(6.4)$ ________
14. $5(7.1)$ ________
15. $5(8.9)$ ________
16. $4(9.2)$ ________
17. $9(11.1)$ ________
18. $7(8.9)$ ________

Copy each statement and add parentheses to make it true.

19. $6 + 6 \div 6 \cdot 6 + 6 = 24$ ________
20. $6 \cdot 6 + 6 \cdot 6 - 6 = 426$ ________
21. $6 + 6 \div 6 \cdot 6 - 6 = 0$ ________
22. $6 - 6 \cdot 6 + 6 \div 6 = 1$ ________
23. A backyard measures 80 ft · 125 ft. A garden is planted in one corner of it. The garden measures 15 ft · 22 ft. How much of the backyard is *not* part of the garden?

____

Name ______________________ Class ______________ Date ______________

1-8 • Guided Problem Solving

GPS Exercise 28:

Anna is buying daisies to use in centerpieces. Each centerpiece has 3 daisies. There are 10 tables in all. Use mental math to find the cost of the daisies if each daisy costs $0.98.

Understand

1. What are you being asked to do?

____

2. Which method are you to use to determine the cost?

____

Plan and Carry Out

3. How many daisies do you need in all?

____

4. Write an expression to find the total cost of the daisies.

____

5. The amount $.98 can also be written as $1.00 – $.02. Rewrite your expression from Step 4 using $1.00 – $.02.

____

6. Simplify the expression.

____

7. How much do the daisies cost?

____

Check

8. Use a calculator to determine the cost of the daisies. Is your answer from step 7 correct?

____

Solve Another Problem

9. Your horticulture club is planting a garden at school as a beautification project. The principal is allowing you to use an area that is 5 yd^2. If it costs $8.93 to buy enough rose bulbs to plant 1 yd^2, how much will it cost to buy bulbs to fill 5 yd^2?

____

Name ________________ Class ________ Date ________

Practice 1-9

Mean, Median, Mode, and Range

Find the mean, median, mode, and range of each data set.

1. hours of piano practice ________________

Hours Mr. Capelli's students practice

2 1 2 0 1 2 2 1 2 2

2. days of snow per month ________________

Monthly snow days in Central City

8 10 5 1 0 0 0 0 0 1 3 12

3. number of students per class ________________

Class size in Westmont Middle School

32 26 30 35 25 24 35 30 29 25

4. ratings given by students to a new movie ________________

Student ratings of a movie

10 9 10 8 9 7 5 3 8 9 9 10 9 9 7

Use the table for Exercises 5–7.

Name	Hourly Wage
Julia	$8.75
Ron	$7.50
Miguel	$25.00
Natasha	$11.00
Robert	$10.50

5. Whose wage is an outlier in the data set?

____

6. Find the mean hourly wage with and without the outlier.

____

7. What effect does the outlier have on the mean?

____

Name ______________________ Class ______________ Date ______________

1-9 • Guided Problem Solving

GPS Exercise 23:

Average Life Expectancy

Animal	Years
Bison	15
Cow	15
Deer	8
Donkey	12
Elk	15
Goat	8
Horse	20
Moose	12
Pig	10
Sheep	12

Understand

1. What does this data set refer to?

____

2. What are you being asked to do?

____

Plan and Carry Out

3. Find the sum of the numbers in the data set. ________

4. Find the mean by dividing the sum of the numbers by the total number of numbers. ________

5. Order the numbers in the data set in increasing order.

____

6. What are the two middle numbers? ________

7. Find the median of the data by finding the mean of the two middle numbers. ________

8. Find the mode by finding which number is listed most often. ________

9. How many modes are there? ________

10. Find the range by subtracting the smallest number from the largest number. ________

Check

11. What do you notice about the mean, median, mode, and range of this data?

____

Solve Another Problem

12. Millie has 3 siblings, Peggy has one sister, Larry has 5 brothers, Joey is an only child, and Marie has 6 siblings. What is the mean number of siblings for this group of people? ________

Name ______________________ Class ______________ Date ______________

1A: Graphic Organizer

For use before Lesson 1-1

Study Skill As you begin a new textbook, look through the table of contents to see what kind of information you will be learning during the year. Notice that some of the topics were introduced last year. Get a head start by reviewing your old notes and problems.

Write your answers.

1. What is the chapter title? ______________________
2. How many lessons are there in this chapter? ______________________
3. What is the topic of the Test-Taking Strategies page? ______________________
4. Complete the graphic organizer below as you work through the chapter.
   - In the center, write the title of the chapter.
   - When you begin a lesson, write the lesson name in a rectangle.
   - When you complete a lesson, write a skill or key concept in a circle linked to that lesson block.
   - When you complete the chapter, use this graphic organizer to help you review.

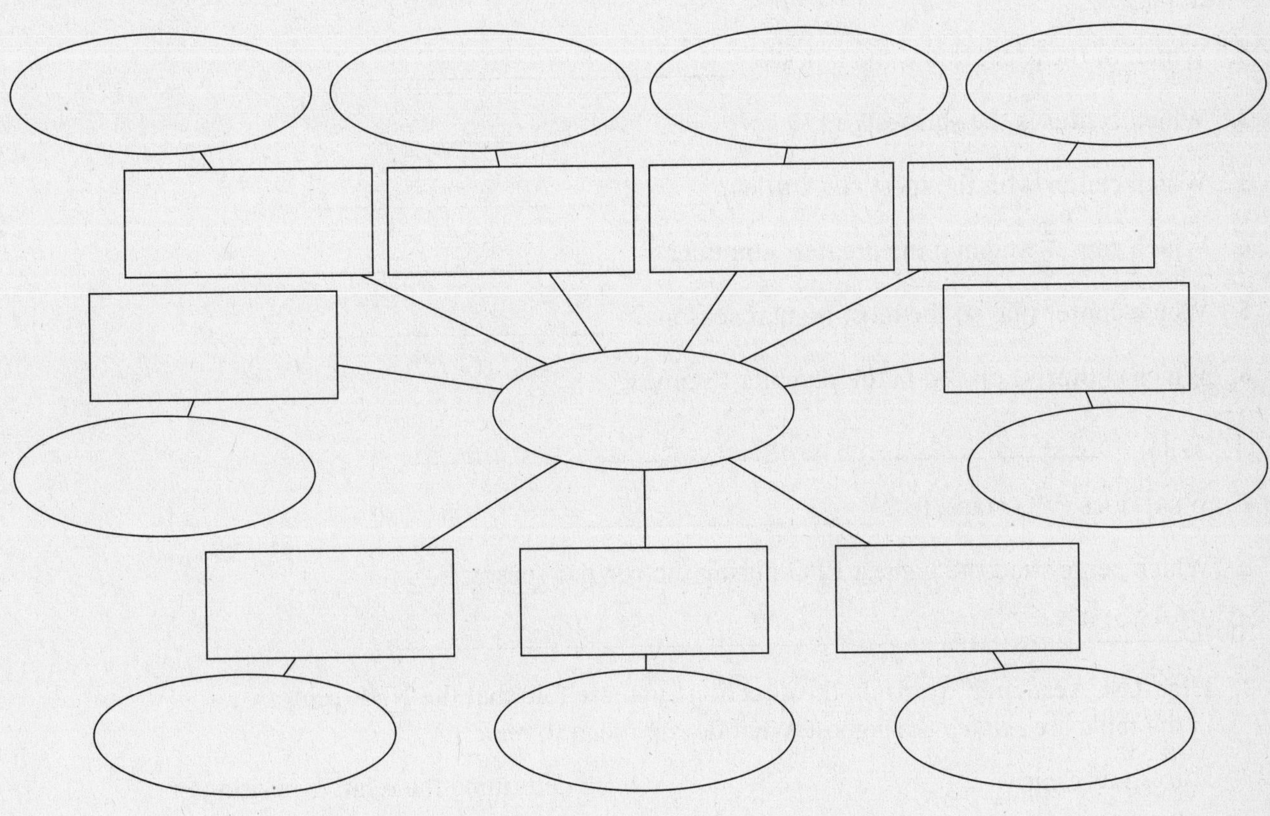

Name ____________ Class ____________ Date ____________

1B: Reading Comprehension

For use after Lesson 1-4

Study Skill Information is often organized in charts and tables. Practice reading charts and tables in books, magazines, and newspapers.

The table below contains information about four of the highest-ranked centers in the history of the National Basketball Association (NBA).

Use the table below to answer the questions.

Player	Height, Weight Playoffs	Number of Seasons to Regular Season	Points Per Game (PPG) During Playoffs	PPG During	NBA Titles	Age at Retirement
Kareem Abdul-Jabbar	7 ft 2 in. 267 lb	20 to 18	24.6	24.3	6	42
Wilt Chamberlain	7 ft 1 in. 275 lb	14 to 13	30.1	22.5	2	37
Shaquille O'Neal	7 ft 1 in. 325 lb	13 to 12	27.6	26.7	2	*
Bill Russell	6 ft 10 in. 220 lb	13 to 13	15.1	16.2	11	35

* still playing

1. Which of these centers is the tallest? ____________
2. Which center is the shortest? ____________
3. Which center won the most NBA titles? ____________
4. Which center weighed the greatest amount? ____________
5. Which center played the most regular seasons? ____________
6. Which center(s) played in the playoffs 13 times?

   ____
7. What does PPG stand for? ____________
8. Which center had the highest PPG during the regular season?

   ____
9. **High-Use Academic Words** In the directions, you are told that the NBA centers in the table are *ranked* the highest. What does it mean to *rank*?

   a. to show clearly

   b. to determine the relative position of

Name ______________________ Class ______________ Date ______________

1C: Reading/Writing Math Symbols

For use after Lesson 1-5

Study Skill Finish one homework assignment before beginning another. Sometimes it helps to complete the most difficult assignment first.

Match the symbol in Column A with its meaning in Column B.

Column A	Column B
1. ·	A. division
2. ≈	B. degrees
3. ÷	C. is approximately equal to
4. ||	D. the opposite of
5. °	E. multiplication
6. ≤	F. is less than or equal to
7. −	G. absolute value

Match the metric abbreviation in Column A with the appropriate word in Column B.

Column A	Column B
8. mL	A. kilometers
9. L	B. decimeters
10. dm	C. milliliters
11. cL	D. centiliters
12. mg	E. grams
13. km	F. liters
14. g	G. milligrams

Name ______________________ Class ______________ Date ______________

1D: Visual Vocabulary Practice

For use after Lesson 1-9

Study Skill If a word is not in the glossary of your textbook, use a dictionary to find its meaning.

Concept List

Associative Property of Addition	Associative Property of Multiplication
Commutative Property of Addition	Distributive Property
mean	order of operations
median	range
mode	

Write the concept that best describes each exercise. Choose from the concept list above.

1. $(3 - (-2)^2) \cdot 5 + 3 =$ $(3 - 4) \cdot 5 + 3 =$ $-1 \times 5 + 3 = -5 + 3 = -2$ ______________	**2.** $(8 + x) + 2x = 8 + (x + 2x)$ ______________	**3.** The number 14 represents this in the data set {14, 30, 14, 31, 30, 18, 14, 12}. ______________
4. The average temperatures in a city over seven days included 54°F, 51°F, 42°F, 47°F, 58°F, 54°F, and 53°F. What does the number $58 - 42 = 16$ represent for this set of temperatures? ______________	**5.** Blanes's grades in history class are 82, 82, 92, 90, and 84. What does the number $\frac{82 + 82 + 92 + 90 + 84}{5} = 86$ represent for this set of grades? ______________	**6.** $8(2^3 + 16) = 8(2^3) + 8(16)$ ______________
7. $b + c = c + b$ ______________	**8.** $14 \cdot (50 \cdot 21) =$ $(14 \cdot 50) \cdot 21$ ______________	**9.** The set {1, 1, 3, 5, 10} represents the number of hours that five students watched TV last week. What does the number 3 represent for this set of hours? ______________

Name ______________________ Class ______________ Date ______________

1E: Vocabulary Check

For use after Lesson 1-6

Study Skill Strengthen your vocabulary. Use these pages and add cues and summaries by applying the Cornell Notetaking style.

Write the definition for each word or term at the right. To check your work, fold the paper back along the dotted line to see the correct answers.

______________________ ______________________ ______________________	absolute value
______________________ ______________________ ______________________	integers
______________________ ______________________ ______________________	compatible numbers
______________________ ______________________ ______________________	Zero Property
______________________ ______________________ ______________________	additive inverses

Name ______________________ Class ______________ Date ______________

1E: Vocabulary Check (continued)

For use after Lesson 1-6

Write the vocabulary word or term for each definition. To check your work, fold the paper forward along the dotted line to see the correct answers.

the distance of a number from 0 on a number line ______________________

the set of positive whole numbers, their opposites, and 0 ______________________

numbers that are easy to compute mentally ______________________

The product of 0 and any number is 0. ______________________

two numbers whose sum is 0 ______________________

Name ______________________ Class ______________ Date ______________

1F: Vocabulary Review Puzzle

For use with the Chapter Review

Study Skill Vocabulary is an important part of every subject you learn. Use flashcards to review new words and their definitions.

Find each of the following words in the word search. Circle the word and then cross it off the word list. Words can be displayed forwards, backwards, up, down, or diagonally.

absolute value	integers	order
median	mode	mean
opposites	outlier	range
compatible	distributive	multiplication

C	Q	E	D	E	T	A	J	P	K	A	Z	L	H	N
F	K	E	E	R	E	D	R	O	N	D	A	H	U	N
M	Z	D	W	I	T	E	P	I	E	B	B	I	P	O
R	N	O	U	R	O	L	C	C	V	E	S	E	F	I
A	O	M	B	A	P	B	M	E	I	T	O	V	X	T
N	P	R	J	N	P	I	E	P	T	I	L	A	S	A
G	F	I	R	L	O	T	T	E	U	F	U	T	E	C
E	I	N	P	M	S	A	R	T	B	E	T	K	T	I
Y	O	T	H	G	I	P	A	A	I	I	E	O	R	L
I	D	E	O	O	T	M	N	R	R	N	V	U	O	P
W	A	G	R	F	E	O	V	O	T	K	A	T	I	I
P	D	E	F	N	S	C	O	O	S	E	L	L	J	T
G	K	R	N	N	A	W	S	O	I	G	U	I	R	L
N	M	S	D	K	A	E	V	N	D	S	E	E	U	U
M	E	D	I	A	N	F	M	A	R	O	M	R	L	M

Name ______________________ Class ______________ Date ______________

Practice 2-1

Exponents and Order of Operations

Write using an exponent.

1. $3 \cdot 3 \cdot 3 \cdot 3 \cdot 3$ ____________
2. $2.7 \cdot 2.7 \cdot 2.7$ ____________
3. $11.6 \cdot 11.6 \cdot 11.6 \cdot 11.6$ ____________
4. $2 \cdot 2 \cdot 2 \cdot 2 \cdot 2 \cdot 2$ ____________
5. $8.3 \cdot 8.3 \cdot 8.3 \cdot 8.3 \cdot 8.3$ ____________
6. $4 \cdot 4 \cdot 4 \cdot 4 \cdot 4 \cdot 4 \cdot 4 \cdot 4$ ____________

Write as the product of repeated factors. Then simplify.

7. $(0.5)^3$ ____________
8. $(-4)^5$ ____________
9. $(2.7)^2$ ____________
10. 2^3 ____________
11. $(-5)^6$ ____________
12. $(8.1)^3$ ____________

Simplify using the order of operations.

13. -4^3 ____________
14. $11 + (-6^3)$ ____________
15. $14 + 16^2$ ____________
16. $8 + 6^4$ ____________
17 $3^2 \cdot 5^4$ ____________
18. $6^2 - 2^4$ ____________
19. $4\ (0.9 + 1.3)^3$ ____________
20. $35 - (4^2 + 5)$ ____________
21. $(3^3 + 6) - 7$ ____________
22. $5\ (0.3 \cdot 1.2)^2$ ____________
23. $5\ (4 + 2)^2$ ____________
24. $(8 - 6.7)^3$ ____________

25. A cubic aquarium has edges measuring 4.3 ft each. Find the volume of the aquarium in cubic feet.

____

26. Lana is 2^3 in. taller than her little sister. How many inches taller is Lana than her sister?

____

Name ______________________ Class ______________ Date ______________

2-1 • Guided Problem Solving

GPS Exercise 29:

A Scanning Electron Microscope can magnify an image to as much as 10^5 times the actual size. How many times is this?

Understand

1. What are you being asked to do?

____

____

2. What do you call the 5 in 10^5?

____

3. What do you call the 10 in 10^5?

____

Plan and Carry Out

4. The number 10^5 is what number? ______________

5. How many zeros are in the number 10^5? ______________

6. How many times does the microscope magnify? ______________

Check

7. Does your answer follow the pattern of powers of 10? Explain.

____

____

____

Solve Another Problem

8. Lucy has a microscope that magnifies an image to as much as 10^3 times the actual size. Aaron has a microscope that magnifies an image to as much as 10^4 times the actual size. What is the difference in these two numbers?

____

Name ____________ Class ____________ Date ____________

Practice 2-2

Prime Factorization

Find the LCM of each pair of numbers.

1. 11, 5 ________
2. 5, 12 ________
3. 12, 7 ________
4. 5, 9 ________
5. 5, 18 ________
6. 5, 20 ________
7. 7, 10 ________
8. 17, 13 ________
9. 14, 8 ________
10. 11, 23 ________
11. 14, 5 ________
12. 16, 9 ________
13. Cameron is making bead necklaces. He has 90 green beads and 108 blue beads. What is the greatest number of identical necklaces he can make if he wants to use all of the beads?

    ____

14. One radio station broadcasts a weather forecast every 18 minutes and another station broadcasts a commercial every 15 minutes. If the stations broadcast both a weather forecast and a commercial at noon, when is the next time that both will be broadcast at the same time?

    ____

Determine whether each number is prime or composite.

15. 97 ________
16. 72 ________
17. 29 ________
18. 120 ________

Write the prime factorization. Use exponents where possible.

19. 42 ________
20. 130 ________
21. 78 ________
22. 126 ________
23. 125 ________
24. 90 ________
25. 92 ________
26. 180 ________

Find the GCD of each pair of numbers.

27. 45, 60 ________
28. 18, 42 ________
29. 32, 80 ________
30. 20, 65 ________
31. 24, 90 ________
32. 17, 34 ________
33. 14, 35 ________
34. 51, 27 ________
35. 42, 63 ________

Name ______________________ Class ______________ Date ______________

2-2 • Guided Problem Solving

GPS Exercise 37:

A movie theatre just added two rooms. One room is large enough for 125 people, and the other can seat up to 350 people. In each room, the seating is arranged in horizontal rows with the same number of seats in each row. What is the greatest number of seats that can make up each row?

Understand

1. Circle the information you will need to solve the problem.
2. What do you need to do to answer the question?

____

____

Plan and Carry Out

3. List the prime factors of 350. ______________
4. List the prime factors of 125. ______________
5. List the factors that 350 and 125 have in common. ______________
6. What is the greatest common factor of 350 and 125? ______________
7. What is the largest number of seats that can make up each row? ______________

Check

8. What is 350 ÷ 25? What is 125 ÷ 25? Do these quotients have any common factors besides 1?

____

____

Solve Another Problem

9. For graduation, the left side of the gymnasium can seat 228 people and the right side can seat 144 people. The principal wants the same number of chairs in each row on both sides. How many chairs does the setup committee need to put in each row?

____

Name ____________ Class ____________ Date ____________

Practice 2-3

Simplifying Fractions

Write each fraction in simplest form.

1. $\frac{8}{12}$ ____________
2. $\frac{9}{15}$ ____________
3. $\frac{16}{20}$ ____________
4. $\frac{20}{25}$ ____________
5. $\frac{15}{18}$ ____________
6. $\frac{14}{30}$ ____________
7. $\frac{11}{44}$ ____________
8. $\frac{24}{36}$ ____________

Write each fraction in simplest form. Give the GCD of the numerator and denominator.

9. $\frac{125}{200}$ _____ GCD = _____
10. $\frac{36}{64}$ _____ GCD = _____
11. $\frac{65}{90}$ _____ GCD = _____
12. $\frac{45}{72}$ _____ GCD = _____
13. $\frac{35}{85}$ _____ GCD = _____
14. $\frac{30}{42}$ _____ GCD = _____

Solve.

15. Emily exercised from 4:05 P.M. to 4:32 P.M. For what part of an hour did Emily exercise? Write the fraction in simplest form.

    ____

16. Luis rode his bike after school for 48 min. For what part of an hour did he ride his bike? Write the fraction in simplest form.

    ____

17. Philip played video games for 55 min before dinner. For what part of an hour did he play?

    ____

18. What part of an hour is your school lunch time?

    ____

19. Survey 12 people to find their favorite kind of pizza from the following choices. Write the results in fraction form. Then shade the pizza shapes using different colors to indicate their choices.

Pizza Favorites

Cheese ____________________

Green Pepper ____________________

Olive ____________________

Mushroom ____________________

Name ______________________ Class ______________ Date ____________

2-3 • Guided Problem Solving

GPS Exercise 27:

The city of San Francisco, California, typically has 160 clear days out of the 365 days in a year. San Francisco's clear days represent what fraction of a year? Write your answer in simplest form.

Understand

1. Circle the information you will need to solve.
2. What are you being asked to do?

____

____

Plan and Carry Out

3. Write the fraction for the expression 160 out of 365.

____

4. List the prime factors of 160.

____

5. List the prime factors of 365.

____

6. List the factors that 160 and 365 have in common.

____

7. Divide both 160 and 365 by the common factors.

____

8. Write the fraction in simplest form. __________

Check

9. Is 160 ÷ 365 the same as 32 ÷ 73? Explain. You may find a calculator helpful.

____

____

Solve Another Problem

10. Gerald received a score of 66 out of 72 on his vocabulary test. Write his score as a fraction in simplest form.

____

Practice 2-4

Comparing and Ordering Fractions

Write the two fractions for these models and compare them with <, >, or =.

1. 

2. 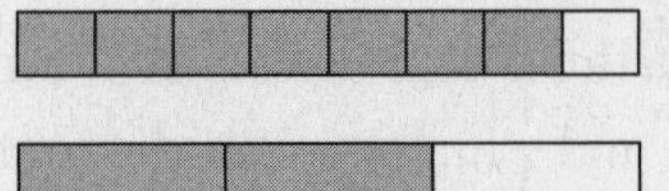

3. 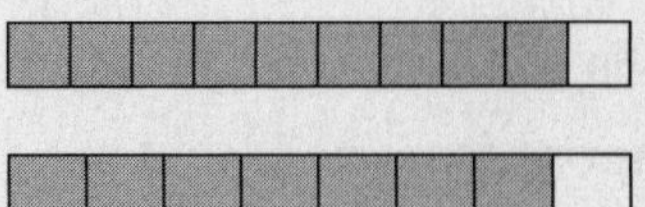

______ ______ ______

Find the LCD of each pair of fractions.

4. $\frac{5}{8}, \frac{5}{6}$ ______
5. $\frac{5}{12}, \frac{7}{8}$ ______
6. $\frac{9}{10}, \frac{1}{2}$ ______
7. $\frac{1}{6}, \frac{3}{10}$ ______
8. $\frac{1}{4}, \frac{2}{15}$ ______
9. $\frac{5}{6}, \frac{8}{15}$ ______

Compare each pair of fractions. Use <, >, or =.

10. $\frac{7}{8}$ ☐ $\frac{3}{10}$
11. $\frac{6}{12}$ ☐ $\frac{4}{8}$
12. $\frac{7}{15}$ ☐ $\frac{11}{15}$
13. $\frac{4}{5}$ ☐ $\frac{6}{10}$
14. $\frac{8}{15}$ ☐ $\frac{1}{2}$
15. $\frac{10}{15}$ ☐ $\frac{8}{12}$
16. $\frac{4}{9}$ ☐ $\frac{7}{9}$
17. $\frac{1}{2}$ ☐ $\frac{11}{20}$
18. $\frac{7}{16}$ ☐ $\frac{1}{2}$

Order from least to greatest.

19. $\frac{1}{4}, \frac{1}{3}, \frac{1}{6}$ ______
20. $\frac{1}{2}, \frac{5}{6}, \frac{7}{8}$ ______
21. $\frac{1}{4}, \frac{2}{5}, \frac{3}{8}$ ______
22. $\frac{7}{8}, \frac{5}{9}, \frac{2}{3}$ ______
23. $\frac{3}{8}, \frac{5}{6}, \frac{1}{2}$ ______
24. $\frac{9}{10}, \frac{11}{12}, \frac{15}{16}$ ______
25. $\frac{3}{4}, \frac{1}{2}, \frac{7}{8}$ ______
26. $\frac{5}{9}, \frac{2}{3}, \frac{7}{12}$ ______
27. $\frac{15}{16}, \frac{7}{8}, \frac{1}{2}$ ______

Solve.

28. A pattern requires a seam of at least $\frac{5}{8}$ in. Rachel sewed a seam $\frac{1}{2}$ in. wide. Did she sew the seam wide enough? Explain.

______

29. Marc needs $\frac{3}{4}$ cup of milk for a recipe. He has $\frac{2}{3}$ cup. Does he have enough? Explain.

______

30. Monica is growing three bean plants as part of a science experiment. Plant A is $\frac{1}{2}$ in. tall. Plant B is $\frac{3}{4}$ in tall. Plant C is $\frac{3}{8}$ in. tall. Order the plants from shortest to tallest.

______

31. During a rainstorm Willow received $\frac{7}{16}$ in. of rain and Riverton received $\frac{5}{8}$ in. of rain. Which community received more rain?

______

Name ______________________ Class ______________ Date ______________

2-4 • Guided Problem Solving

GPS Exercise 29:

You want to nail a board that is $\frac{1}{2}$ in. thick onto a wall. You can choose from nails that are $\frac{3}{8}$ in. long and $\frac{3}{4}$ in. long. Which size nail is the better choice? Explain.

Understand

1. Circle the information you will need to solve.
2. What are you being asked to do?

____

____

3. In order to compare fractions what must you do?

____

Plan and Carry Out

4. What is the common denominator for $\frac{1}{2}, \frac{3}{8}, \frac{3}{4}$? ______________
5. Write an equivalent fraction for $\frac{1}{2}$ and $\frac{3}{4}$ with the denominator found in Step 4. ______________
6. Which nail is longer than $\frac{4}{8}$ in.? ______________
7. Which size nail is the better choice, the $\frac{3}{8}$ in. nail or the $\frac{3}{4}$ in. nail? ______________
8. Explain why you chose the nail you did in Step 8.

____

____

____

Check

9. What is $\frac{3}{4} - \frac{1}{2}$? What is $\frac{3}{8} - \frac{1}{2}$?

____

Solve Another Problem

10. Louise used the $\frac{1}{2}$ in., the $\frac{11}{16}$ in., and the $\frac{5}{8}$ in. wrench from her mom's toolbox. Now her mom wants Louise to put them back in the toolbox from smallest to largest. What order should the wrenches be in?

____

Name ____________ Class ____________ Date ____________

Practice 2-5

Mixed Numbers and Improper Fractions

1. Write a mixed number and an improper fraction for the model below.

____

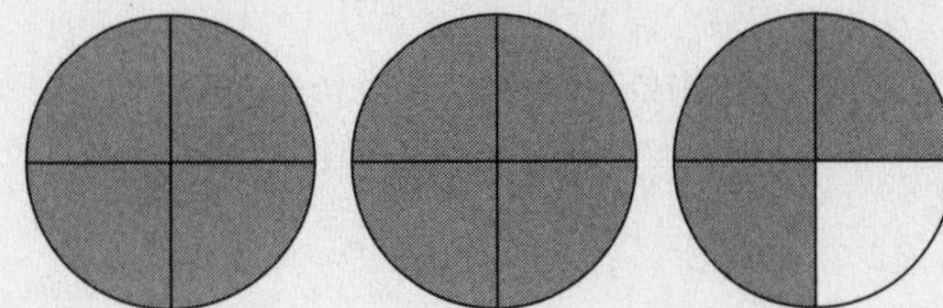

Write each mixed number as an improper fraction. You may find a model helpful.

2. $2\frac{3}{8}$ ____________
3. $5\frac{1}{3}$ ____________
4. $1\frac{7}{10}$ ____________
5. $4\frac{5}{8}$ ____________
6. $3\frac{5}{12}$ ____________
7. $1\frac{15}{16}$ ____________

Write each improper fraction as a mixed number in simplest form. You may find a model helpful.

8. $\frac{25}{3}$ ____________
9. $\frac{42}{7}$ ____________
10. $\frac{18}{4}$ ____________
11. $\frac{27}{12}$ ____________
12. $\frac{11}{6}$ ____________
13. $\frac{20}{3}$ ____________
14. $\frac{125}{5}$ ____________
15. $\frac{34}{7}$ ____________
16. $\frac{40}{6}$ ____________

The distance around the inside of a shopping mall is $\frac{12}{16}$ mi.

17. Juan jogged around the mall 4 times. How far did he jog?

____

18. Aaron walked around the mall 3 times. How far did he walk?

____

The distance around an indoor running track is $\frac{1}{6}$ mile.

19. Aruna jogged around the track 16 times. How far did she jog?

____

20. Theresa walked around the track 22 times. How far did she walk?

____

21. Shade the figures below to represent $3\frac{5}{8}$. How many eighths are shaded?

____

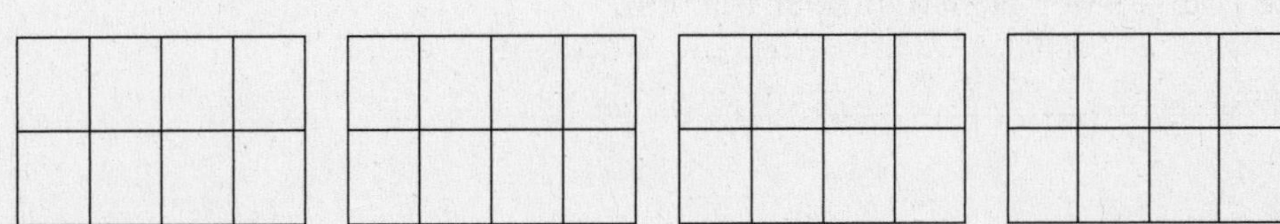

Name ______________________ Class ______________ Date ____________

2-5 • Guided Problem Solving

GPS Exercise 33:

A tailor designs a skirt that is $25\frac{1}{4}$ in. long. What is the length in eighths of an inch? Write your answer as an improper fraction.

Understand

1. What are you being asked to do?

____

____

2. What is an improper fraction?

____

____

3. How many eighths of an inch are in one inch? ____________

Plan and Carry Out

4. Write an expression that will be used to solve the problem.

____

5. In order to combine these two numbers, what must you do first?

____

6. How many eighths of an inch are in $25\frac{1}{4}$ in. ? ____________

7. What is the length in eighths of an inch?

____

Check

8. Rewrite the answer to Step 7 as a mixed number.

____

Solve Another Problem

9. There are $8\frac{3}{4}$ cups of flour in a batch of cookies. If there are 6 servings in a batch of cookies, how many cups of flour are in each serving? Write your answer as an improper fraction.

____

Name ______________ Class ______________ Date ______________

Practice 2-6

Fractions and Decimals

Write each fraction as a decimal.

1. $\frac{3}{5}$ ______________
2. $\frac{7}{8}$ ______________
3. $\frac{7}{9}$ ______________
4. $\frac{5}{16}$ ______________
5. $\frac{1}{6}$ ______________
6. $\frac{5}{8}$ ______________
7. $\frac{1}{3}$ ______________
8. $\frac{2}{3}$ ______________
9. $\frac{9}{10}$ ______________
10. $\frac{7}{11}$ ______________
11. $\frac{9}{20}$ ______________
12. $\frac{3}{4}$ ______________
13. $\frac{4}{9}$ ______________
14. $\frac{9}{11}$ ______________
15. $\frac{11}{20}$ ______________

Write each decimal as a mixed number or fraction in simplest form.

16. 0.6 ______________
17. 0.45 ______________
18. 0.62 ______________
19. 0.8 ______________
20. 0.325 ______________
21. 0.725 ______________
22. 4.75 ______________
23. 0.33 ______________
24. 0.925 ______________
25. 3.8 ______________
26. 4.7 ______________
27. 0.05 ______________
28. 0.65 ______________
29. 0.855 ______________
30. 0.104 ______________
31. 0.47 ______________
32. 0.894 ______________
33. 0.276 ______________

Order from greatest to least.

34. $0.\overline{2}, \frac{1}{5}, 0.02$

____

35. $1.\overline{1}, 1\frac{1}{10}, 1.101$

____

36. $\frac{6}{5}, 1\frac{5}{6}, 1.\overline{3}$

____

37. $4.\overline{3}, \frac{9}{2}, 4\frac{3}{7}$

____

38. A group of gymnasts were asked to name their favorite piece of equipment. 0.33 of the gymnasts chose the vault, $\frac{4}{9}$ chose the beam, and $\frac{1}{7}$ chose the uneven parallel bars. List their choices in order of preference from greatest to least.

____

Name ______________________ Class ______________ Date ______________

2-6 • Guided Problem Solving

GPS Exercise 33:

About 12,500 icebergs break away from Greenland each year. Of these, about 375 float into the Atlantic Ocean.

a. What fraction of icebergs float into the Atlantic Ocean?
b. Write your answer for part (a) as a decimal.
c. What fraction of icebergs do *not* float into the Atlantic Ocean?

Understand

1. What are you being asked to do?

____

2. Circle the information you will need to solve the problem.

Plan and Carry Out

3. Which number should go in the denominator of your fraction for part (a)? Which number should go in the numerator? Write the fraction.

____

4. Write your answer to Step 4 as a decimal (divide the numerator by the denominator).

____

5. How will you find the fraction of icebergs that do *not* float into the Atlantic Ocean?

____

6. Find the fraction of icebergs that do not float into the Atlantic Ocean.

____

Check

7. Multiply the total number of icebergs by your answer to Step 5. Is the answer 375? Add your answer to Step 4 and your answer to Step 7. Is the sum 1?

____

Solve Another Problem

8. Of the 245 people who attended a local picnic, 49 wore blue jeans.
   a. What fraction of people wore blue jeans?
   b. Write your answer for part (a) as a decimal.

____

____

Name ______________________ Class ______________ Date ______________

Practice 2-7

Rational Numbers

Compare. Use <, =, or >.

1. $-\frac{2}{9}$ ☐ $-\frac{4}{9}$

2. $-\frac{1}{6}$ ☐ $-\frac{2}{3}$

3. $-\frac{5}{12}$ ☐ $-\frac{3}{4}$

4. -1.2 ☐ -2.1

5. -0.6 ☐ -0.52

6. -1.23 ☐ -1.25

7. -5.3 ☐ $-5.\overline{3}$

8. $-3\frac{1}{4}$ ☐ -3.25

9. $-4\frac{2}{5}$ ☐ -4.12

Order from least to greatest.

10. $\frac{5}{4}, 1.5, -\frac{3}{2}, -0.5$

____

11. $\frac{1}{11}, -0.9, 0.09, \frac{1}{10}$

____

12. $0.1\overline{2}, -\frac{11}{12}, -\frac{1}{6}, -0.1$

____

13. $\frac{2}{3}, 0.6, -\frac{5}{6}, -6.6$

____

14. $1.312, 1\frac{3}{8}, -1\frac{3}{10}, -1.33$

____

15. $1, \frac{4}{5}, -\frac{8}{9}, -1$

____

Use mental math to compare each pair of fractions using <, =, or >.

16. $\frac{1}{6}$ ☐ $\frac{1}{8}$

17. $\frac{8}{9}$ ☐ $\frac{8}{12}$

18. $\frac{1}{4}$ ☐ $\frac{1}{5}$

19. $\frac{3}{9}$ ☐ $\frac{3}{7}$

20. $\frac{5}{50}$ ☐ $\frac{1}{60}$

21. $\frac{9}{10}$ ☐ $\frac{10}{12}$

22. $\frac{1}{12}$ ☐ $\frac{1}{15}$

23. $\frac{5}{6}$ ☐ $\frac{3}{4}$

24. $\frac{1}{65}$ ☐ $\frac{3}{60}$

Compare.

25. Four puppies measured $5\frac{1}{4}$ in., $5\frac{3}{8}$ in., $5\frac{5}{8}$ in., and $5\frac{5}{16}$ in. long at birth. Order the lengths from least to greatest.

____

26. Samuel is $\frac{5}{8}$ in. taller than Jackie. Shelly is 0.7 in. taller than Jackie. Who is the tallest?

____

Name ______________________ Class ______________ Date ____________

2-7 • Guided Problem Solving

GPS Exercise 27:

About $\frac{1}{25}$ of a toad's eggs survive to adulthood. About 0.25 of a frog's eggs and $\frac{1}{5}$ of a green turtle's eggs survive to adulthood. Which animal's eggs have the highest survival rate?

Understand

1. Circle the information you will need to solve.
2. What are you being asked to do?

   ____

   ____
3. In order to find the greatest number, what must you do first?

   ____

Plan and Carry Out

4. Write $\frac{1}{25}$ as a decimal. ______________
5. Write $\frac{1}{5}$ as a decimal. ______________
6. Which is the largest decimal, 0.04, 0.2, or 0.25? ______________
7. Which animal's eggs have the highest survival rate? ______________

Check

8. What fraction is 0.25 equal to? Is it the greatest value?

   ____

Solve Another Problem

9. In order to organize the nails in a garage, Anne and Jeff measured the nails. Anne used fractions to measure her 3 groups of nails and found that they were $\frac{3}{5}$ in., $\frac{7}{12}$ in., and $\frac{4}{9}$ in. Jeff used decimals to measure his two groups and found that they were 0.62 in., and 0.31 in. Which nail is the longest?

   ____

Name ______________________ Class ______________ Date ______________

2A: Graphic Organizer

For use before Lesson 2-1

Study Skill Develop consistent study habits. Block off the same amount of time each evening for schoolwork. Plan ahead by setting aside extra time when you have a big project or test coming up.

Write your answers.

1. What is the chapter title? ______________________
2. How many lessons are there in this chapter? ______________________
3. What is the topic of the Test-Taking Strategies page? ______________________
4. Complete the graphic organizer below as you work through the chapter.
   - In the center, write the title of the chapter.
   - When you begin a lesson, write the lesson name in a rectangle.
   - When you complete a lesson, write a skill or key concept in a circle linked to that lesson block.
   - When you complete the chapter, use this graphic organizer to help you review.

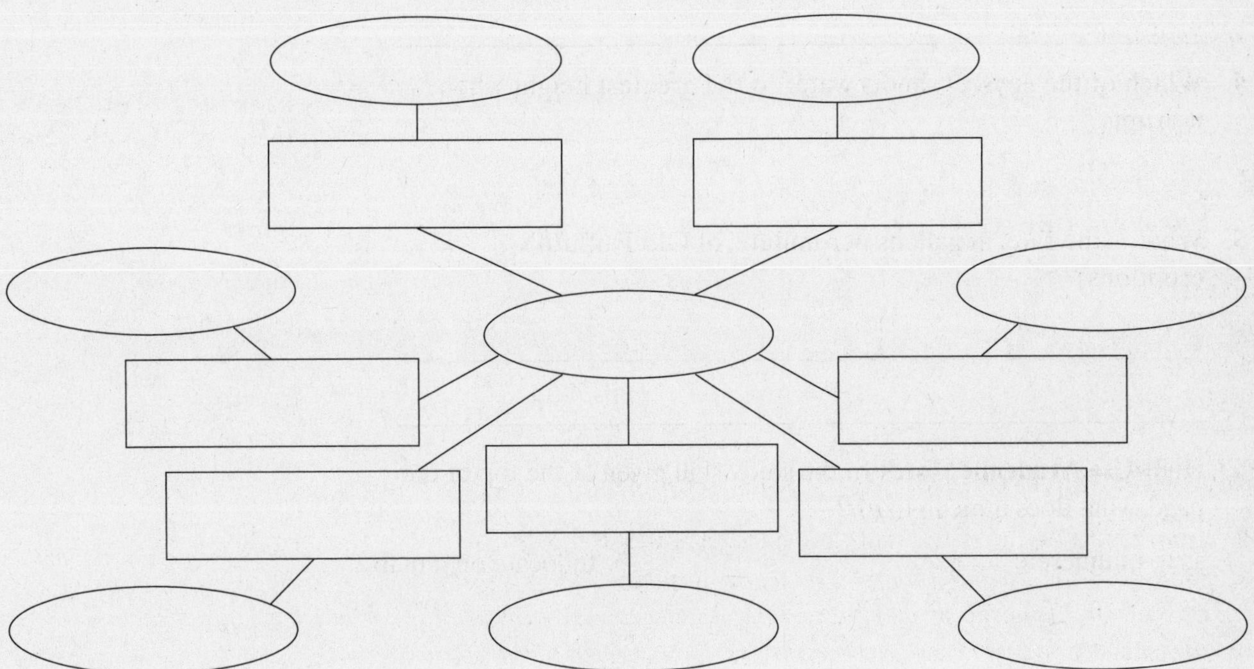

Name ______________________ Class ______________ Date ______________

2B: Reading Comprehension

For use after Lesson 2-5

Study Skill Never go to class unprepared. List your assignments, books needed, and supplies to help you prepare.

Read the paragraph and answer the questions.

Old Faithful is the most famous geyser at Yellowstone National Park. It erupts approximately every $1\frac{1}{4}$ hours for up to 5 minutes. When it erupts, a mixture of water and steam shoots into the air as high as 170 feet. The amount of water expelled during each eruption ranges from 10,000 to 12,000 gallons. Giant Geyser and Steamboat Geyser, two other geysers at Yellowstone, shoot water to heights of 200 feet and 380 feet, respectively.

1. What is the paragraph about?

   ____

2. Which number in the paragraph is written as a mixed number?

   ____

3. For what fraction of an hour does Old Faithful erupt?

   ____

4. Which of the geysers shoots water to the greatest height when it erupts?

   ____

5. What is the rate, in gallons per minute, of Old Faithful's eruptions?

   ____

   ____

6. **High-Use Academic Words** In the study skill given at the top of the page, what does it mean to *list*?

   a. to enumerate

   b. to locate on a map

Name ______________ Class ______________ Date ______________

2C: Reading/Writing Math Symbols

For use after Lesson 2-7

Study Skill Use flashcards to help you memorize math symbols and their meanings.

Write each statement in words.

1. $-7 < 6$ ______________
2. $4^3 = 64$ ______________
3. $-3 > -5$ ______________
4. $|-5| = 5$ ______________
5. $3^2 = 9$ ______________
6. $3.01 \approx 3$ ______________
7. $\frac{8}{4} = 2$ ______________
8. $\frac{1}{3} < \frac{3}{5}$ ______________
9. $4.\overline{6} > 0$ ______________
10. $5^4 = 625$ ______________

Write each statement using mathematical symbols.

11. Three and seven tenths is less than 4 and one half.

____

12. The absolute value of 2.6 is 2.6.

____

13. Negative three-fourths is greater than negative ten.

____

14. Four and three thousandths is approximately equal to four.

____

15. Two raised to the fifth power is thirty-two.

____

16. Six cubed is two hundred sixteen.

____

Name ______________________ Class ______________ Date ______________

2D: Visual Vocabulary Practice

For use after Lesson 2-7

Study Skill Mathematics builds on itself, so build a strong foundation.

Concept List

equivalent fractions	greatest common divisor	improper fraction
least common denominator	least common multiple	prime factorization
repeating decimal	mixed number	simplest form

Write the concept that best describes each exercise. Choose from the concept list above.

1. $\frac{6}{4}$ ______________	**2.** The number 24 represents this for the numbers 48 and 72. ______________	**3.** $0.312312312\ldots = 0.\overline{312}$ ______________
4. 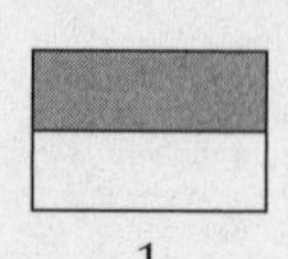 $\frac{1}{2} = \frac{3}{6}$ ______________	**5.** The number 12 represents this for the fractions $\frac{1}{6}$ and $\frac{3}{4}$. ______________	**6.** $4\frac{3}{12}$ ______________
7. The number 60 represents this for the numbers 12 and 15. ______________	**8.** $\frac{3}{20}$ ______________	**9.** $108 = 2^2 \cdot 3^3$ ______________

Name ______________________ Class ______________ Date ____________

2E: Vocabulary Check

For use after Lesson 2-6

Study Skill Strengthen your vocabulary. Use these pages and add cues and summaries by applying the Cornell Notetaking style.

Write the definition for each word or term at the right. To check your work, fold the paper back along the dotted line to see the correct answers.

exponent

composite number

mixed number

terminating decimal

simplest form

Name ______________________ Class ______________ Date ______________

2E: Vocabulary Check (continued)

For use after Lesson 2-6

Write the vocabulary word or term for each definition. To check your work, fold the paper forward along the dotted line to see the correct answers.

how many times a number, or base, is used as a factor ______________________

a whole number that has more than two divisors ______________________

the sum of a whole number and a fraction ______________________

a decimal that stops, or terminates ______________________

a fraction where the numerator and denominator have no common factors other than 1 ______________________

2F: Vocabulary Review Puzzle

For use with the Chapter Review

Study Skill Use a notebook or a section of a loose-leaf binder for math assignments. Review problems that gave you trouble.

Unscramble each of the key words from the chapter to help you fill in the famous quote by Lewis Carroll. Match the letters in the numbered cells with the numbered cells at the bottom.

NENPTEXO

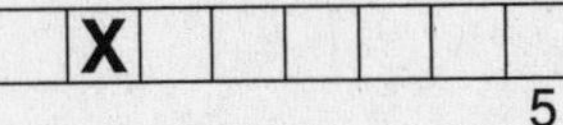

SMOTEPICO BREMUN

OPWER

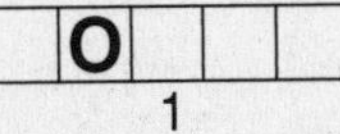

LORNIATA RUNMEB

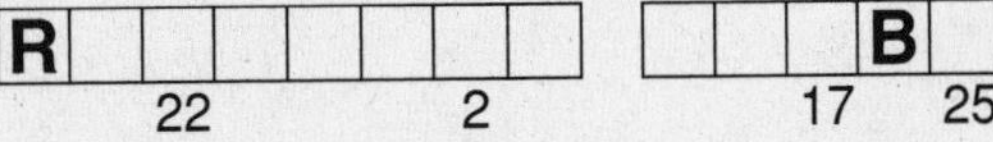

SIVIEBIDL

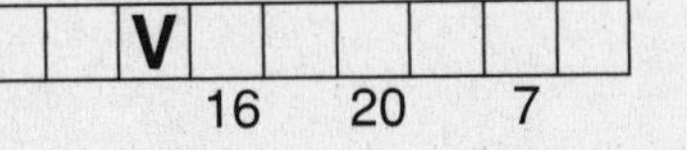

TARTEEGS COOMNM ISODRVI

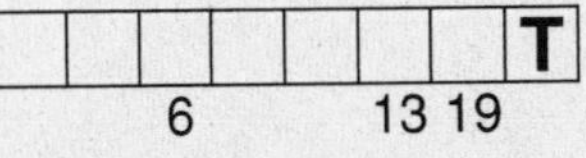

C ______ I ______

MIEPLLUT

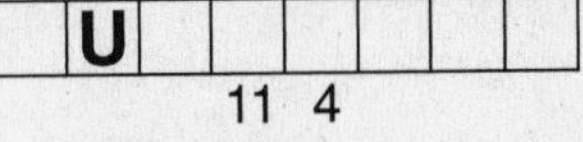

LESAT COOMNM METLULPI

E ___ 21 ___ M ___ ___ 8 P 14

RIPME MUNREB

___ M ___ M 10 23

MIEDX MUEBRN

___ X ___ 24 12

ROMPIERP FRTAINOC

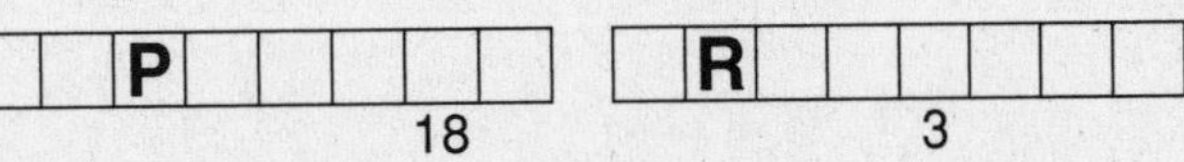

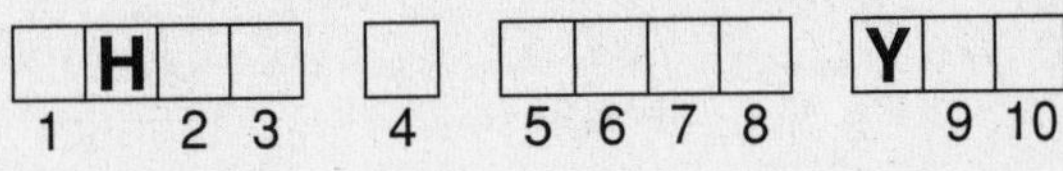

___ H ___ ___ 11 12 13 14 ___ 15 16 17 18 19 ___ 20 21 ___ 22 23 24 25

Name ______________________ Class ______________ Date ______________

Practice 3-1

Estimating With Fractions and Mixed Numbers

Use benchmarks to estimate each sum or difference.

1. $\frac{1}{6} + \frac{5}{8}$ ______
2. $\frac{7}{8} - \frac{1}{16}$ ______
3. $\frac{9}{10} + \frac{7}{8}$ ______
4. $\frac{1}{10} + \frac{5}{6}$ ______
5. $\frac{4}{5} - \frac{1}{6}$ ______
6. $\frac{11}{12} - \frac{5}{16}$ ______
7. $2\frac{1}{6} + 7\frac{1}{9}$ ______
8. $4\frac{9}{10} - 3\frac{5}{8}$ ______
9. $4\frac{7}{8} + 8\frac{1}{5}$ ______
10. $14\frac{3}{4} + 9\frac{7}{8}$ ______
11. $7\frac{11}{15} - 6\frac{7}{16}$ ______
12. $3\frac{11}{15} - 2\frac{9}{10}$ ______

Use rounding to estimate each product or quotient.

13. $13\frac{1}{8} \div 6\frac{1}{5}$ ______
14. $5\frac{1}{6} \cdot 8\frac{4}{5}$ ______
15. $8\frac{1}{6} \div 1\frac{9}{10}$ ______
16. $27\frac{6}{7} \div 3\frac{2}{3}$ ______
17. $20\frac{4}{5} \cdot 2\frac{2}{7}$ ______
18. $9\frac{1}{3} \div 2\frac{7}{8}$ ______
19. $19\frac{4}{5} \div 4\frac{5}{8}$ ______
20. $9\frac{2}{13} \div 3\frac{1}{18}$ ______
21. $42\frac{1}{6} \div 6\frac{1}{16}$ ______
22. $15\frac{1}{20} \cdot 3\frac{1}{10}$ ______
23. $72\frac{2}{15} \div 8\frac{3}{4}$ ______
24. $3\frac{5}{6} \cdot 10\frac{1}{12}$ ______

Solve each problem.

25. Each dress for a wedding party requires $7\frac{1}{8}$ yd of material. Estimate the amount of material you would need to make 6 dresses.

____

26. A fabric store has $80\frac{3}{8}$ yd of a particular fabric. About how many pairs of curtains could be made from this fabric if each pair requires $4\frac{1}{8}$ yd of fabric?

____

27. Adam's car can hold $16\frac{1}{10}$ gal of gasoline. About how many gallons are left if he started with a full tank and has used $11\frac{9}{10}$ gal?

____

28. Julia bought stock at $\$28\frac{1}{8}$ per share. The value of each stock increased by $\$6\frac{5}{8}$. About how much is each share of stock now worth?

____

Estimate each answer.

29. $6\frac{2}{9} - 2\frac{7}{8}$ ______
30. $\frac{1}{8} + \frac{9}{10}$ ______
31. $8\frac{2}{9} \cdot 10\frac{4}{9}$ ______
32. $6\frac{1}{4} \div 2\frac{3}{11}$ ______
33. $5\frac{1}{11} \cdot 8\frac{13}{15}$ ______
34. $\frac{21}{40} - \frac{5}{89}$ ______
35. $\frac{81}{100} - \frac{1}{2}$ ______
36. $11\frac{5}{9} \div 2\frac{1}{2}$ ______
37. $\frac{3}{5} + \frac{7}{8}$ ______

Name ______________________ Class ______________ Date ______________

3-1 • Guided Problem Solving

GPS Exercise 41:

Writing in Math You need $9\frac{9}{16}$ lb of chicken. The store sells chicken in half-pound packages. How many packages should you order? Explain.

Understand

1. What are you being asked to do?

____

2. How do you know when to round up or when to round down with a fraction?

____

____

____

Plan and Carry Out

3. What is the numerator of the fraction? ______________
4. What is half of the denominator of the fraction? ______________
5. Is the numerator bigger or smaller than half of the denominator? ______________
6. Do you round the fraction up or down? ______________
7. How many pounds of chicken do you need? ______________
8. How many packages of chicken will you need to buy? ______________

Check

9. What is $9 \div 16$? Round to the nearest whole number. Does your answer make sense?

____

____

____

Solve Another Problem

10. You are making curtains to cover the top of four windows. Each window is $15\frac{5}{8}$ in. wide. You buy material by the whole yard. How many yards should you buy?

____

Name ______________________ Class ______________ Date ______________

Practice 3-2

Adding and Subtracting Fractions

Write a number statement for each model.

1\. ______________

2\. 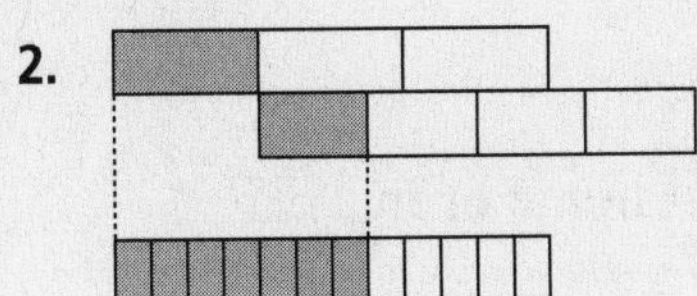

____

3\. 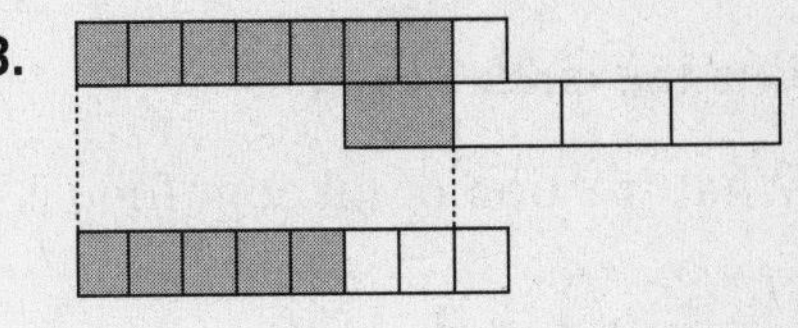

____

Find each sum or difference. You may find a model helpful.

4\. $\frac{1}{6} + \frac{7}{8}$ ________

5\. $\frac{9}{10} - \frac{1}{6}$ ________

6\. $\frac{1}{6} + \frac{1}{6}$ ________

7\. $\frac{1}{10} + \frac{2}{5}$ ________

8\. $\frac{5}{6} + \frac{1}{12}$ ________

9\. $\frac{2}{3} - \frac{1}{2}$ ________

10\. $\frac{7}{9} - \frac{1}{3}$ ________

11\. $\frac{3}{4} - \frac{1}{4}$ ________

12\. $\frac{1}{5} + \frac{3}{4}$ ________

13\. $\frac{1}{3} + \frac{1}{2}$ ________

14\. $\frac{1}{8} + \frac{1}{12}$ ________

15\. $\frac{7}{10} - \frac{1}{3}$ ________

Use the table at the right for Exercises 16–21. Tell which two snacks combine to make each amount.

Snack	Serving Amount
Raisins	$\frac{1}{4}$ c
Walnuts	$\frac{3}{8}$ c
Almonds	$\frac{1}{8}$ c
Sesame sticks	$\frac{2}{3}$ c
Mini pretzels	$\frac{5}{8}$ c
Dried apricots	$\frac{1}{6}$ c

16\. $\frac{5}{6}$ c ______________________

17\. $\frac{1}{2}$ c ______________________

18\. $\frac{3}{4}$ c ______________________

19\. $\frac{11}{12}$ c ______________________

20\. 1 c ______________________

21\. $\frac{19}{24}$ c ______________________

____

Name ______________________ Class ______________ Date ______________

3-2 • Guided Problem Solving

GPS Exercise 33:

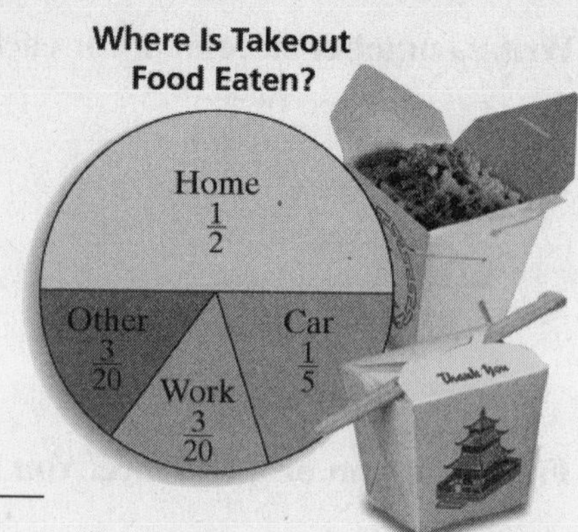

Use the circle graph.

What fraction of takeout food is eaten at home or in a car?

Understand

1. What are you being asked to do?

____

Plan and Carry Out

2. What fraction of takeout food is eaten at home?

____

3. What fraction of takeout food is eaten in a car?

____

4. Write an expression combining these two fractions.

____

5. What is the least common denominator (LCD) of these two fractions?

____

6. Using the answer to question 5, rewrite the expression from question 4 using equivalent fractions with a common denominator.

____

7. Add the numerators of the fractions from question 6. What fraction of takeout is eaten at home or in a car?

____

Check

8. Add the remaining fractions in the circle graph to your answer. Did you get 1?

____

Solve Another Problem

9. According to the graph above, what fraction of takeout food is eaten in a car or at work?

____

Name ______________________ Class ______________ Date ______________

Practice 3-3

Adding and Subtracting Mixed Numbers

Find each sum.

1. $5\frac{1}{3} + 3\frac{2}{3}$
2. $7\frac{1}{4} + 4\frac{3}{8}$
3. $2\frac{1}{8} + 6\frac{5}{8}$
4. $8\frac{1}{5} + 4\frac{3}{10}$
5. $9\frac{1}{6} + 6\frac{1}{4}$
6. $3\frac{2}{3} + 10\frac{5}{6}$

Find each difference.

7. $6\frac{11}{12} - 4\frac{5}{12}$
8. $12 - 5\frac{3}{10}$
9. $14\frac{1}{2} - 7\frac{1}{5}$
10. $9 - 5\frac{5}{6}$
11. $13\frac{3}{4} - 10\frac{1}{2}$
12. $15\frac{1}{6} - 6\frac{5}{12}$

Find each sum or difference.

13. $1\frac{1}{6} - \frac{3}{4}$
14. $4\frac{1}{2} - 2\frac{7}{8}$
15. $9\frac{3}{4} + 7\frac{7}{8}$
16. $5\frac{1}{6} - 4\frac{7}{12}$
17. $9\frac{8}{15} + 11\frac{5}{12}$
18. $\frac{14}{15} - \frac{1}{2}$
19. $9\frac{2}{3} + 3\frac{5}{6}$
20. $2\frac{1}{10} + 1\frac{2}{5}$
21. $6\frac{7}{16} - 2\frac{7}{8}$

Write a mixed number for each time period. Be sure each fraction is in lowest terms.

22. 8:00 A.M. to 9:20 A.M.
23. 9:00 A.M. to 2:45 P.M.
24. 8:30 A.M. to 10:40 P.M.

Name ____________________ Class ____________ Date ____________

3-3 • Guided Problem Solving

GPS Exercise 27:

On Saturday you hiked $4\frac{3}{8}$ mi. On Sunday, you hiked $3\frac{1}{2}$ mi. How far did you hike during the weekend?

Understand

1. Circle the information you will need to solve.
2. What are you being asked to do?

   ____

3. Estimate the sum of the distances.

   ____

Plan and Carry Out

4. Add the whole numbers. ____________
5. In order to add $\frac{3}{8} + \frac{1}{2}$, what do you need to find first?

   ____

6. What is the common denominator for $\frac{3}{8} + \frac{1}{2}$? ____________
7. Add. $\frac{3}{8} + \frac{1}{2}$ ____________
8. Add. $7 + \frac{7}{8}$ ____________
9. How far did you hike during the weekend? ____________

Check

10. Is your answer reasonable according to the estimate you made in Step 3?

    ____

    ____

Solve Another Problem

11. On a white-water rafting trip you paddled $1\frac{3}{4}$ mi the first day and $2\frac{3}{8}$ mi the second day. How many miles did you raft on both days?

    ____

Name ______________________ Class ______________ Date ______________

Practice 3-4

Multiplying Fractions and Mixed Numbers

Find each product.

1. $\frac{5}{6} \cdot \frac{3}{5}$ ________
2. $\frac{7}{8} \cdot \frac{4}{5}$ ________
3. $\frac{9}{10} \cdot \frac{5}{12}$ ________
4. $\frac{5}{8} \cdot \frac{3}{5}$ ________
5. $\frac{1}{6}$ of 36 ________
6. $\frac{5}{9} \cdot 36$ ________
7. $\frac{3}{4} \cdot 36$ ________
8. $2 \cdot \frac{9}{10}$ ________
9. $8 \cdot \frac{9}{10}$ ________
10. $\frac{1}{3} \cdot 3\frac{1}{3}$ ________
11. $\frac{5}{6}$ of $1\frac{3}{5}$ ________
12. $\frac{1}{8}$ of $1\frac{4}{5}$ ________
13. $3 \cdot 4\frac{1}{2}$ ________
14. $5 \cdot 2\frac{1}{4}$ ________
15. $3 \cdot 2\frac{2}{3}$ ________
16. $3\frac{2}{3} \cdot 1\frac{1}{2}$ ________
17. $4\frac{1}{6} \cdot 2\frac{2}{5}$ ________
18. $3\frac{1}{4} \cdot 2\frac{1}{6}$ ________

Solve.

19. A sheet of plywood is $\frac{5}{8}$ in. thick. How tall is a stack of 21 sheets of plywood?

____

20. A poster measures 38 cm across. If a photocopy machine is used to make a copy that is $\frac{3}{5}$ of the original size, what is the width of the copy?

____

21. A one-kilogram object weighs about $2\frac{1}{5}$ pounds. Find the weight, in pounds, of a computer monitor with mass $7\frac{3}{8}$ kilograms.

____

22. The population of Sweden is about $1\frac{11}{16}$ times as great as the population of Denmark. Find the population of Sweden if the population of Denmark is about 5,190,000.

____

Name _______________ Class _______________ Date _______________

3-4 • Guided Problem Solving

GPS Exercise 33:

The length of a track around a field is $\frac{1}{4}$ mi. You jog $3\frac{1}{2}$ times around the track. How far do you jog?

Understand

1. Circle the information you will need to solve.
2. What are you being asked to do?

____

3. What operation will you use to solve the problem?

____

Plan and Carry Out

4. What is the length of the track? _______________
5. How many times did you run around the track? _______________
6. Write a multiplication expression to solve the problem. _______________
7. How far do you jog? _______________

Check

8. How many times would you have to run around the track to run one mile? Is your answer reasonable? Explain.

____

____

Solve Another Problem

9. One can of paint covers $2\frac{1}{2}$ walls. You have $\frac{3}{4}$ of a can of paint. How many walls can you paint?

____

Name ____________ Class ____________ Date ____________

Practice 3-5

Dividing Fractions and Mixed Numbers

Find the reciprocal of each number.

1. $\frac{1}{2}$ ______
2. $\frac{9}{16}$ ______
3. $\frac{4}{5}$ ______
4. $1\frac{1}{4}$ ______
5. $2\frac{9}{10}$ ______
6. $3\frac{1}{6}$ ______

Find each quotient.

7. $\frac{3}{4} \div \frac{1}{4}$ ______
8. $\frac{5}{6} \div \frac{1}{12}$ ______
9. $\frac{1}{12} \div \frac{5}{6}$ ______
10. $6 \div \frac{3}{4}$ ______
11. $5 \div \frac{9}{10}$ ______
12. $\frac{4}{5} \div 2$ ______
13. $\frac{7}{8} \div 3$ ______
14. $\frac{4}{9} \div 8$ ______
15. $1\frac{1}{2} \div \frac{2}{3}$ ______
16. $\frac{3}{4} \div 1\frac{1}{3}$ ______
17. $2\frac{1}{2} \div 1\frac{1}{4}$ ______
18. $1\frac{3}{4} \div \frac{3}{4}$ ______
19. $1\frac{7}{10} \div \frac{1}{2}$ ______
20. $4\frac{1}{2} \div 2\frac{1}{2}$ ______
21. $6 \div 3\frac{4}{5}$ ______
22. $4\frac{3}{4} \div \frac{7}{8}$ ______
23. $5\frac{5}{6} \div 1\frac{1}{3}$ ______
24. $3\frac{3}{8} \div 1\frac{1}{4}$ ______
25. $6\frac{1}{2} \div 1\frac{1}{2}$ ______
26. $2\frac{9}{10} \div 1\frac{3}{4}$ ______
27. $3\frac{1}{4} \div 1\frac{1}{3}$ ______

Solve each problem.

28. Rosa makes $2\frac{1}{2}$ c of pudding. How many $\frac{1}{3}$ c servings can she get from the pudding?

______

29. One type of lightning bug glows once every $1\frac{1}{2}$ s. How many times can it glow in 1 min?

______

30. Bea can run $\frac{1}{6}$ mi in 2 min. How long should it take her to run 2 mi?

______

31. Joe drives 20 mi in $\frac{1}{2}$ h. How long will it take him to drive 50 mi?

______

Name ______________________ Class ______________ Date ____________

3-5 • Guided Problem Solving

GPS Exercise 38:

A manatee can swim 5 mi in $1\frac{1}{4}$ h. If the manatee swims at the same average speed, how far can it swim in 1 h?

Understand

1. Circle the information you will need to solve.
2. What are you being asked to do?

____

____

Plan and Carry Out

3. Write a ratio comparing 5 miles to $1\frac{1}{4}$ hours.

____

4. Write a ratio comparing x miles to 1 hour.

____

5. Write a proportion comparing the ratios in Steps 3 and 4.

____

6. How far can the manatee swim in 1 hour?

____

Check

7. Will the manatee swim more or less than 5 miles in 1 hour? Is your answer reasonable? Explain.

____

____

Solve Another Problem

8. Glenda ran 8 miles in $2\frac{1}{2}$ hours. If she runs at the same average speed, how far can she run in 1 hour?

____

Name ______________ Class ______________ Date ______________

Practice 3-6

Changing Units in the Customary System

Tell whether you would multiply or divide to change from one unit of measure to the other.

1. tons to pounds ______________

2. pints to quarts ______________

3. feet to yards ______________

4. gallons to pints ______________

5. cups to quarts ______________

6. pounds to ounces ______________

Change each unit of length, capacity, or weight.

7. 9 qt = ________ gal

8. $2\frac{1}{4}$ t = ________ lb

9. $3\frac{1}{2}$ yd = ________ in.

10. 4 yd = ________ ft

11. 60 c = ________ qt

12. 246 in. = ________ ft

13. 1,750 oz = ________ lb

14. 84 ft = ________ yd

15. 198 in. = ________ yd

16. 480 fl oz = ________ pt

17. $\frac{1}{4}$ gal = ________ fl oz

18. $\frac{1}{2}$ mi = ________ ft

19. $\frac{1}{10}$ mi = ________ in.

20. 2 lb 6 oz = ________ lb

21. 2 qt 8 fl oz = ________ qt

Solve.

22. United States farms produced 2,460,000,000 bushels of soybeans in 1994. How many quarts is this? (A bushel is 32 quarts.)

____

23. In 1994, Brian Berg built an 81-story "house" using playing cards. The house was $15\frac{2}{3}$ ft tall. How many inches is this?

____

Choose an appropriate customary unit of measure.

24. capacity of a mug ______________

25. length of a family room ______________

26. distance between two capital cities ______________

27. weight of a shampoo bottle ______________

Name ______________________ Class ______________ Date ____________

3-6 • Guided Problem Solving

GPS Exercise 40:

The length of the Amazon River in South America is about 4,000 mi. How many feet is this?

Understand

1. Circle the information you will need to solve.
2. What are you being asked to do?

____

Plan and Carry Out

3. How many feet are there in 1 mile?

____

4. Do you multiply or divide to find the number of feet in 4,000 miles?

____

5. Write a multiplication expression to solve this problem.

____

6. How many feet are there in 4,000 mi?

____

Check

7. Should the number of feet in 4,000 miles be more or less than 4,000? Explain why.

____

Solve Another Problem

8. A fishing boat is working 90 miles from shore. How many feet from shore is this?

____

Name ______________________ Class ______________ Date ______________

3A: Graphic Organizer

For use before Lesson 3-1

Study Skill You should fully understand the basic concepts in each chapter before moving on to more complex material. Be sure to ask questions when you are not comfortable with what you have learned.

Write your answers.

1. What is the chapter title? ______________________
2. How many lessons are there in this chapter? ______________
3. What is the topic of the Test-Taking Strategies page? ______________
4. Complete the graphic organizer below as you work through the chapter.
   - In the center, write the title of the chapter.
   - When you begin a lesson, write the lesson name in a rectangle.
   - When you complete a lesson, write a skill or key concept in a circle linked to that lesson block.
   - When you complete the chapter, use this graphic organizer to help you review.

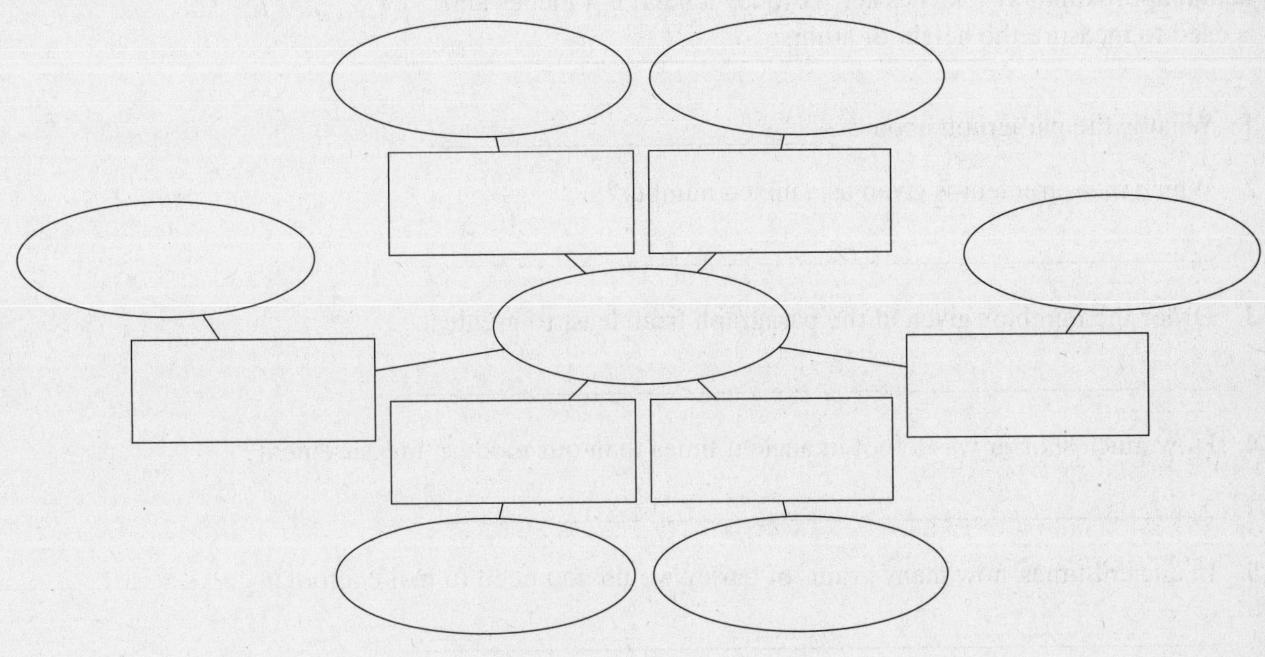

Name ______________________ Class ______________ Date ______________

3B: Reading Comprehension

For use after Lesson 3-6

Study Skill Make a realistic study schedule. Set specific goals for yourself, rather than general ones. For example, read Chapter 2, do problems 1–20, or study for a math test.

Read the paragraph below and answer the questions.

In ancient times, people measured things by comparing them to parts of the body. For example, a foot length or a finger width was considered an acceptable measurement. Later, other common objects were used to represent measurements. Below is a list of some common lengths and their early standards of measurement.

Inch: the width of a man's thumb, 3 grains of barley placed end to end

Foot: the length of an average man's foot, about $11\frac{1}{42}$ inches

Yard: the length of a man's belt, or the distance from a man's nose to the tip of his outstretched arm

Span: the length of a man's stretched out hand, about 9 inches

Hand: approximately 5 inches across, today a hand is 4 inches and is used to measure the height of a horse

1. What is the paragraph about? ______________________

2. Which measurement is given as a mixed number?

   ____

3. Order the numbers given in the paragraph from least to greatest.

   ____

4. How much shorter was a foot in ancient times than our modern measurement?

   ____

5. In ancient times, how many grains of barley would you need to make a foot?

   ____

6. In modern times, how many grains of barley would you need to make a foot?

   ____

7. **High-Use Academic Words** In question three, what does it mean to *order*?

   a. to arrange information in a sequence
   b. to determine the value of

Name ______________________ Class ______________ Date ______________

3C: Reading/Writing Math Symbols

For use after Lesson 3-6

Study Skill Read problems carefully. Pay special attention to units when working with measurements.

Match each abbreviation in Column A with the appropriate customary units in Column B.

Column A	Column B
1. lb	A. ounces
2. c	B. quarts
3. oz	C. pounds
4. yd	D. pints
5. pt	E. gallons
6. ft	F. yards
7. qt	G. feet
8. gal	H. cups

Write each of the following using appropriate mathematical symbols.

9. one hundred kilometers ______________

10. forty-seven pounds ______________

11. three and seven tenths ounces ______________

12. two and five tenths milliliters ______________

13. five and thirty-three hundredths grams ______________

14. four and three quarters inches ______________

15. thirteen meters ______________

16. five and one third tons ______________

Name ________________ Class ________________ Date ________________

3D: Visual Vocabulary Practice

For use after Lesson 3-5

High-Use Academic Words

Study Skill When learning a new concept, try to draw a picture to illustrate it.

Concept List

compare	table	estimate
equivalent	convert	define
order	figure	sum

Write the concept that best describes each exercise. Choose from the concept list above.

1. 3 yd = 9 ft

____

2. $-5 + 20 + 13 + (-2) = 26$

____

3. Two numbers are *reciprocals* if their product is one.

____

4.

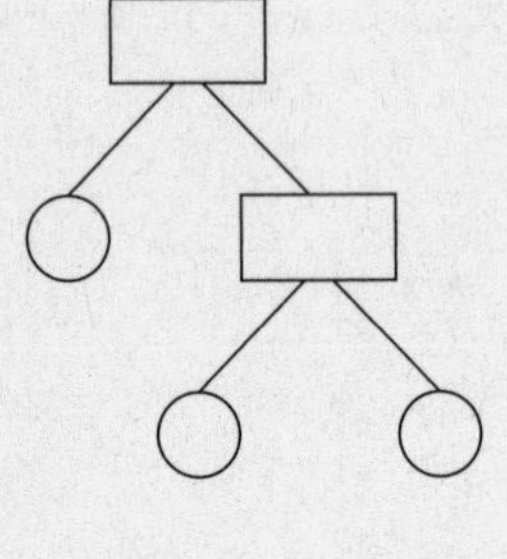

____

5. $5^2 < 2^5$

____

6. $\frac{2}{5}$ and $\frac{4}{10}$

____

7. $-28, 4, \frac{1}{2}, -2, 0.1$

$-28, -2, 0.1, \frac{1}{2}, 4$

____

8. $23.15 + 5.79 \approx 23 + 6$

____

9. **Average Lifespan**

Insect	Weeks
Ant	4
Butterfly	2
Cockroach	104
Mosquito	2

____

3E: Vocabulary Check

For use after Lesson 3-6

Study Skill Strengthen your vocabulary. Use these pages and add cues and summaries by applying the Cornell Notetaking style.

Write the definition for each word or term at the right. To check your work, fold the paper back along the dotted line to see the correct answers.

______________________	benchmark
______________________	prime number
______________________	reciprocals
______________________	mean
______________________	opposites

Name ______________________ Class ______________ Date ______________

3E: Vocabulary Check (continued)

For use after Lesson 3-6

Write the definition for each word or term at the right. To check your work, fold the paper forward along the dotted line to see the correct answers.

a convenient number used to replace fractions that are less than 1 ______________________

a whole number with exactly two divisors, −1 and the number itself ______________________

two numbers whose product is 1 ______________________

the sum of the data divided by the number of data items ______________________

two numbers that are the same distance from 0 on the number line, but in opposite directions ______________________

Name ______________________ Class ______________ Date ______________

3F: Vocabulary Review Puzzle

For use with the Chapter Review

Study Skill Take short breaks between assignments. You will be able to concentrate on a new assignment more easily if you take a brief "time out" before starting.

Complete the crossword puzzle using the words below. For help, use the glossary in your textbook.

improper fraction	denominator	numerator	benchmark	mode
mixed number	reciprocals	composite	median	prime

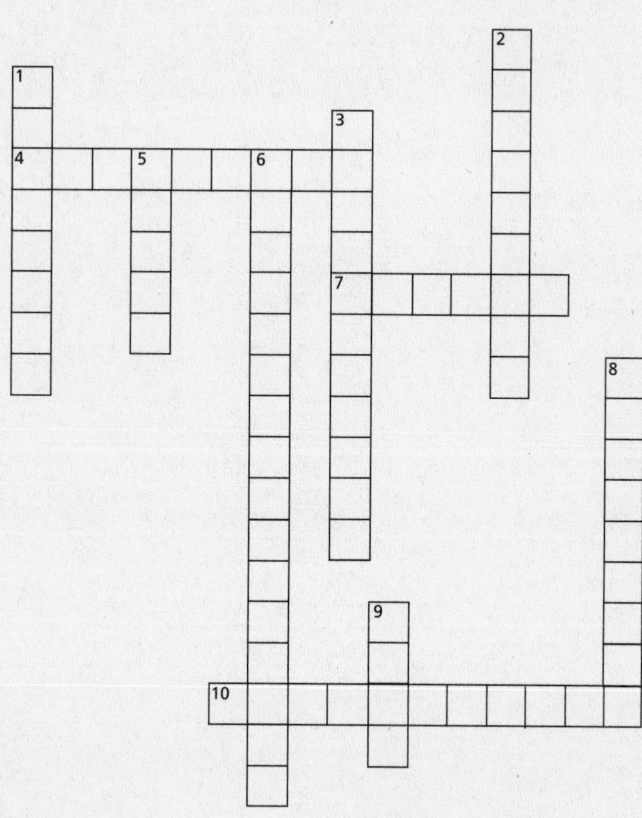

ACROSS

4. number with more than two divisors
7. number that is in the middle of a data set when the values are ranked in order from least to greatest
10. sum of a whole number and a fraction

DOWN

1. two numbers with a product of 1.
2. value that can be used as a reference point
3. bottom number in a fraction
5. number with exactly two divisors
6. numerator is greater than or equal to the denominator
8. top number in a fraction
9. number that occurs most often in a data set

Name ______________________ Class ______________ Date ______________

Practice 4-1

Evaluating and Writing Algebraic Expressions

Evaluate each expression using the values $m = 7, r = 8$, and $t = 2$.

1. $5m - 6$
2. $4m + t$
3. $r \div t$
4. $m \cdot t$
5. $5t + 2m$
6. $r \cdot m$
7. $3m - 5t$
8. $(m \cdot r) \div t$
9. mrt

Write an algebraic expression for the *n*th term of each table.

10.

A	0	1	2	3	n
B	3	5	7	9	?

11.

A	0	1	2	3	n
B	1	4	7	10	?

Write a word phrase for each algebraic expression.

12. $n + 16$
13. $3.2n$
14. $25.6 - n$
15. $n \div 24$
16. $\frac{45}{n}$
17. $15.4 - n$

Write an algebraic expression for each word phrase.

18. 12 more than m machines
19. six times the daily amount of fiber f in your diet
20. your aunt's age a minus 25
21. the total number of seashells s divided by 10
22. You and four friends plan a surprise party. Each of you contributes the same amount of money m for food.
    a. Write an algebraic expression for the total amount of money contributed for food.
    b. Evaluate your expression for $m = \$5.25$.

Name ______________________ Class ______________ Date ______________

4-1 • Guided Problem Solving

GPS Exercise 28:

Estimation This section of a page from a telephone directory shows a column with 11 names in 1 inch. Each page has four 10-inch columns. Write an algebraic expression for the approximate number of names in p pages of the directory.

6-4462 **Daalling V** 8 Everett All............
2-3302 [illegible]y R..........
4-1775 **Dabady V** 94 Burns de All........
2-0014 **Dabagh L** 13 Lanca ter R.......
6-3356 **Dabagh W** Dr 521 eston All..
4-7322 **Dabar G** 98 River A...............
6-1530 **Dabarera F** 34 Ros land All....
2-2279 **Dabas M** 17 Rivers e R..........
4-9978 **D'Abate D** 86 Moss Hill Rd All..
2-6745 **D'Abate G** 111 Sou Central R
4-5456 **Dabbous H** 670 Wa ren Dr All..
6-3064 **Dabbraccio F** 151 entury All..
6-2257 **Dabby D** 542 Walnu All..........
2-9987 [illegible] Green R..
6-5643 **Dabcovich M** 72 Main All........

Understand

1. What are you being asked to do?

____

2. What is an algebraic expression?

____

____

3. What does p represent?

____

____

Plan and Carry Out

4. How many names are in 1 in. of one column? ____________

5. How many names are in one 10-in. column? ____________

6. How many names are in four 10-in. columns? ____________

7. How many names are listed on one page? ____________

8. How many names are listed on p pages? ____________

9. Write an algebraic expression for the approximate number of names in p pages of the directory. ____________

Check

10. Substitute $p = 1, 2$, and 3 in the expression and solve. Does your expression provide reasonable values?

____

Solve Another Problem

11. The yearbook committee can fit 1 student picture in one inch of a row. If there are eight 6-inch rows on each page, write an expression for the approximate number of pictures that can fit on p pages.

____

Name ______________________ Class ______________ Date ____________

Practice 4-2

Using Number Sense to Solve Equations

Find the solution of each equation from the given numbers.

1. $30p = 900$; 3, 20, 30, or 60

2. $\frac{h}{9} = 11$; 3, 30, 72, or 99

3. $t + 32.4 = 62$; 29.6, 31.4, or 18.6

4. $r - 17 = 40$; 23, 57 or 63

Use mental math to solve each equation.

5. $5t = 25$

6. $8w = 64$

7. $p + 5 = 12$

8. $a + 2 = 15$

9. $\frac{h}{6} = 4$

10. $\frac{g}{8} = 6$

11. $y - 11 = 28$

12. $d - 4 = 12$

13. $w - 10 = 15$

Estimate the solution of each equation to the nearest whole number.

14. $18.92 - t = 14.23$

15. $21.8 + y = 31.64$

16. $18.43 + x = 123.4$

17. The seventh-grade class has been collecting aluminum cans for recycling. The class has collected 210 cans. Their goal is to collect 520 cans. Write an equation and estimate the number of aluminum cans needed to reach their goal.

18. A seamstress bought some bolts of fabric at \$25.30 each. She spent a total of \$227.70. Write an equation and estimate the number of bolts of fabric that she purchased.

19. For your party you purchased balloons for \$.79 each. You spent a total of \$11.85. Write an equation and estimate the number of balloons purchased.

Name ______________________ Class ______________ Date ______________

4-2 • Guided Problem Solving

GPS Exercise 24:

Solve using mental math or estimation. If you estimate, round to the nearest whole number before you add or subtract.

$$p - 7.35 = 46.71$$

Understand

1. What are you being asked to do?

____

2. Will you use estimation, mental math, or both to solve this problem?

____

Plan and Carry Out

3. Write the equation you are being asked to solve.

____

4. Round the numbers in the equation to the nearest whole number.

____

5. Write the meaning of the equation in Step 4 in the blank below.

____

6. Use mental math to find which number minus 7 equals 47.

____

7. What is the approximate value of p?

____

Check

8. Subtract 7 from your answer. Did you get 47?

____

Solve Another Problem

9. **Estimate by rounding to the nearest whole number and solve.**

$t + 5.43 = 39.96$

____

Name ______________ Class ______________ Date ______________

Practice 4-3

Solving Equations by Adding

Solve each equation. Check your answer.

1. $n - 2 = 5$ ______
2. $x - 1 = -3$ ______
3. $7 = a - 2$ ______
4. $p - 2 = -6$ ______
5. $-9 = -4 + a$ ______
6. $-2 = c - 2$ ______
7. $x - (-3) = 7$ ______
8. $a - (6) = 5$ ______
9. $s - 16 = 6$ ______
10. $p - (2) = 19$ ______
11. $r - 7 = -13$ ______
12. $25 = a - (3)$ ______

Solve each equation. Write your answer in simplest form.

13. $t - \frac{3}{8} = \frac{1}{8}$ ______
14. $-\frac{2}{9} = r - \frac{5}{9}$ ______
15. $c - \frac{3}{5} = \frac{1}{6}$ ______
16. $y - \frac{1}{7} = \frac{3}{4}$ ______

Solve each equation.

17. $d - 19.3 = 37.5$ ______
18. $-1.8 = h - 4.7$ ______
19. $z - \frac{3}{14} = -\frac{2}{5}$ ______
20. $k - 4\frac{1}{5} = 3\frac{3}{4}$ ______

21. Michael bought a \$25.00 gift for a friend. After he bought the gift, Michael had \$176.89. Write and solve an equation to calculate how much money Michael had before he bought the gift.

____

22. This spring it rained a total of 11.5 inches. This was 3 inches less than last spring. Write and solve an equation to find the amount of rain last season.

____

Name ______________________ Class ______________ Date ______________

4-3 • Guided Problem Solving

GPS Exercise 24:

Suppose a student collects 12 ladybugs for a project one day. This is 9 fewer than the number of ladybugs the student collected the previous day. Write and solve an equation to find the number of ladybugs the student collected the previous day.

Understand

1. Circle the information you will need to solve.
2. What are you being asked to do?

   ____

   ____

3. What will your variable represent?

   ____

   ____

Plan and Carry Out

4. How many ladybugs did the student collect the second day? ______________
5. Determine a variable for the number of ladybugs the student collected the previous day. ______________
6. Write an expression for the phrase *9 fewer than the number of ladybugs the student collected the previous day.* ______________
7. Write an equation that compares the answer to step 4 with the answer to Step 6. ______________
8. Solve the equation written in Step 7. ______________
9. How many ladybugs did the student collect the previous day? ______________

Check

10. Substitute the answer to Step 9 into the equation for the variable and solve.

    ____

Solve Another Problem

11. Jason is 72 in. tall. If Kenny is 15 in. shorter than Jason, write and solve an equation for the height of Kenny.

    ____

Name ________________ Class ____________ Date ____________

Practice 4-4

Solving Equations by Subtracting

Solve each equation. Check your answer.

1. $x + 5 = 8$
2. $g + 12 = 21$
3. $13 = 4 + r$
4. $z + 5 = 3$
5. $4 = f + 12$
6. $-3 = d + 29$
7. $y + 4 = -19$
8. $-7 = n + 13$
9. $-23 = s + 7$
10. $j + 12 = -4$
11. $-32 = e + 4$
12. $q + 14 = -37$

Solve each equation. Write your answer in simplest form.

13. $q + \frac{2}{7} = \frac{6}{7}$
14. $\frac{8}{9} = r + \frac{2}{3}$
15. $j + \frac{3}{8} = -\frac{1}{4}$
16. $-1\frac{3}{10} = p + \frac{3}{5}$

Solve each equation.

17. $1.3 = m + 7.8$
18. $7.3 + t = 10.1$
19. $-15.2 = 2.7 + w$
20. $4.1 + g = -5.9$

21. Rachel collects seashells. During a trip to the beach, she finds 14 new seashells, bringing her collection up to 74 seashells in all. Write and solve an equation to find the number of seashells Rachel had before her trip to the beach.

22. Carlos's puppy, Maya, gained 11.5 pounds over a period of four months. Maya now weighs 58.6 pounds. Write and solve an equation to find Maya's weight four months ago.

23. After earning $12.50 for mowing her neighbor's yard, Tina has a total of $17.84. Write and solve an equation to find the amount of money Tina had before mowing her neighbor's yard.

Name ______________________ Class ______________ Date ____________

4-4 • Guided Problem Solving

GPS Exercise 29:

Bianca's class collected 132 cans of food to donate to a local charity. This was 19 cans more than Tim's class collected. How many cans of food did Tim's class collect?

Understand

1. Circle the information you will need to solve the problem.
2. What are you being asked to do?

   ____

3. What will your variable represent?

   ____

   ____

Plan and Carry Out

4. Determine a variable for the number of cans Tim's class collected.

   ____

5. Write an expression for the phrase *19 cans more than the number of cans Tim's class collected.*

   ____

6. How many cans did Bianca's class collect?

   ____

7. Write an equation that compares the answer in Step 5 to Step 6.

   ____

8. Solve the equation you wrote for Step 7.

   ____

9. How many cans did Tim's class collect?

   ____

Check

10. Substitute your answer to Step 9 for the variable in the equation and solve.

    ____

Solve Another Problem

11. Raquel can run 4.2 miles. If Raquel can run 1.6 miles farther than Jason, how far can Jason run? Write and solve an equation to find your answer.

    ____

Name ________________ Class ________________ Date ________________

Practice 4-5

Solving Equations by Multiplying

Solve each equation by multiplying. Check your answer.

1. $\frac{n}{2} = 126$
2. $\frac{d}{3} = -81$
3. $-\frac{t}{4} = 56$
4. $\frac{k}{-3} = 6$
5. $-18 = \frac{y}{-2}$
6. $\frac{y}{16} = 3$
7. $-7 = \frac{r}{12}$
8. $\frac{w}{9} = -5$
9. $\frac{v}{-3} = -15$
10. $13 = \frac{x}{-4}$
11. $28 = \frac{a}{7}$
12. $\frac{t}{-42} = 3$
13. $24 = \frac{f}{-4}$
14. $15 = \frac{j}{12}$
15. $\frac{k}{8} = 408$
16. $\frac{b}{-96} = -3$

Solve each equation.

17. $\frac{1}{4}x = 13$
18. $\frac{1}{3}y = 21$
19. $\frac{2}{5}t = 14$
20. $-\frac{3}{7}r = 6$
21. $-15 = \frac{5}{6}p$
22. $-21 = -\frac{7}{2}j$

Write and solve an equation to represent each situation.

23. Five people divide a large bag of beads evenly, giving each person 19 beads. How many beads were in the bag?

24. Jennifer sold 18 books at her garage sale. Of all the items sold at Jennifer's garage sale, $\frac{3}{7}$ were books. How many items did Jennifer sell at her garage sale?

Name ______________________ Class ______________ Date ______________

4-5 • Guided Problem Solving

GPS Exercise 30:

Beth needs boards that are $\frac{3}{4}$ foot long. She has a board that is 8 feet long. How many $\frac{3}{4}$-foot sections can she cut from it?

Understand

1. Circle the information you will need to solve the problem.
2. What are you being asked to do?

    ____

3. What will your variable represent? ______________

Plan and Carry Out

4. Determine a variable for the number of $\frac{3}{4}$-foot sections Beth cuts.

    ____

5. Write an expression to represent the total length of the $\frac{3}{4}$-foot sections Beth cuts.

    ____

6. How long is Beth's board? ______________
7. Write an equation that compares the expression from Step 5 and the answer to Step 6. ______________
8. Solve the equation written in Step 7. ______________
9. How many $\frac{3}{4}$-foot sections can Beth cut? ______________

Check

10. Multiply your answer by $\frac{3}{4}$ foot. Is this number less than or equal to 8?

    ____

Solve Another Problem

11. Marc makes 15 pints of soup. If one serving of soup is $\frac{3}{4}$ pint, how many servings of soup did Marc make?

    ____

Name ______________________ Class ______________ Date ______________

Practice 4-6

Solving Equations by Dividing

Solve each equation by dividing. Check your answer.

1. $3r = 48$ ____________
2. $7q = 147$ ____________
3. $276 = 12p$ ____________
4. $-7z = -91$ ____________
5. $-215 = 5b$ ____________
6. $-102 = -6l$ ____________
7. $13n = 247$ ____________
8. $1{,}474 = 22t$ ____________
9. $-18.5 = -3.7q$ ____________
10. $-5.2d = 31.2$ ____________
11. $27.5 = 2.5s$ ____________
12. $2q = 7.2$ ____________

Solve each equation.

13. $-26x = 83.2$ ____________
14. $-134.4 = 21z$ ____________
15. $-5.1y = 214.2$ ____________
16. $8.1p = 97.2$ ____________
17. $179.2 = 5.6t$ ____________
18. $-192.2 = -3.1r$ ____________

Write and solve an equation to represent each situation.

19. One of the largest flowers, the Rafflesia, weighs about 15 lb. How many Rafflesia flowers can be placed in a container that can hold a maximum of 240 lb?

____

20. "Heavy water" is a name given to a compound used in some nuclear reactors. Heavy water costs about $1,500 per gallon. If a nuclear plant spent $10,500 on heavy water, how many gallons of heavy water were bought?

____

Name ______________________ Class ______________ Date ____________

4-6 • Guided Problem Solving

GPS Exercise 23:

A local park rents paddle boats. Their ad is shown on the right. How many hours can you rent a boat if you have $22 to spend?

Lake Lee
Paddle Boat Rental
$5.50 per hour

Understand

1. Circle the information you will need to solve the problem.
2. What are you being asked to do?

____

3. What will your variable represent?

____

Plan and Carry Out

4. Determine a variable to represent the number of hours you rent the boat. ____________________
5. Write an expression to represent the total cost of renting a paddle boat for a given number of hours.

____

6. How much money can you spend? ____________
7. Write an equation that compares the expression from Step 5 and the answer to Step 6.

____

8. Solve the equation you wrote in Step 7.

____

9. For how many hours can you rent a boat? ____________

Check

10. Multiply your answer by $5.50. Is this number less than or equal to $22?

____

Solve Another Problem

11. Bethany's bread recipe calls for 2.5 cups of flour. How many batches of bread can she bake if she has 13.5 cups of flour? Write an equation to solve the problem.

____

Name ______________________ Class ______________ Date ____________

4A Graphic Organizer

For use before Lesson 4-1

Study Skill Take notes when your teacher presents new material in class and when you read the lesson yourself. Organize these notes as a way to study, reviewing them as you go.

Write your answers.

1. What is the chapter title? ______________________
2. How many lessons are there in this chapter? ______________
3. What is the topic of the Test-Taking Strategies page? ______________
4. Complete the graphic organizer below as you work through the chapter.
   - In the center, write the title of the chapter.
   - When you begin a lesson, write the lesson name in a rectangle.
   - When you complete a lesson, write a skill or key concept in a circle linked to that lesson block.
   - When you complete the chapter, use this graphic organizer to help you review.

Name ______________________ Class ______________ Date ______________

4B: Reading Comprehension

For use after Lesson 4-2

Study Skill As you learn more vocabulary, more concepts are within your reach.

Read the paragraph below and answer the questions that follow.

November is American Indian and Alaska Native Heritage Month. According to the U.S. Census Bureau, more than 4 million people in the United States identified themselves as American Indian or Alaska native in 2004. That is 1.5% of the total U.S. population. About 687,000 people with this heritage live in California, giving it the largest American Indian and Alaska native population of any state. However, $\frac{1}{5}$ of the Alaska population is American Indian or Alaska native. This is a much greater fraction than in California.

1. What is the subject of this paragraph?

   ____

2. What is the largest number in the paragraph?

   ____

3. What is the smallest number?

   ____

4. Which state has the greatest number of people with American Indian and Alaska native ancestry?

   ____

5. The population of Alaska is about 665,000. How many Alaskans have American Indian or Alaska native heritage?

   ____

6. Explain how California can have the greatest population but not the largest fraction of people with this ancestry.

   ____

7. **High-Use Academic Words** In Exercise 6, what does the word *explain* mean?

   a. to put or use in place of something else

   b. to give facts and details that make an idea easier to understand

Name ______________________ Class ______________ Date ______________

4C: Reading/Writing Math Symbols

For use after Lesson 4-4

Study Skill Mathematics builds on itself, so build a strong foundation.

Match each expression with its word form.

1. $x - 3$
2. $4m$
3. $\frac{7}{x}$
4. $m + 6$
5. $m \div 5$

A. six more than a number
B. the quotient of a number and five
C. a number decreased by three
D. seven divided by a number
E. four multiplied by a number

Write a mathematical expression or equation for each word description.

6. nine less than the product of eleven and x

   ____

7. a number plus four equals thirteen

   ____

8. the quotient of x and 4

   ____

9. the absolute value of a number

   ____

Write two different word phrases for each of the following expressions.

10. $x - 10$

   ____

   ____

11. $5m$

   ____

   ____

12. $3^2 + m$

   ____

   ____

Name ______________________ Class ______________ Date ____________

4D: Visual Vocabulary Practice

For use after Lesson 4-6

Study Skill Making sense of mathematical symbols is like reading a foreign language that uses different letters.

Concept List

Addition Property of Equality	Subtraction Property of Equality
Division Property of Equality	Multiplication Property of Equality
variable	solution of an equation
open sentence	algebraic expression
Inverse operations	

Write the concept that best describes each exercise. Choose from the concept list above.

1. If $5 - y = 2 - 3y$, then $5 - y + 3y = 2 - 3y + 3y$. __________	**2.** $8 + x$ __________	**3.** $-36x = 144$ $x = -4$ -4 represents this for $-36x = 144$. __________
4. z in the equation $\frac{2z}{5} = 12$ __________	**5.** If $7m = 1 + 2m$, then $7m - 2m = 1 + 2m - 2m$. __________	**6.** $3z + \frac{1}{4} = 21$ __________
7. If $5b = 3$, then $\frac{5b}{5} = \frac{3}{5}$. __________	**8.** + and – or · and ÷ __________	**9.** If $\frac{1}{9}z = 8$, then $9 \cdot \left(\frac{1}{9}z\right) = 9 \cdot 8$. __________

Name ______________________ Class ______________ Date ____________

4E: Vocabulary Check

For use after Lesson 4-6

Study Skill Strengthen your vocabulary. Use these pages and add cues and summaries by applying the Cornell Notetaking style.

Write the definition for each word or term at the right. To check your work, fold the paper back along the dotted line to see the correct answers.

variable

algebraic expression

equation

open sentence

inverse operations

Name ________________ Class ________________ Date ________________

4E: Vocabulary Check (continued)

For use after Lesson 4-6

Write the vocabulary word or term for each definition. To check your work, fold the paper forward along the dotted line to see the correct answers.

a symbol that represents one or more numbers ________________

a mathematical phrase with at least one variable ________________

a mathematical sentence with an equal sign ________________

an equation with one or more variables ________________

operations that undo each other ________________

Name _______________ Class _______________ Date _______________

4F: Vocabulary Review

For use with the Chapter Review

Study Skill Review notes that you have taken in class as soon as possible to clarify any points you missed and to refresh your memory.

Circle the word that best completes the sentence.

1. A (*variable, expression*) is a letter that stands for a number.
2. An (*expression, equation*) is a mathematical statement with an equal sign.
3. A (*solution, sentence*) is a value for a variable that makes an equation true.
4. To solve an equation, use (*inverse, variable*) operations.
5. Two numbers are (*opposites, reciprocals*) if their product is 1.
6. The statement $4 + (9 + 3) = (4 + 9) + 3$ is an example of the (*Commutative Property of Addition, Associative Property of Addition*).
7. The (*opposite, absolute value*) of 15 is -15.
8. The (*mean, median*) is the middle number in a data set when the data is arranged from least to greatest.
9. You can use the (*commutative, identity*) property to change the order in an expression.
10. The statement $a + 0 = a$ is an example of the (*Identity Property of Zero, Identity Property of Multiplication*).
11. The (*absolute value, opposite*) of a number is its distance from 0 on a number line.
12. (*Rational numbers, Integers*) are the set of whole numbers, their opposites, and zero.
13. Two numbers whose sum is 0 are (*additive, opposite*) inverses.
14. A(n) (*outlier, range*) is a data value that is much greater or less than the other values in the data set.
15. Using the (*distributive property, order of operations*), you can calculate that $12 + 5 \cdot 2$ equals 22.

Name ______________________ Class ______________ Date ______________

Practice 5-1

Ratios

Write a ratio in three ways, comparing the first quantity to the second.

1. Ten years ago in Louisiana, schools averaged 182 pupils for every 10 teachers.

   ____

2. Between 1899 and 1900, 284 out of 1,000 people in the United States were 5–17 years old.

   ____

Use the chart below for Exercises 3–4.

Three seventh-grade classes were asked whether they wanted chicken or pasta served at their awards banquet.

Room Number	Chicken	Pasta
201	10	12
202	8	17
203	16	10

3. In room 201, what is the ratio of students who prefer chicken to students who prefer pasta?

   ____

4. Combine the totals for all three rooms. What is the ratio of the number of students who prefer pasta to the number of students who prefer chicken?

   ____

Write each ratio as a fraction in simplest form.

5. 12 to 18 ________ 6. 81 : 27 ________ 7. $\frac{6}{28}$ ________

Tell whether the ratios are *equivalent* or *not equivalent*.

8. 12 : 24, 50 : 100 ______________

9. $\frac{22}{1}, \frac{1}{22}$ ______________

10. 2 to 3, 24 to 36 ______________

11. A bag contains green, yellow, and orange marbles. The ratio of green marbles to yellow marbles is 2 : 5. The ratio of yellow marbles to orange marbles is 3 : 4. What is the ratio of green marbles to orange marbles?

   ____

Name ______________________ Class ______________ Date ______________

5-1 • Guided Problem Solving

GPS Exercise 27:

To make pancakes, you need 2 cups of water for every 3 cups of flour. Write an equivalent ratio to find how much water you will need with 9 cups of flour.

Understand

1. Circle the information you will need to solve the problem.
2. What are you being asked to do?

____

____

3. Why will a ratio help you to solve the problem?

____

____

Plan and Carry Out

4. What is the ratio of the cups of water to the cups of flour? ____________
5. How many cups of flour are you using? ____________
6. Write an equivalent ratio to use 9 cups of flour. ____________
7. How many cups of water are needed for 9 cups of flour? ____________

Check

8. Why is the number of cups of water triple the number of cups needed for 3 cups of flour?

____

____

Solve Another Problem

9. Rebecca is laying tile in her bathroom. She needs 4 black tiles for every 16 white tiles. How many black tiles are needed if she uses 128 white tiles?

____

Name ______________________ Class ____________ Date ____________

Practice 5-2

Unit Rates and Proportional Reasoning

Find the unit rate for each situation. Round to the nearest hundredth, if necessary.

1. travel 250 mi in 5 h

2. earn $75.20 in 8 h

3. read 80 pages in 2 h

4. type 8,580 words in 2 h 45 min

5. manufacture 2,488 parts in 8 h

6. 50 copies of a book on 2 shelves

Find each unit cost. Then determine the better buy.

7. paper: 100 sheets for $.99
   500 sheets for $4.29

8. peanuts: 1 lb for $1.29
   12 oz for $.95

9. crackers: 15 oz for $2.99
   12 oz for $2.49

10. apples: 3 lb for $5.99
    5 lb for $8.99

11. mechanical pencils: 4 for $1.25
    25 for $5.69

12. bagels: 4 for $2.19
    6 for $3.49

13. a. Yolanda and Yoko ran in a 100-yd dash. When Yolanda crossed the finish line, Yoko was 10 yd behind her. The girls then repeated the race, with Yolanda starting 10 yd behind the starting line. If each girl ran at the same rate as before, who won the race? By how many yards?

    b. Assuming the girls run at the same rate as before, how far behind the starting line should Yolanda be in order for the two to finish in a tie?

Name ______________________ Class ______________ Date ______________

5-2 • Guided Problem Solving

GPS Exercise 25a:

Population density is the number of people per unit of area. Alaska has the lowest population density of any state in the United States. It has 626,932 people in 570,374 mi^2. What is its population density? Round to the nearest person per square mile.

Understand

1. What is *population density*?

____

____

2. What are you being asked to do?

____

3. What does the phrase *people per unit of area* imply?

____

____

____

Plan and Carry Out

4. What is the population of Alaska? ______________
5. What is the area of Alaska? ______________
6. Write a division expression for the population density. ______________
7. What is its population density? ______________
8. Round to the nearest person per square mile. ______________

Check

9. Why is the population density only about 1 person/mi^2?

____

____

Solve Another Problem

10. Mr. Boyle is buying pizza for the percussion band. The bill is $56.82 for 5 pizzas. If there are 12 members of the band, how much does the pizza cost per member? Round to the nearest cent.

____

Name ____________ Class ____________ Date ____________

Practice 5-3

Proportions

Determine whether the ratios can form a proportion.

1. $\frac{12}{16}, \frac{30}{40}$ ____________
2. $\frac{8}{12}, \frac{15}{21}$ ____________
3. $\frac{27}{21}, \frac{81}{56}$ ____________
4. $\frac{45}{24}, \frac{75}{40}$ ____________
5. $\frac{5}{9}, \frac{80}{117}$ ____________
6. $\frac{15}{25}, \frac{75}{125}$ ____________
7. $\frac{2}{14}, \frac{20}{35}$ ____________
8. $\frac{9}{6}, \frac{21}{14}$ ____________
9. $\frac{24}{15}, \frac{16}{10}$ ____________
10. $\frac{3}{4}, \frac{8}{10}$ ____________
11. $\frac{20}{4}, \frac{17}{3}$ ____________
12. $\frac{25}{6}, \frac{9}{8}$ ____________

Do the ratios form a proportion?

13. $\frac{14}{10} \stackrel{?}{=} \frac{9}{7}$ ____________
14. $\frac{18}{8} \stackrel{?}{=} \frac{36}{16}$ ____________
15. $\frac{6}{10} \stackrel{?}{=} \frac{15}{25}$ ____________
16. $\frac{7}{16} \stackrel{?}{=} \frac{4}{9}$ ____________
17. $\frac{6}{4} \stackrel{?}{=} \frac{12}{8}$ ____________
18. $\frac{19}{3} \stackrel{?}{=} \frac{114}{8}$ ____________
19. $\frac{5}{14} \stackrel{?}{=} \frac{6}{15}$ ____________
20. $\frac{60}{27} \stackrel{?}{=} \frac{8}{3.6}$ ____________
21. $\frac{27}{1.5} \stackrel{?}{=} \frac{450}{25}$ ____________
22. $\frac{3}{18} \stackrel{?}{=} \frac{4}{20}$ ____________
23. $\frac{5}{2} \stackrel{?}{=} \frac{15}{6}$ ____________
24. $\frac{200}{15} \stackrel{?}{=} \frac{4}{0.3}$ ____________

Solve.

25. During the breaststroke competitions of the 1992 Olympics, Nelson Diebel swam 100 meters in 62 seconds, and Mike Bowerman swam 200 meters in 130 seconds. Are the rates proportional?

____

26. During a vacation, the Vasquez family traveled 174 miles in 3 hours on Monday, and 290 miles in 5 hours on Tuesday. Are the rates proportional?

____

Name ______________________ Class ______________ Date ______________

5-3 • Guided Problem Solving

GPS Exercise 34:

A certain shade of green paint requires 4 parts blue to 5 parts yellow. If you mix 16 quarts of blue paint with 25 quarts of yellow paint, will you get the desired shade of green? Explain.

Understand

1. Circle the information you will need to solve the problem.
2. What are you being asked to do?

   ____

   ____

3. Will a ratio help you to solve the problem? Explain.

   ____

   ____

Plan and Carry Out

4. What is the ratio of blue parts to yellow parts? ____________
5. What is the ratio of blue quarts to yellow quarts? ____________
6. Check to see if the cross products of the two ratios are equal.

   ____

7. Are the ratios the same? ______________________
8. Will you get the desired shade of green? Explain.

   ____

Check

9. How do you know that the ratios are not the same?

   ____

Solve Another Problem

10. There are 15 boys and 12 girls in your math class. There are 5 boys and 3 girls in your study group. Determine if the boy to girl ratio is the same in study group as it is in your math class. Explain.

    ____

    ____

Name ______________________ Class ______________ Date ______________

Practice 5-4

Solving Proportions

Solve each proportion using mental math.

1. $\frac{n}{14} = \frac{20}{35}$ ______________
2. $\frac{9}{6} = \frac{21}{n}$ ______________
3. $\frac{24}{n} = \frac{16}{10}$ ______________
4. $\frac{3}{4} = \frac{n}{10}$ ______________

Solve each proportion using cross products.

5. $\frac{k}{8} = \frac{14}{4}$

   $k =$ ______________
6. $\frac{u}{3} = \frac{10}{5}$

   $u =$ ______________
7. $\frac{14}{6} = \frac{d}{15}$

   $d =$ ______________
8. $\frac{5}{1} = \frac{m}{4}$

   $m =$ ______________
9. $\frac{36}{32} = \frac{n}{8}$

   $n =$ ______________
10. $\frac{5}{30} = \frac{1}{x}$

    $x =$ ______________
11. $\frac{t}{4} = \frac{5}{10}$

    $t =$ ______________
12. $\frac{9}{2} = \frac{v}{4}$

    $v =$ ______________

Solve.

13. A contractor estimates it will cost $2,400 to build a deck to a customer's specifications. How much would it cost to build five similar decks?

    ____

14. A recipe requires 3 c of flour to make 27 dinner rolls. How much flour is needed to make 9 rolls?

    ____

Solve using a proportion.

15. Mandy runs 4 km in 18 min. She plans to run in a 15 km race. How long will it take her to complete the race?

    ____

16. Ken's new car can go 26 miles per gallon of gasoline. The car's gasoline tank holds 14 gal. How far will he be able to go on a full tank?

    ____

17. Eleanor can complete two skirts in 15 days. How long will it take her to complete eight skirts?

    ____

18. Three eggs are required to make two dozen muffins. How many eggs are needed to make 12 dozen muffins?

    ____

Name ______________________ Class ______________ Date ____________

5-4 • Guided Problem Solving

GPS Exercise 33:

Your heart rate is the number of heartbeats per minute.

- What is your heart rate if you count 18 beats in 15 seconds?
- How many beats do you count in 15 secounds if your heart rate is 96 beats/min? Explain your choice of method.

Understand

1. What are you being asked to do in the first part of the problem?

   ____

2. What are you being asked to do in the secound part of the problem?

   ____

3. Circle the information you will need to use to answer the question.

   ____

Plan and Carry Out

4. How many seconds are in 1 minute? ____________
5. Write a proportion comparing 18 beats in 15 seconds to an unknown number of beats in 1 minute. ____________
6. Solve the proportion in Step 4 to find your heart rate if you count 18 beats in 15 seconds. ____________
7. Write a proportion comparing 96 beats in 60 seconds to an unknown number of beats in 15 seconds. ____________
8. Solve the proportion to find the number of beats you count in 15 seconds if your heart rate is 96 beats/min. ____________
9. Explain why it works well to use a proportion to solve this problem. If you think a different method would be easier, explain why you prefer that method. ____________

Check

10. Rewrite proportions with your answers, using a value given in the problem as an unknown. When you solve the proportion, does your answer match the value given in the problem?

    ____

Solve Another Problem

11. Ryan can swim 1,800 yards in 1 hour. How many yards can he swim in 20 minutes?

    ____

Practice 5-5

Using Similar Figures

△ *MNO* is similar to △ *JKL*. Complete each statement.

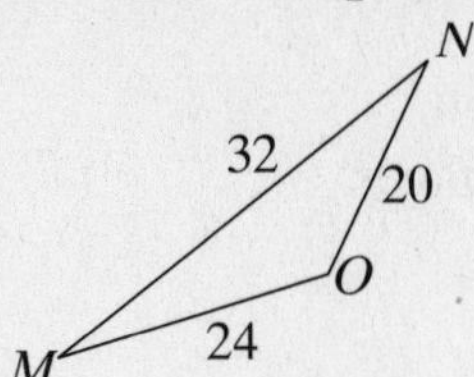

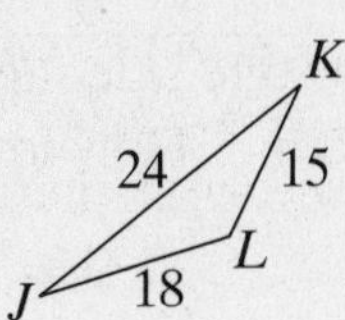

1. $\angle M$ corresponds to __________.
2. $\angle L$ corresponds to __________.
3. $\overline{JL}$ corresponds to __________.
4. $\overline{MN}$ corresponds to __________.
5. What is the ratio of the lengths of the corresponding sides? __________

The figures in each pair are similar. Find the value of each variable.

6.

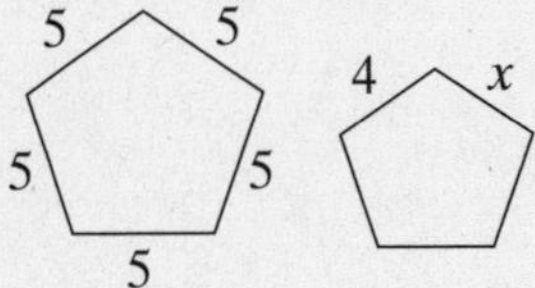

7.

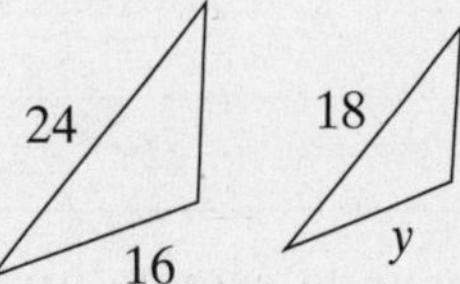

8.

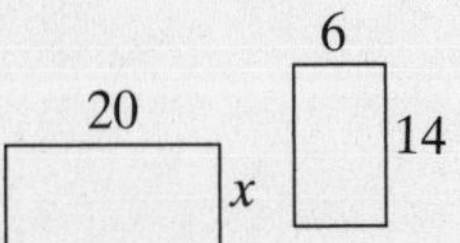

9.

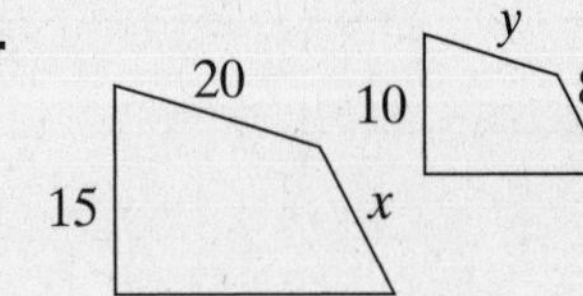

10.

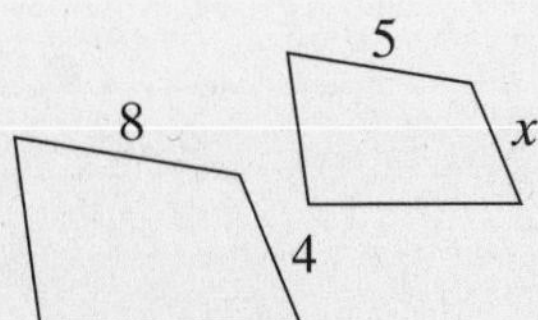

11.

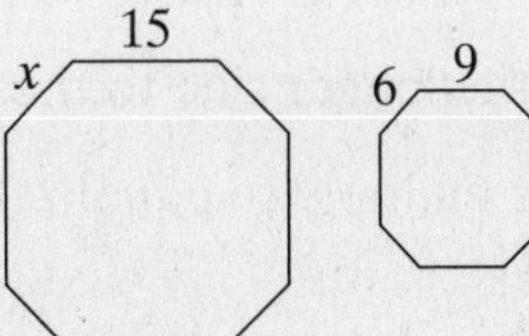

12. On a sunny day, if a 36-inch yardstick casts a 21-inch shadow, how tall is a building whose shadow is 168 ft?

____

13. Oregon is about 400 miles from west to east, and 300 miles from north to south. If the image of Oregon on a map is 15 inches tall (from north to south), about how wide is the image of Oregon on the map?

____

Name ______________________ Class ______________ Date ______________

5-5 • Guided Problem Solving

GPS Exercise 12:

A rectangle with an area of 32 in.^{2} has one side measuring 4 in. A similar rectangle has an area of 288 in.^{2}. How long is the longer side of the larger rectangle?

Understand

1. What are you being asked to do?

____

____

2. Will a proportion that equates the ratio of the areas to the ratio of the shorter sides result in the desired answer? Explain.

____

____

____

3. What measure should you determine first?

____

____

Plan and Carry Out

4. What is the length of the longer side of the rectangle whose area is 32 in.^{2} and whose shorter side is 4 in.? __________

5. What is the ratio of the longer side to the shorter side? __________

6. What pairs of factors multiply to equal 288?

____

7. Which pair of factors has a ratio of $\frac{2}{1}$? __________

8. What is the length of the longer side? __________

Check

9. Why must the ratio between the factors be $\frac{2}{1}$?

____

____

Solve Another Problem

10. A triangle with perimeter 26 in. has two sides that are 8 in. long. What is the length of the third side of a similar triangle which has two sides that are 12 in. long? __________

Practice 5-6

Maps and Scale Drawings

The scale of a map is 2 cm : 21 km. Find the actual distances for the following map distances.

1. 9 cm ______________
2. 12.5 cm ______________
3. 14 cm ______________
4. 3.6 cm ______________
5. 4.5 cm ______________
6. 7.1 cm ______________

A scale drawing has a scale of $\frac{1}{4}$ in. : 12 ft. Find the length on the drawing for each actual length.

7. 8 ft ______________
8. 30 ft ______________
9. 15 ft ______________
10. 18 ft ______________
11. 20 ft ______________
12. 40 ft ______________

Use a metric ruler to find the actual distance between each pair of towns. Round to the nearest kilometer.

13. Hickokburg to Kidville ______________
14. Dodgetown to Earp City ______________
15. Dodgetown to Kidville ______________
16. Kidville to Earp City ______________
17. Dodgetown to Hickokburg ______________
18. Earp City to Hickokburg ______________

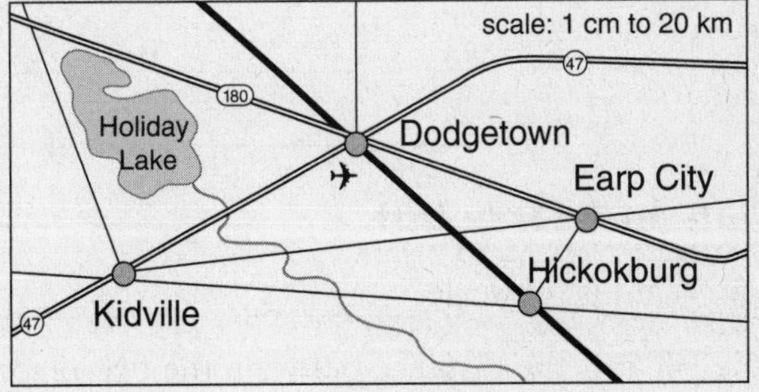

Solve.

19. The scale drawing shows a two-bedroom apartment. The master bedroom is 9 ft × 12 ft. Use an inch ruler to measure the drawing.

   a. The scale is ______________.

   b. Write the actual dimensions in place of the scale dimensions.

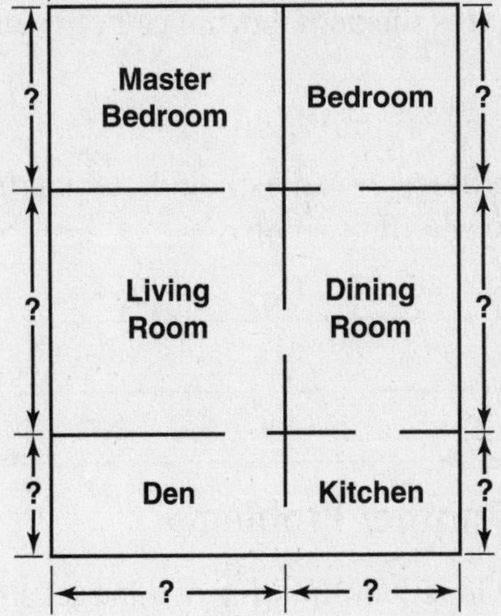

Name ________________ Class ________________ Date ________________

5-6 • Guided Problem Solving

GPS Exercise 21:

Writing in Math You are looking at a map with a scale of 2 in. = 17 ft. Explain how you find the actual distance between two places that are 3 in. apart on the map.

Understand

1. What are you being asked to do?

____

____

2. What points should you include in your explanation?

____

____

3. What is a scale?

____

____

Plan and Carry Out

4. What is the scale? _______________

5. What is the distance between the two places on the map?

____

6. Write a proportion using the scale, the distance on the map, and the unknown length of the drawing. _______________

7. What is the actual distance between the two places? _______________

Check

8. Use Steps 4–7 to explain how you found the actual distance between the two places.

____

____

____

Solve Another Problem

9. The length of the wing of a model airplane is 3 in. If the scale of the model to the actual plane is 1 in. = 25 ft, what is the length of the actual wing?

____

Name ______________________ Class ______________ Date ______________

5A: Graphic Organizer

For use before Lesson 5-1

Study Skill As you read over the material in the chapter, keep a paper and pencil handy to write down notes and questions in your math notebook. Review notes taken in class as soon as possible.

Write your answers.

1. What is the chapter title? ______________________
2. How many lessons are there in this chapter? ______________________
3. What is the topic of the Test-Taking Strategies page? ______________________
4. Complete the graphic organizer below as you work through the chapter.
   - In the center, write the title of the chapter.
   - When you begin a lesson, write the lesson name in a rectangle.
   - When you complete a lesson, write a skill or key concept in a circle linked to that lesson block.
   - When you complete the chapter, use this graphic organizer to help you review.

Name ______________________ Class ______________ Date ______________

5B: Reading Comprehension

For use after Lesson 5-3

Study Skill When you read mathematics, look for words like "more than," "less than," "above," "times as many," "divided by." These clues will help you decide what operation you need to solve a problem.

Read the paragraph and answer the questions that follow.

> A tropical storm is classified as a hurricane when it has wind speeds in excess of 74 mi/h. The winds of Hurricane Paul (2006) reached 31 mi/h above the minimum. How fast were the winds of Hurricane Paul?

Source: earthobservatory.nasa.gov/NaturalHazard/shownh.php3?img_id=13935

1. What numbers are in the paragraph? ______________

2. What question are you asked to answer?

   ____

   ____

3. What units will you use in your answer? ______________

4. Does a storm with winds of 74 mi/h qualify as a hurricane? Explain.

   ____

   ____

   ____

5. When did Hurricane Paul occur? ______________

6. How much above the minimum were Hurricane Paul's winds?

   ____

7. Let x represent Hurricane Paul's wind speed. Write an equation to help you solve the problem.

   ____

8. What is the answer to the question asked in the paragraph?

   ____

9. **High-Use Academic Words** In Exercise 7, what does it mean to *solve*?

   a. to find an answer for
   b. to keep something going

Name ______________________ Class ______________ Date ______________

5C: Reading/Writing Math Symbols

For use after Lesson 5-4

Study Skill When you take notes in any subject, use abbreviations and symbols whenever possible.

Write each statement or expression using the appropriate mathematical symbols.

1. the ratio of a to b ______________________

2. x to 4 is less than 5 to 2 ______________________

3. 4 more than 5 times n ______________________

4. 5 : 24 is not equal to 1 : 5 ______________________

Write each mathematical statement in words.

5. $x \leq 25$

____

____

6. $|-20| > |15|$

____

____

____

7. 1 oz $\approx$ 28 g

____

____

8. $\frac{1}{3} = \frac{4}{12}$

____

____

Match the symbolic statement or expression in Column A with its written form in Column B.

Column A	Column B
9. $k < 12$	A. 12 times x
10. $\lvert -5 \rvert$	B. negative 2 plus negative 4 is p
11. $n \geq 15$	C. the ratio of 4 to 8
12. $x = -4 + 5$	D. k is less than 12
13. 4 : 8	E. the quotient of x and 9
14. $12x$	F. x equals negative 4 plus 5
15. $-2 + (-4) = p$	G. the absolute value of negative 5
16. $x \div 9$	H. n is greater than or equal to 15

Name ____________________ Class ____________ Date ____________

5D: Visual Vocabulary Practice

For use after Lesson 5-6

Study Skill When you come across something you don't understand, view it as an opportunity to increase your brain power.

Concept List

cross products	equivalent ratios	indirect measurement
proportion	rate	scale
similar polygons	unit cost	unit rate

Write the concept that best describes each exercise. Choose from the concept list above.

1. $\frac{18}{16}$ and 4.5 : 4 __________	**2.** A 6-ft-tall person standing near a building has a shadow that is 60 ft long. This can be used to determine the height of the building. __________	**3.** A bakery sells a dozen donuts for \$3.15. This can also be represented as $\frac{\$3.15}{12 \text{ donuts}}$. __________
4. The expression "45 words per minute" represents this. __________	**5.** $\frac{30}{75} = \frac{2}{5}$ __________	**6.** For the equation $\frac{15}{16} = \frac{z}{4}$, these are 15(4) and 16$z$. __________
7. The equation $\frac{1}{2}$ in. = 50 mi represents this on a map. __________	**8.** $\frac{\$4.25}{5 \text{ lb}} = \$.85/\text{lb}$ __________	**9.** Rectangle 25.5 by 12; rectangle 8.5 by 4 __________

Name ______________________ Class ______________ Date ____________

5E: Vocabulary Check

For use after Lesson 5-6

Study Skill Strengthen your vocabulary. Use these pages and add cues and summaries by applying the Cornell Notetaking style.

Write the definition for each word or term at the right. To check your work, fold the paper back along the dotted line to see the correct answers.

______________________________	polygon
______________________________	proportion
______________________________	unit rate
______________________________	ratio
______________________________	scale

5E: Vocabulary Check (continued)

For use after Lesson 5-6

Write the vocabulary word or term for each definition. To check your work, fold the paper forward along the dotted line to see the correct answers.

a closed figure formed by three or more line segments that do not cross _______________

an equation stating that two ratios are equal _______________

the rate for one unit of a given quantity _______________

a comparison of two quantities by division _______________

a ratio that compares a length in a drawing or model to the corresponding length in the actual object _______________

Name ______________________ Class ______________ Date ______________

5F: Vocabulary Review Puzzle

For use with the Chapter Review

Study Skill Use a special notebook or section of a loose-leaf binder for math.

Complete the crossword puzzle. For help, use the Glossary in your textbook.

Here are the words you will use to complete this crossword puzzle:

equation	divisor	figures	fraction
polygon	mixed number	prime	proportion
ratio	scale drawing		

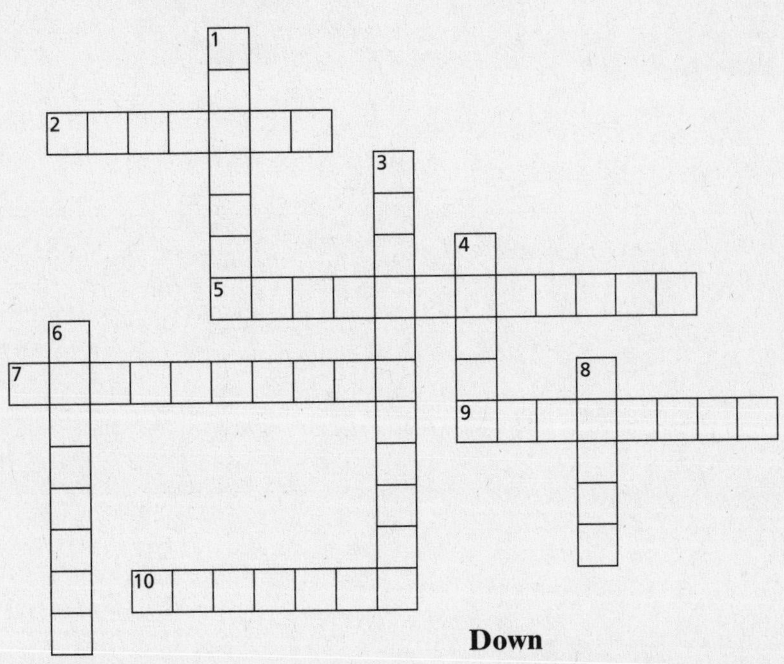

Across

2. a closed plane figure formed by 3 or more line segments that do not cross
5. enlarged or reduced drawing of an object
7. equation stating two ratios are equal
9. a mathematical sentence with an equal sign
10. a whole number that divides another whole number evenly

Down

1. Similar ____________ have the same shape but not necessarily the same size.
3. the sum of a whole number and a fraction
4. a number with only two divisors, 1 and the number itself
6. a number in the form $\frac{a}{b}$
8. a comparison of two numbers by division

Name ____________ Class ____________ Date ____________

Practice 6-1

Percents, Fractions, and Decimals

Write each percent as a fraction in simplest form and as a decimal.

1. 65% ____________ **2.** 37.5% ____________ **3.** 80% ____________ **4.** 25% ____________

5. 18% ____________ **6.** 46% ____________ **7.** 87% ____________ **8.** 8% ____________

9. 43% ____________ **10.** 55% ____________ **11.** 94% ____________ **12.** 36% ____________

Write each number as a percent. Round to the nearest tenth of a percent where necessary.

13. $\frac{8}{15}$ ____________ **14.** $\frac{7}{50}$ ____________ **15.** 0.56 ____________

16. 0.0413 ____________ **17.** $\frac{3}{8}$ ____________ **18.** $\frac{7}{12}$ ____________

19. 0.387 ____________ **20.** 0.283 ____________ **21.** $\frac{2}{9}$ ____________

Write each number as a percent. Place the number into the puzzle without using the percent sign or decimal point.

22.

Across

1. 0.134
3. $\frac{53}{100}$
5. 0.565
7. $1\frac{7}{50}$
9. 0.456
10. 0.63
11. $\frac{11}{200}$
13. 0.58
14. $\frac{191}{200}$
16. 0.605

Down

2. 0.346
4. 0.324
5. $\frac{1}{2}$
6. 0.515
8. $\frac{33}{200}$
9. 0.4385
10. $\frac{659}{1,000}$
12. $\frac{1,087}{20,000}$
15. $\frac{14}{25}$

1.	2.		■	■
■		■	3.	4.
5.		6.	■	
	■	7.	8.	
■	9.			■
10.		■	11.	12.
13.		■	■	
14.		15.	■	
■	■	16.		

Name ____________________ Class ____________ Date ____________

6-1 • Guided Problem Solving

GPS Exercise 32:

You answer 32 questions correctly on a 45-question test. You need a score of at least 70% to pass. Do you pass? Explain.

Understand

1. What are you being asked to do? ____________

2. Circle the information you will need to solve. ____________

Plan and Carry Out

3. How many questions did you answer correctly? ____________

4. How many questions were on the test? ____________

5. Write a fraction comparing the number of questions you answered correctly to the total number of questions on the test.

____

6. Use a calculator to convert the fraction to a decimal. Round to the nearest thousandth.

____

7. Convert your answer from Step 6 to a percent by moving the decimal to the left two places. What percent of the questions did you answer correctly?

____

8. Compare your score to 70%. Did you pass? Explain.

____

Check

9. Multiply the percent you found in Step 7 by 45 and round to the nearest number. Based on this calculation, did you answer 32 questions correctly?

____

Solve Another Problem

10. To win a free-throw contest, Miguel needs to make 85% or more of the free throws he attempts. He makes 22 out of 27 free throws. Approximately what percent of free throws did Miguel make? Did Miguel win the contest?

____

Name ____________ Class ____________ Date ____________

Practice 6-2

Percents Greater Than 100% or Less Than 1%

Classify each of the following as: (A) less than 1%, (B) greater than 100%, or (C) between 1% and 100%.

1. $\frac{1}{2}$ ________
2. $\frac{4}{3}$ ________
3. $\frac{2}{300}$ ________
4. $\frac{3}{10}$ ________
5. 1.03 ________
6. 0.009 ________
7. 0.635 ________
8. 0.0053 ________

Use >, <, or = to compare the numbers in each pair.

9. $\frac{1}{4}$ ☐ 20%
10. $\frac{1}{2}$% ☐ 50
11. 0.008 ☐ 8%
12. 150% ☐ $\frac{5}{4}$
13. 3 ☐ 300%
14. $\frac{7}{250}$ ☐ 0.3%

Write each fraction or mixed number as a percent. Round to the nearest tenth of a percent if necessary.

15. $1\frac{2}{5}$ ________
16. $1\frac{37}{100}$ ________
17. $\frac{0.8}{100}$ ________
18. $5\frac{1}{4}$ ________
19. $1\frac{7}{10}$ ________
20. $1\frac{25}{40}$ ________
21. $1\frac{17}{20}$ ________
22. $\frac{7}{500}$ ________
23. $1\frac{1}{8}$ ________

Write each decimal as a percent.

24. 0.003 ________
25. 1.8 ________
26. 0.0025 ________
27. 5.3 ________
28. 0.0041 ________
29. 0.083 ________
30. 0.0009 ________
31. 0.83 ________
32. 20 ________

Write each percent as a decimal and as a fraction in simplest form.

33. 175% ________ ________
34. 120% ________ ________
35. $\frac{2}{5}$% ________ ________
36. $\frac{5}{8}$% ________ ________
37. 750% ________ ________
38. $8\frac{1}{4}$% ________ ________

39. In 1990, the population of Kansas was 2,477,574, which included 21,965 Native Americans. What percent of the people living in Kansas were Native Americans?

____

40. The mass of Earth is $\frac{1}{318}$ of the mass of Jupiter. What percent is this?

____

Name ____________________ Class ____________ Date ____________

6-2 • Guided Problem Solving

GPS Exercise 34:

Write the percent as a decimal and as a fraction in simplest form.

On March 1, the snowpack in the Northern Great Basin of Nevada was 126% of the average snowpack.

Understand

1. What is the relevant information?

____

____

2. What are you being asked to do?

____

3. How do you convert a percent to a decimal?

____

Plan and Carry Out

4. When changing 126% to a fraction, what will be your numerator and denominator?

____

5. Write this fraction as a mixed number in simplest form.

____

6. Convert 126% to a decimal. ____________________

Check

7. Multiply the answer to Step 6 by 100. Does it equal the percent?

____

Solve Another Problem

Write the percent as a decimal and as a fraction in simplest form.

8. Of the students in a class, 66% are female.

____

Name ____________ Class ____________ Date ____________

Practice 6-3

Finding a Percent of a Number

Find each answer.

1. 20% of 560
2. 42% of 200
3. 9% of 50
4. 40% of 70
5. 25% of 80
6. 50% of 80
7. 40% of 200
8. 5% of 80
9. 75% of 200

Find each answer using mental math.

10. 14% of 120
11. 30% of 180
12. 62.5% of 24
13. 34% of 50
14. 25% of 240
15. 85.5% of 23
16. 120% of 56
17. 80% of 90
18. 42% of 120

Estimate each answer.

19. 24% of 104
20. 31% of 92
21. 8% of 61
22. 47% of 206
23. 73% of 196
24. 4% of 79
25. 79% of 19
26. 18% of 44
27. 88% of 99

Solve.

28. A bicycle goes on sale at 75% of its original price of $160. What is its sale price?

Name ______________________ Class ______________ Date ______________

6-3 • Guided Problem Solving

GPS Exercise 40:

In 2005, about 74,000 acres of land burned in California wildfires. The Topanga fire, in Los Angeles County, accounted for around 32% of this land. About how many acres were burned in the Topanga fire?

Understand

1. What is the relevant information in the problem?

____

2. What are you being asked to do?

____

____

3. How will changing 32% to an equivalent decimal help you solve the problem?

____

Plan and Carry Out

4. What is the percent of acres of land that were burned in the Topanga fire?

____

____

5. Write 32% as a decimal. ______________

6. What is the total number of acres of land that burned in California wildfires in 2005? ______________

7. Multiply your decimal answer from Step 5 by 74,000.

____

8. How many acres of land were burned in the Topanga fire? ______

Check

9. What is 50% of 74,000? Is the number of acres of land burned in the Topanga fire less than this?

____

Solve Another Problem

10. Your mother says that 80% of your shirts are dirty. If you have 30 shirts, how many are dirty?

____

Name ____________ Class ____________ Date ____________

Practice 6-4

Solving Percent Problems Using Proportions

Use a proportion to solve.

1. 48 is 60% of what number?

2. What is 175% of 85?

3. What percent of 90 is 50?

4. 76 is 80% of what number?

5. What is 50% of 42.88?

6. 96 is 160% of what number?

7. What percent of 24 is 72?

8. What is 85% of 120?

9. What is 80% of 12?

10. 56 is 75% of what number?

Solve.

11. The sale price of a bicycle is $120. This is 80% of the original price. Find the original price.

12. The attendance at a family reunion was 160 people. This was 125% of last year's attendance. How many people attended the reunion last year?

13. A company has 875 employees. On "Half-Price Wednesday," 64% of the employees eat lunch at the company cafeteria. How many employees eat lunch at the cafeteria on Wednesdays?

14. There are 1,295 students attending a small university. There are 714 women enrolled. What percent of students are women?

Name ______________________ Class ______________ Date ______________

6-4 • Guided Problem Solving

GPS Exercise 30:

At the library, you find 9 books on a certain topic. The librarian tells you that 55% of the books on this topic have been signed out. How many books does the library have on the topic?

Understand

1. Circle the information you will need to solve.
2. What are you being asked to do?

____

____

3. If 55% of the books have been signed out, what percent of the books have *not* been signed out?

____

Plan and Carry Out

4. Choose a variable to represent the total number of books the library has on the topic.

____

5. How many books did you find on the topic? ____________
6. Write a proportion comparing the percent of books in the library to the number of books in the library.

____

7. Solve the proportion. ____________________
8. How many books does the library have on the topic? ____________

Check

9. Is 55% of your answer plus 9 equal to your answer?

____

Solve Another Problem

10. There are 12,000 people attending a concert. You learn that 20% of the people who bought tickets to the concert did not attend. How many people bought tickets to the concert?

____

____

Practice 6-5

Solving Percent Problems Using Equations

Write and solve an equation. Round answers to the nearest tenth.

1. What percent of 64 is 48?

2. 16% of 130 is what number?

3. 25% of what number is 24?

4. What percent of 18 is 12?

5. 48% of 83 is what number?

6. 40% of what number is 136?

7. What percent of 530 is 107?

8. 74% of 643 is what number?

9. 62% of what number is 84?

10. What percent of 84 is 50?

11. 37% of 245 is what number?

12. 12% of what number is 105?

Solve.

13. A cafe offers senior citizens a 15% discount off its regular price of $8.95 for the dinner buffet.

    a. What percent of the regular price is the price for senior citizens?

    b. What is the price for senior citizens?

14. In 1990, 12.5% of the people in Oregon did not have health insurance. If the population of Oregon was 2,880,000, how many people were uninsured?

Name ______________________ Class ______________ Date ______________

6-5 • Guided Problem Solving

GPS Exercise 27:

The attendance at the school play on Friday was 95% of the attendance on Saturday night. If 203 people attended on Saturday night, estimate how many attended on Friday.

Understand

1. What are you being asked to do?

   ____

2. Circle the information you will need to answer the question.

   ____

Plan and Carry Out

3. What percentage of Saturday's attendance was Friday's attendance?

   ____

4. How many people attended the play on Saturday night?

   ____

5. Write your answer to Step 3 as a decimal.

   ____

6. Write an equation showing the Friday-night attendance as a percent of the Saturday-night attendance. Let f represent the Friday-night attendance.

   ____

7. Solve the equation in Step 6. How many people attended the play Friday night?

   ____

Check

8 Compare your answer with 203. Is your answer less than 203?

   ____

Solve Another Problem

9. Jamie walks 1,395 yards to get to her friend's house. She walks 80% of this distance to get to school in the mornings. How far does Jamie walk to get to school?

   ____

Name ______________________ Class ______________ Date ______________

Practice 6-6

Tips and Discounts

Find the amount of each tip.

1. 20% tip on a $45.75 meal

____

2. 15% tip on a $32.50 taxi fare

____

3. 15% tip on a $17.45 delivery

____

Find the total cost of each meal after paying a 15% tip.

4. $17.94 ____________
5. $55.60 ____________
6. $32.75 ____________
7. $60.25 ____________
8. $7.29 ____________
9. $9.82 ____________

Find the discount and total cost of each item.

10. 35% discount on a $55.30 pair of shoes

discount ______________

total cost ______________

11. 60% discount on a $27.75 book

discount ______________

total cost ______________

12. 20% discount on a $72.99 lamp

discount ______________

total cost ______________

13. 45% discount on a $12.35 shirt

discount ______________

total cost ______________

14. 75% discount on a $69.45 rug

discount ______________

total cost ______________

15. 15% discount on a $15.39 towel

discount ______________

total cost ______________

Name ______________________ Class ______________ Date ______________

6-6 • Guided Problem Solving

GPS Exercise 22:

Your neighbor pays $40 to mow her lawn and always adds a 15% tip. You and your friend decide to mow the lawn together and split the earnings in half. How much will each of you make from the job?

Understand

1. What are you being asked to do?

____

2. Circle the information you will need to solve.

Plan and Carry Out

3. How much does your neighbor pay to mow her lawn?

____

4. What percent of this amount does she add as a tip?

____

5. Find the amount of the tip by multiplying your answer from Step 3 by your answer from Step 4.

____

6. Add the tip amount to the amount your neighbor pays to find how much money you and your friend will earn.

____

7. Divide the total amount earned by 2. How much will each of you earn for mowing your neighbor's yard?

____

Check

8. Multiply the amount you and your friend each make by 2. Is this the amount of money you both earned with the tip included?

____

Solve Another Problem

9. James works as a waiter. He waits on a table whose total bill is $37.00. They give him a 15% tip. If he gives $1 to the busboy for his help, how much money did James make?

____

Name ______________ Class ______________ Date ______________

Practice 6-7

Interest

Find the amount of interest earned on each principal at the given rate.

1. $455, 7% ______________
2. $920, 3% ______________
3. $239, 2% ______________
4. $560, 5% ______________
5. $175, 8% ______________
6. $765, 4% ______________

Find the balance in each account after one year for the given principal and annual interest rate.

7. $372, 4% ______________
8. $175, 3.5% ______________
9. $824, 6% ______________
10. $120, 7% ______________
11. $264, 5.5% ______________
12. $615, 2.5% ______________

Use mental math to find the simple interest on each principal at an annual interest rate of 5%.

13. $200 ______________
14. $460 ______________
15. $140 ______________
16. $580 ______________

Solve.

17. One year ago, Marshall made a deposit in a bank account that had an annual interest rate of 5.5%. He now has $279.58 in his bank account. How much money did Marshall originally deposit?

____

18. Roshanda deposited $460 in a bank account. After one year of gaining interest, her account totaled $478.40. What was the account's annual interest rate?

____

Name ______________________ Class ______________ Date ______________

6-7 • Guided Problem Solving

GPS Exercise 22:

Ethan deposited \$198 in an account that earns 2.5% annual interest. He wants to buy a sound system that sells for \$210. Will he have enough money in the account at the end of one year? Explain.

Understand

1. What are you being asked to do?

____

2. Circle the information you will need to solve.

Plan and Carry Out

3. What is the principal that Ethan deposited in the bank? ______________

4. What is the annual interest rate that Ethan earns? ______________

5. Write the equation for finding the balance on an account after one year. ______________

6. Substitute the values in Steps 4 and 5 into the equation for annual balance and solve. ______________

7. How much money will Ethan have in his account after a year? Will he have enough to buy the sound system? ______________

Check

8. Instead of using the equation for finding the balance on an account after a year, find the simple interest Ethan will make on his principal in one year and add this amount to his principal. Is this the same amount that you found in Step 7?

____

Solve Another Problem

9. Phyllis deposits \$340 in a bank account earning 4.4% annual interest. She wants to enroll in a summer language school for \$350. Will she have enough money in her account to do this after one year?

____

Name ______________________ Class ______________ Date ______________

6A: Graphic Organizer

For use before Lesson 6–1

Study Skill As you read over the material in the chapter, keep a paper and pencil handy to write down notes and questions that you have.

Write your answers.

1. What is the chapter title? ______________________
2. How many lessons are there in this chapter? ______________________
3. What is the topic of the Test-Taking Strategies page? ______________________
4. Complete the graphic organizer below as you work through the chapter.
   - In the center, write the title of the chapter.
   - When you begin a lesson, write the lesson name in a rectangle.
   - When you complete a lesson, write a skill or key concept in a circle linked to that lesson block.
   - When you complete the chapter, use this graphic organizer to help you review.

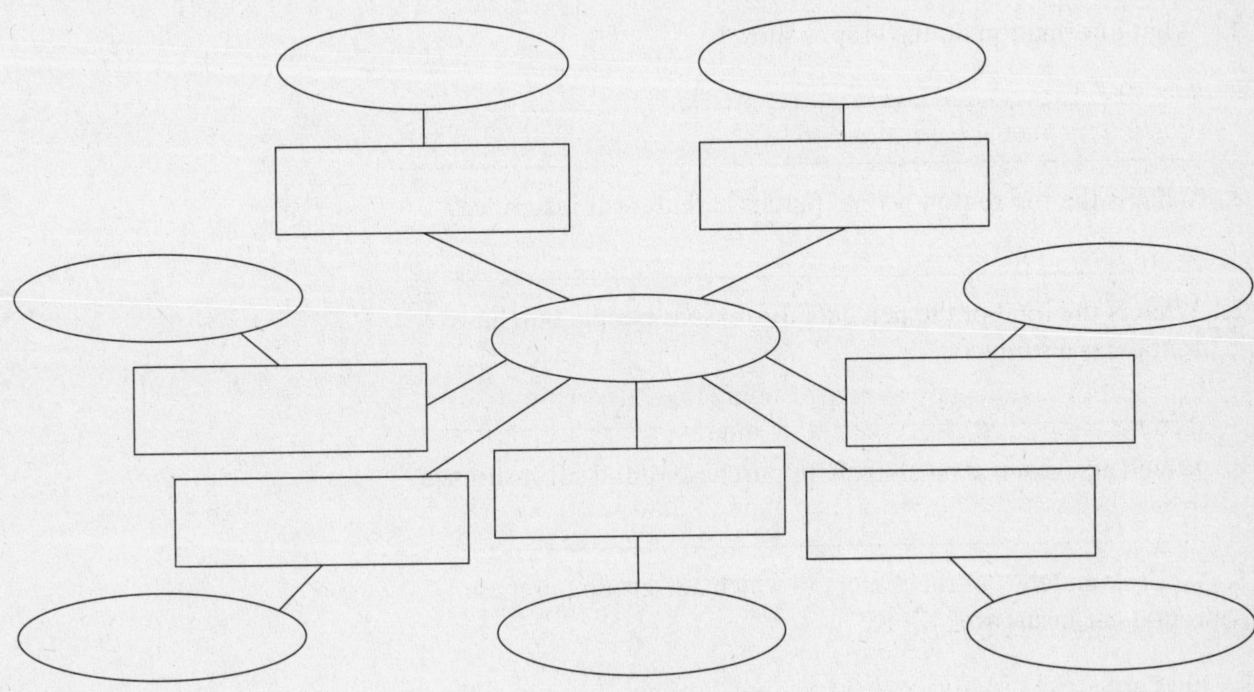

Name ______________________ Class ______________ Date ______________

6B: Reading Comprehension

For use after Lesson 6-1

Study Skill Use a special notebook (or section of a loose-leaf binder) for your math handouts and homework. Keep your notebook neat and organized by reviewing its contents often.

Use the graphs shown below to answer the questions that follow.

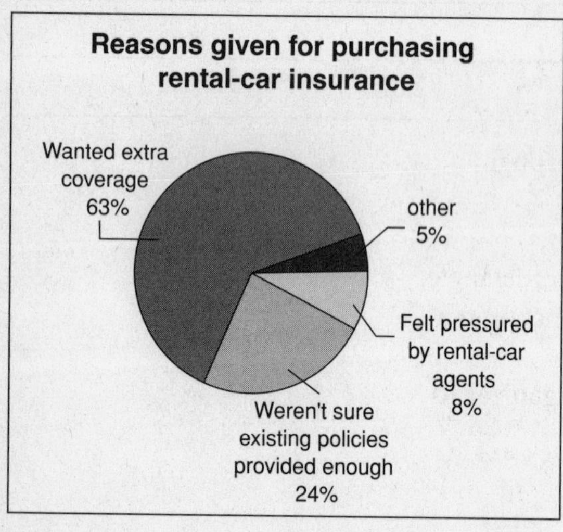

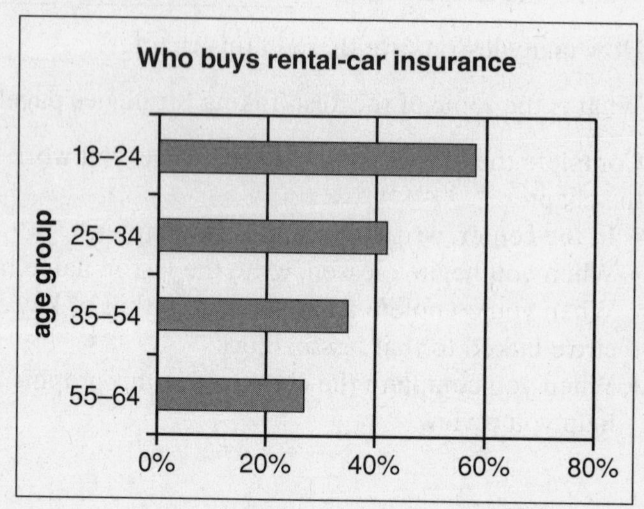

1. What information do the graphs show?

____

____

2. What is the top reason people purchase rental-car insurance?

____

3. What is the total of the percents for reasons people purchase rental-car insurance?

____

4. Which age group is most likely to purchase rental-car insurance?

____

5. Approximately $\frac{1}{3}$ of the renters in which age group purchase rental-car insurance?

____

6. Approximately $\frac{1}{4}$ of the renters purchase rental-car insurance for what reason?

____

7. **High-Use Academic Words** In Exercise 1, what does the word *show* mean?

a. to display

b. to put in a sequence

Name ______________________ Class ______________ Date ______________

6C: Reading/Writing Math Symbols

For use after Lesson 6-4

Study Skill When working on your math homework, use a pencil and have an eraser nearby.

Write each of the following using appropriate mathematical symbols and abbreviations.

1. 3 feet to 1 yard ______________________
2. 47 and 6 tenths percent ______________________
3. thirty-eight hundredths ______________________
4. 1 meter to 100 centimeters ______________________
5. 106 percent ______________________
6. seven tenths percent ______________________
7. 8 quarts to 2 gallons ______________________
8. 93 and 32 hundredths percent ______________________
9. the absolute value of negative 16 ______________________
10. 78 out of 100 ______________________

Write each of the following in words.

11. $|-7.3| = 7.3$

____

12. 30.08%

____

13. 0.87%

____

14. 2 h : 120 min

____

15. $\frac{55}{100}$

____

16. $\frac{1}{10} = 10\%$

____

Name ______________________ Class ______________ Date ______________

6D: Visual Vocabulary Practice

For use after Lesson 6-7

High-Use Academic Words

Study Skill When making a sketch, make it simple but make it complete.

Concept List

represent	graph	solve
model	explain	pattern
substitute	calculate	verify

Write the concept that best describes each exercise. Choose from the concept list above.

1.

35% of 70 is
$0.35 \cdot 70 = 24.5$

____

2.

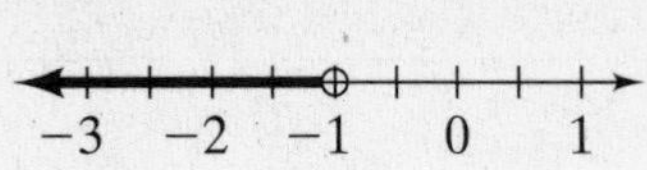

____

3.

5 : 7
5 to 7
$\frac{5}{7}$

____

4.

$$n + 76 = 64$$
$$n + 76 - 76 = 64 - 76$$
$$n = -12$$

____

5.

Sales tax is a percent of a purchase price you must pay when buying certain items. The formula for sales tax is sales tax = tax rate × purchase price.

____

6.

If $\frac{t}{18} = \frac{7}{126}$, then $t = 1$.
Check: $1 \cdot 126 = 7 \cdot 18$

____

7.

A	B
3	15
6	30
9	45
12	60
15	75

____

8.

$7a = 161$; a is either 23 or 26

$7(21) \stackrel{?}{=} 147$ False
$7(23) \stackrel{?}{=} 161$ True

____

9.

____

Name ______________________ Class ______________ Date ______________

6E: Vocabulary Check

For use after Lesson 6-7

Study Skill Strengthen your vocabulary. Use these pages and add cues and summaries by applying the Cornell Notetaking style.

Write the definition for each word or term at the right. To check your work, fold the paper back along the dotted line to see the correct answers.

______________________	interest
______________________	discount
______________________	balance
______________________	percent
______________________	principal

Name ______________________ Class ______________ Date ______________

6E: Vocabulary Check (continued)

For use after Lesson 6-7

Write the vocabulary word or term for each definition. To check your work, fold the paper forward along the dotted line to see the correct answers.

money earned on money deposited in a bank ______________________

the difference between the original price and the sale price of an item ______________________

the principal plus the interest earned ______________________

a ratio that compares a number to 100 ______________________

the original amount of money borrowed or deposited ______________________

6F: Vocabulary Review

For use with the Chapter Review

Study Skill When you have to match words and descriptions from two columns, read the list of words and the definitions carefully and completely so you can quickly find the obvious matches. Then do the rest, one at a time. Cross out words and definitions as you use them.

Match the word in Column A with its definition in Column B.

Column A	Column B
1. percent	A. difference between the original price and the sale price
2. divisor	B. equation stating two ratios are equal
3. discount	C. whole number that divides into another whole number evenly
4. ratio	D. the original amount of money borrowed from a bank, or deposited in an account
5. proportion	E. comparison of two numbers by division
6. principal	F. ratio comparing a number to 100

Match the word in Column A with its definition in Column B.

Column A	Column B
7. mode	G. the principal plus the interest earned
8. equation	H. enlarged or reduced drawing of an object
9. interest	J. statement that two expressions are equal
10. tip	K. number that occurs most often in a data set
11. scale drawing	L. money earned from depositing money in a bank account
12. balance	M. percent of a bill that you give to a person for providing a service

Name ____________ Class ____________ Date ____________

Practice 7-1

Lines and Planes

Describe the lines or line segments as *parallel* or *intersecting*.

1. the rows on a spreadsheet ____________
2. the marks left by a skidding car ____________
3. sidewalks on opposite sides of a street ____________
4. the cut sides of a wedge of apple pie ____________
5. the wires suspended between telephone poles ____________
6. the hands of a clock at 7:00 P.M. ____________
7. the trunks of grown trees in a forest ____________

Use the diagram below for Exercises 8–12.

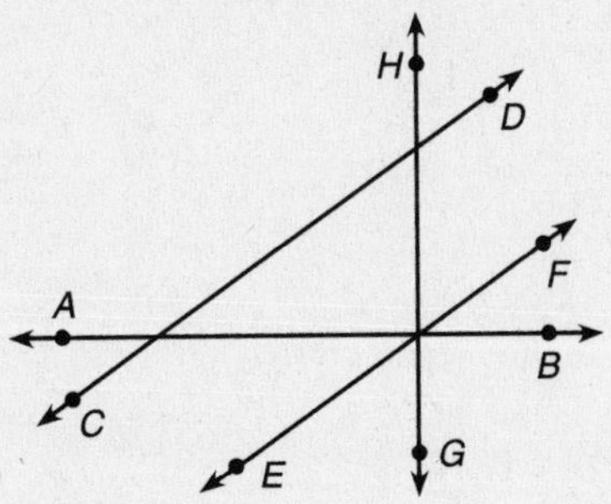

8. Name a pair of parallel lines. ____________
9. Name a segment. ____________
10. Name three points. ____________
11. Name two rays. ____________
12. Name a pair of intersecting lines. ____________

Use a straightedge to draw each figure.

13. a line parallel to $\overline{UV}$

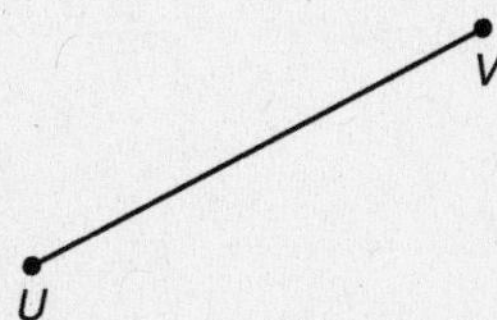

14. a line intersecting $\overline{XY}$

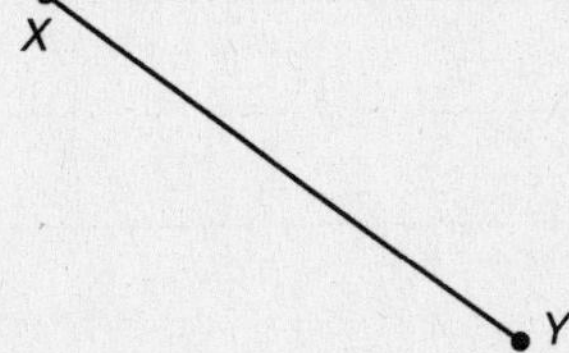

Name ______________________ Class ______________ Date ______________

7-1 • Guided Problem Solving

GPS Exercise 23:

Are the rungs on a ladder parallel, intersecting, or skew?

Understand

1. What is a ladder? Draw a sketch of one.

____

____

2. What are the rungs of a ladder? Circle the rungs on your sketch.

____

____

3. What are you being asked to do?

____

____

Plan and Carry Out

4. Do the rungs have any points in common? ______________
5. Are the rungs in the same plane? ______________
6. Are the rungs intersecting? ______________
7. Are the rungs skew? ______________
8. Are the rungs parallel? ______________

Check

9. Define *parallel*. Does this describe the rungs?

____

____

Solve Another Problem

10. Are the lines on your palm parallel, intersecting, or skew?

____

____

____

Name ______________________ Class ______________ Date ______________

Practice 7-2

Identifying and Classifying Angles

In exercises 1–6, classify each angle as *acute, right, obtuse,* or *straight.*

1.

2.

3.

______ ______ ______

4. $m\angle A = 180°$

5. $m\angle B = 43°$

6. $m\angle D = 90°$

______ ______ ______

Use the figure at the right to name the following.

7. two lines ______

8. three segments ______

9. a pair of congruent angles ______

10. four right angles ______

11. two pairs of obtuse vertical angles ______

12. two pairs of adjacent supplementary angles ______

13. two pairs of complementary angles ______

Solve.

14. If $m\angle A = 23°$, what is the measure of its complement?

______

15. If $m\angle T = 163°$, what is the measure of its supplement?

______

16. If a 67° angle is complementary to $\angle Q$, what is the measure of $\angle Q$?

______

17. Use the dot grid to draw two supplementary angles, one of which is 45°. Do *not* use a protractor.

Name ____________ Class ____________ Date ____________

7-2 • Guided Problem Solving

GPS Exercise 27:

Writing in Math Can an angle ever have the same measure as its complement? Explain.

Understand

1. What are you being asked to do?

____

____

2. What do you have to do to explain your answer?

____

____

____

Plan and Carry Out

3. What is the definition of complementary angles?

____

4. If an angle and its complement have the same measure, explain the relationship between the angle and 90°.

____

5. Determine the measure of the angle. _______________

6. Can an angle ever have the same measure as its complement?

____

Check

7. Explain your answer.

____

____

Solve Another Problem

8. Can an angle ever have the same measure as its supplement? Explain.

____

____

Name ______________________ Class ______________ Date ______________

Practice 7-3

Triangles

Find the value of x in each triangle.

1. 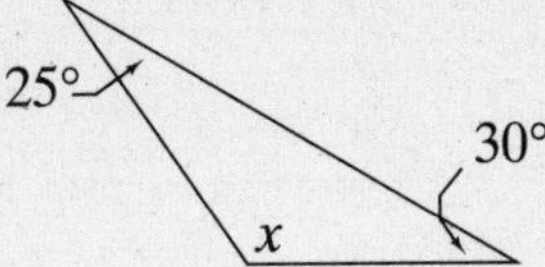

2. 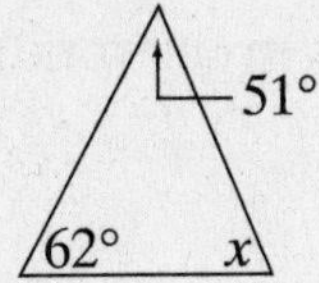

3. 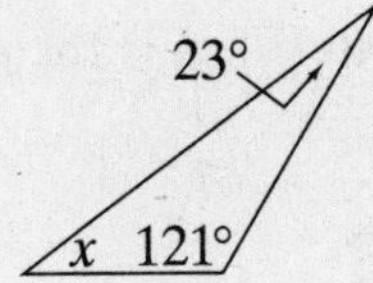

4. 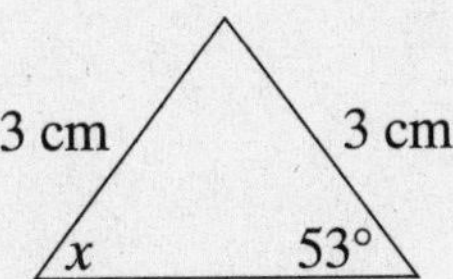

5. 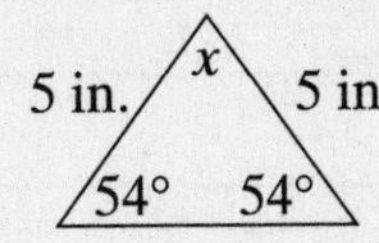

6. 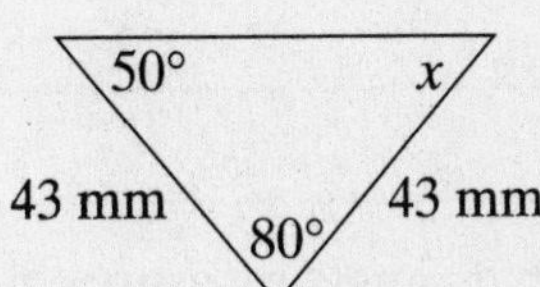

Classify each triangle.

7. The measures of two angles are 53° and 76°.

8. Two sides have the same length.

9. The measure of one angle is 90°.

10. All three sides have the same length.

11. The measures of the angles of a triangle are 40°, 50°, and 90°.

   a. Classify the triangle by its angles.

   b. Can the triangle be equilateral? Why or why not?

   c. Can the triangle be isosceles? Why or why not?

   d. Can you classify the triangle by its sides? Why or why not?

Name ______ Class ______ Date ______

7-3 • Guided Problem Solving

GPS Exercise 18:

Writing in Math What is the measure of $\angle E$? Show your work and justify your steps.

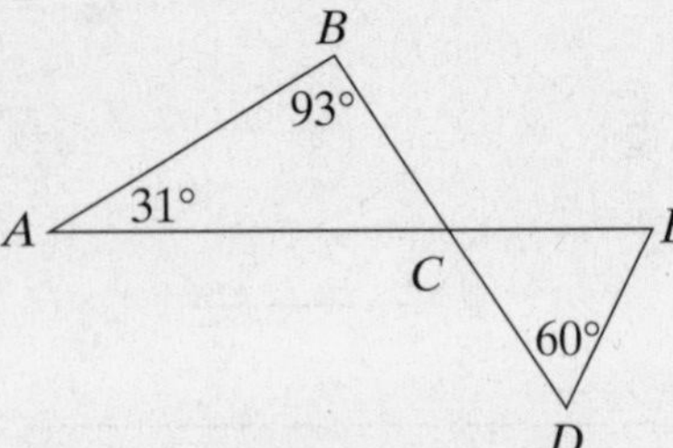

Understand

1. What are you being asked to do?

______

______

2. Which angle measures do you know?

______

Plan and Carry Out

3. What is the sum of the measures of the angles in a triangle?

______

4. What is the sum of the measures of angles A and B?

______

5. Use the results from Steps 3 and 4 to determine the measure of $\angle ACB$. What is the measure of $\angle ECD$?

______

6. What is the sum of the measures of angles $\angle ECD$ and $\angle D$?

______

7. Use the results from Steps 3 and 6 to determine $m\angle E$.

______

Check

8. How do you justify using 180° to find the measure of the unknown angles?

______

Solve Another Problem

9. Suppose $m\angle A = 62°$, $m\angle B = 43°$, and $m\angle D = 73°$. Find the measure of $\angle E$.

______

______

Name ______________________ Class ______________ Date ______________

Practice 7-4

Quadrilaterals and Other Polygons

Identify each polygon and classify it as *regular* or *irregular.*

1. 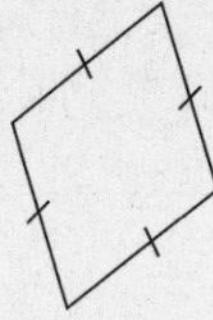

2. 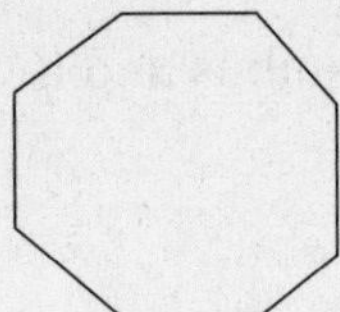

3. 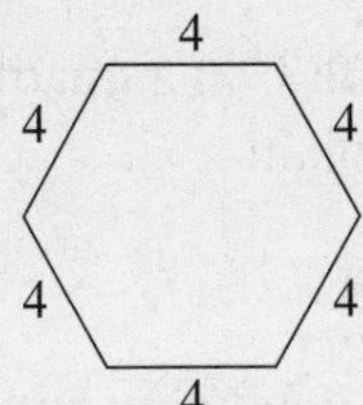

State all correct names for each quadrilateral. Then circle the best name.

4. 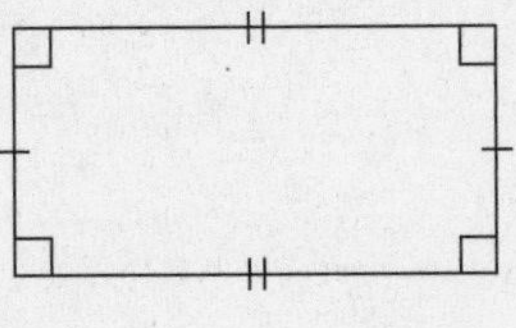

5. 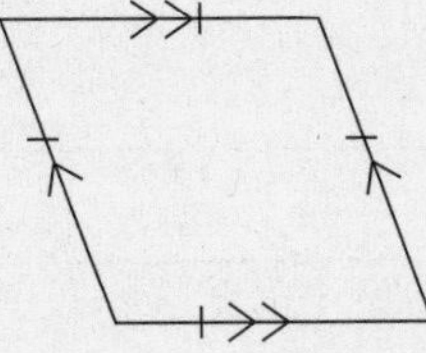

6. 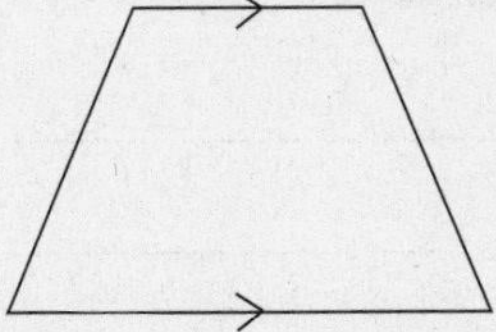

Use dot paper to draw each quadrilateral.

7. a rectangle that is not a square

8. a rhombus with at least two right angles

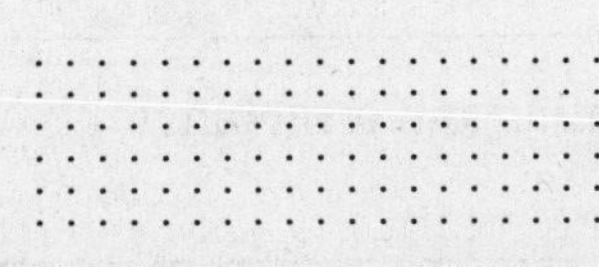

9. a trapezoid with no right angles

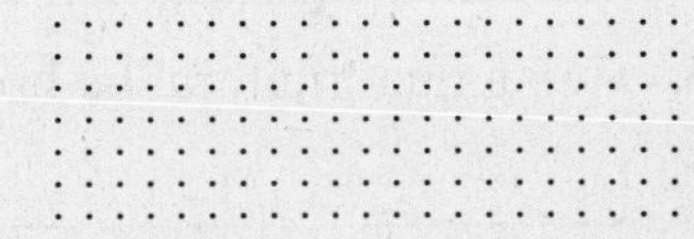

10. List all additional side lengths and angle measures you can find for the trapezoid *JKLM*, where $\overline{KL}$ is parallel to $\overline{JM}$, $\angle K$ is a right angle, and the length of $\overline{LM}$ is 10 cm.

Name ______________________ Class ______________ Date ______________

7-4 • Guided Problem Solving

GPS Exercise 21:

Writing in Math Can a quadrilateral be both a rhombus and a rectangle? Explain.

Understand

1. What are you being asked to do?

____

____

2. In order to answer this question, what definitions do you need to know?

____

____

Plan and Carry Out

3. What is a quadrilateral?

____

4. What is a rhombus?

____

5. What is a rectangle?

____

6. Can a quadrilateral be both a rhombus and a rectangle?

____

Check

7. Explain your answer to Step 6 by giving an example of a shape that is both a rhombus and a rectangle.

____

____

____

Solve Another Problem

8. If all squares are types of rectangles, are all rhombuses types of rectangles? Explain.

____

Name ______________________ Class ______________ Date ______________

Practice 7-5

Using the Properties of Angles

Find the measure of each numbered angle.

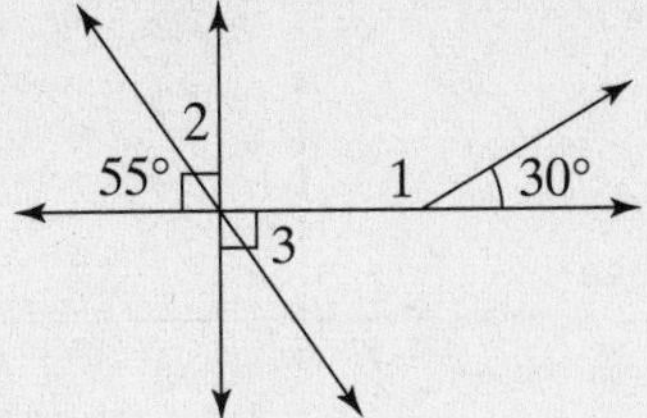

1. ______________ 2. ______________ 3. ______________

Find the measure of $\angle ABC$ in each figure.

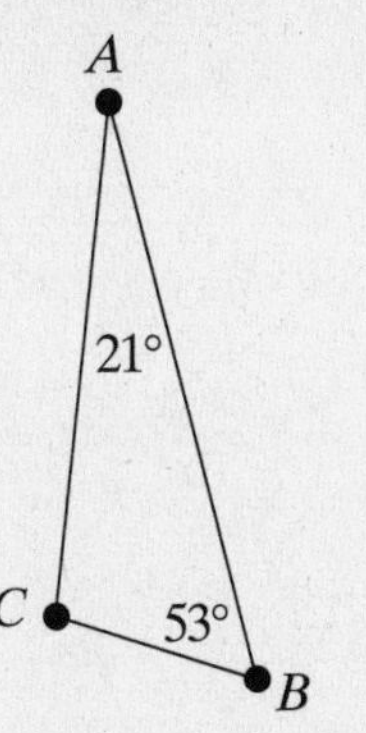

C
72°
34°
A
B

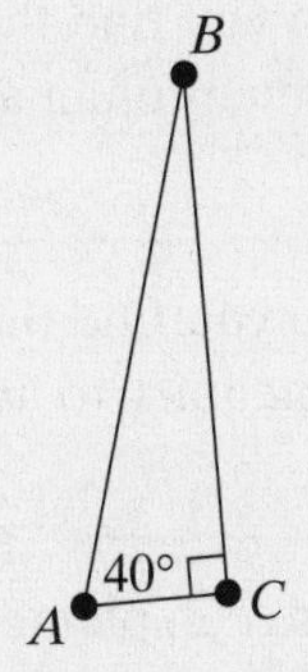

4. ______________ 5. ______________ 6. ______________

Find the measure of each numbered angle.

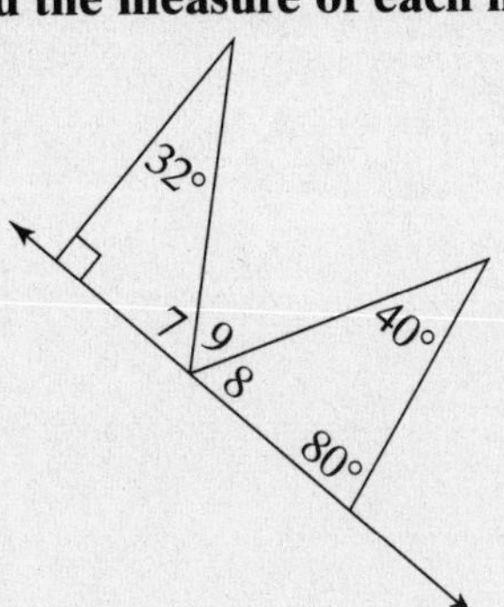

7. ______________ 8. ______________ 9. ______________

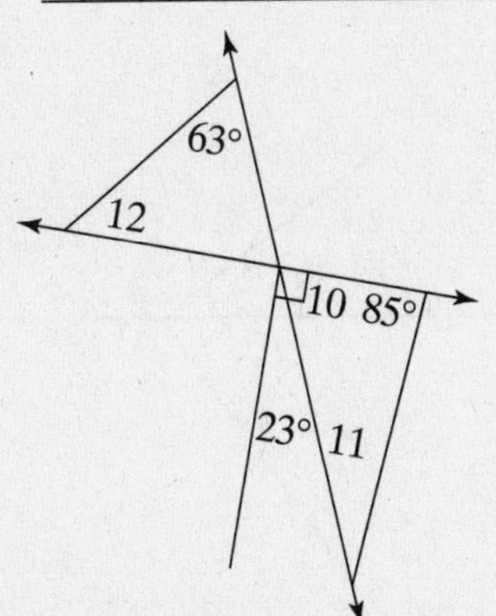

10. ______________ 11. ______________ 12. ______________

Name ______________________ Class ______________ Date ______________

7-5 • Guided Problem Solving

GPS Exercise 14:

Find the measure of each numbered angle.

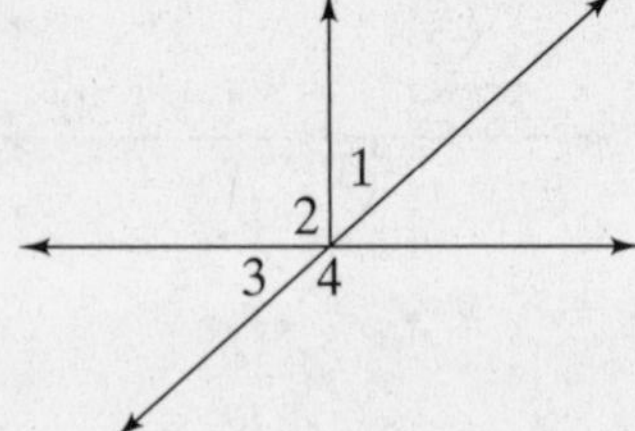

Understand

1. What are you being asked to do?

____

Plan and Carry Out

2. How do you find the measure of an unknown angle that is the complement of an angle with a known measurement?

____

3. How do you find the measure of an unknown angle that is supplementary to an angle with a known measurement?

____

4. $\angle 1$ is the complement of a 40° angle. Find $m\angle 1$.

____

5. $\angle 4$ is supplementary to a 40° angle. Find $m\angle 4$.

____

6. $\angle 3$ is supplementary to $\angle 4$. Find $m\angle 3$.

____

7. $\angle 2$ is supplementary to a 90° angle. Find $m\angle 2$.

____

Check

8. Add the measure of all of the angles in the diagram. Do they add to 360°?

____

Solve Another Problem

9. Find the measure of each numbered angle.

____

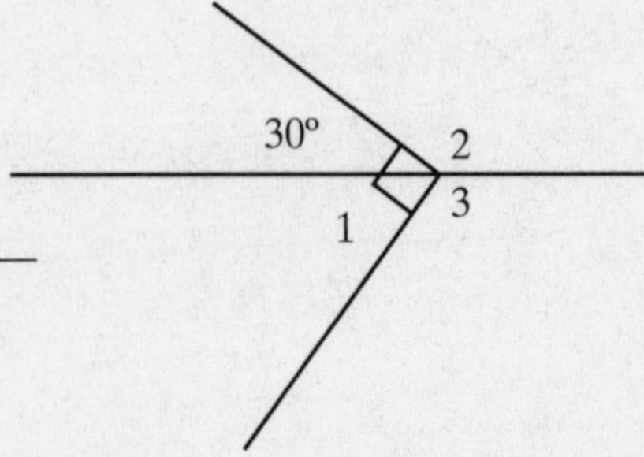

Name ______________________ Class ______________ Date ____________

Practice 7-6

Circles

Name each of the following for circle *O*.

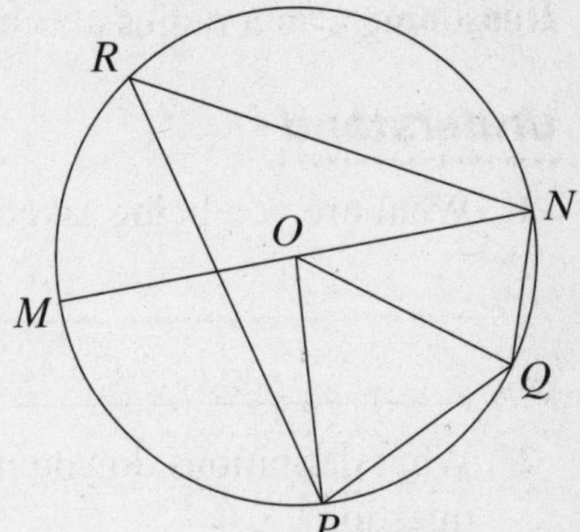

1. two chords ______________

2. three radii ______________

3. a diameter ______________

4. a central angle ______________

5. a semicircle ______________

6. two arcs ______________

7. the longest chord ______________

8. the shortest chord ______________

Name all of the indicated arcs for circle *Q*.

9. all arcs shorter than a semicircle ______________

10. all arcs longer than a semicircle ______________

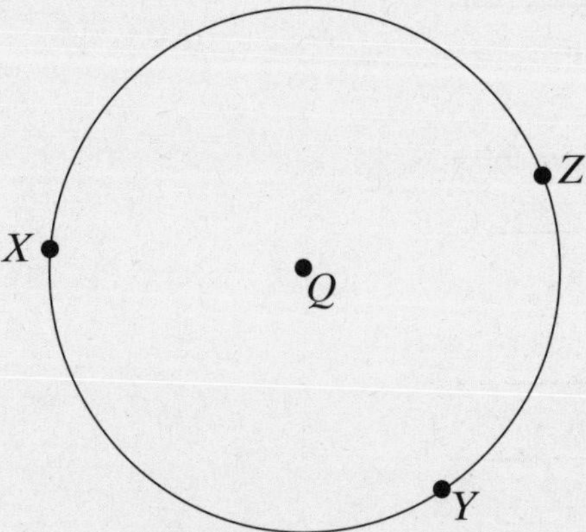

11. Use a compass to draw and label a circle *Q*. Label a semicircle $\overset{\frown}{ABC}$ and an arc $\overset{\frown}{AX}$.

Name ______________________ Class ______________ Date ____________

7-6 • Guided Problem Solving

GPS Exercise 22:

Reasoning Can a radius also be a chord? Explain.

Understand

1. What are you being asked to do?

____

____

2. What definitions do you need to know in order to answer the question?

____

Plan and Carry Out

3. What is a radius?

____

____

4. Where are the endpoints of a radius?

____

____

5. What is a chord?

____

____

6. Can a radius also be a chord? ________________

Check

7. Explain your answer in Step 6.

____

____

____

Solve Another Problem

8. Can a diameter also be a chord? Explain.

____

____

Name ________________ Class ____________ Date ____________

Practice 7-7

Circle Graphs

Use the information in each table to create a circle graph.

1. The data show the total number of space vehicles that either successfully reached or exceeded orbit around Earth.

Years	Number of Successful United States Space Launches
1957–1959	15
1960–1969	470
1970–1979	258
1980–1989	153
1990–1995	146

2. The data represent the percent of private schools in the United States that have an annual tuition in each of the given ranges.

Annual Tuition	% of Private Schools
Less than $500	13
$500–$1,000	28
$1,001–$1,500	26
$1,501–$2,500	15
More than $2,500	18

3. The data represent a poll taken in a seventh-grade class.

Favorite Color for a Car	Number of Seventh Graders
Red	14
Blue	9
White	3
Green	1

a. What percent of seventh graders like blue cars? ____________

b. What percent of seventh graders like green cars? ____________

c. What percent of seventh graders like either red *or* blue cars?

____

d. What percent of seventh graders like a car color *other than* white?

____

Name ______________________ Class ______________ Date ______________

7-7 • Guided Problem Solving

GPS Exercise 16:

The table shows how many days each week students do volunteer work. Use the table to make a circle graph.

Days	1	2	3	4	5
Students	11	5	5	2	2

Understand

1. What are you being asked to do?

____

2. How many students total volunteered?

____

Plan and Carry Out

3. Use a proportion to find the angle of measure for the number of students who volunteered on Day 1.

____

4. Repeat Step 3 for Day 2.

____

5. Repeat Step 3 for Day 3.

____

6. Repeat Step 3 for Day 4.

____

7. Repeat Step 3 for Day 5.

____

8. Use the central angles you found in Steps 3–7 to draw the circle graph.

Check

9. Does the section for 1 day take up a large portion of the circle?

____

Solve Another Problem

10. You are in charge of the activities page in the school yearbook. You want to show how many students are participating in each activity. Use the data in the table to make a circle graph.

Activity	Sports	Band	Student Council	Horticulture	Clubs
Students	28	15	5	3	10

Name ______________________ Class ______________ Date ______________

7A: Graphic Organizer

For use before Lesson 7-1

Study Skill Take notes while you study. Writing something down might help you remember it better. Go back and review your notes when you study for quizzes and tests.

Write your answers.

1. What is the chapter title? ______________________
2. How many lessons are there in this chapter? ______________________
3. What is the topic of the Test-Taking Strategies page? ______________________
4. Complete the graphic organizer below as you work through the chapter.
   - In the center, write the title of the chapter.
   - When you begin a lesson, write the lesson name in a rectangle.
   - When you complete a lesson, write a skill or key concept in a circle linked to that lesson block.
   - When you complete the chapter, use this graphic organizer to help you review.

Name ______________________ Class ______________ Date ______________

7B: Reading Comprehension

For use after Lesson 7-7

Study Skill Review notes that you have taken in class as soon as possible to clarify any points you missed. Be sure to ask questions if you need extra help.

Here is a circle graph for a monthly household budget. Use the graph to answer the questions that follow.

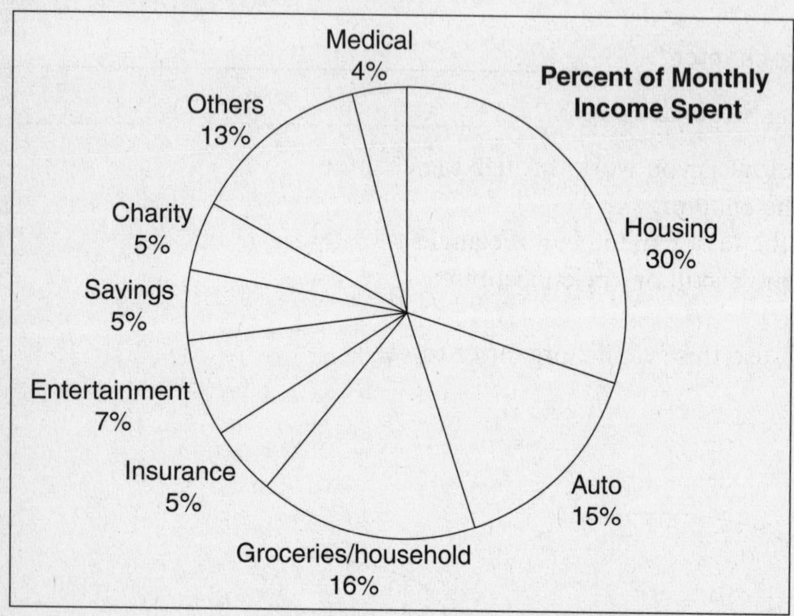

1. On which category was the largest percent of income spent? ______________
2. On which category was the smallest percent of income spent? ______________
3. Why are the insurance, savings, and charity sectors the same size?

   ____
4. What is the total of the percents listed in the circle graph? ______________
5. If the monthly income is $2,400, how much should be spent on an automobile?

   ____
6. How much of a $1,900 monthly income should be saved? ______________
7. If $60 is the amount budgeted for entertainment, what is the monthly income?

   ____
8. **High-Use Academic Words** What does it mean to *review*, as mentioned in the study skill?

   a. to put in order

   b. to study again

Name ______________________ Class ______________ Date ______________

7C: Reading/Writing Math Symbols

For use after Lesson 7-6

Study Skill When you take notes, use abbreviations and symbols such as @ (at), # (number), and w/ (with) to save time and reduce writing.

Match the symbol in Column A with its meaning in Column B.

Column A	Column B
1. $\angle ABC$	A. the measure of angle ABC
2. $\overline{AB}$	B. the length of segment AB
3. $\overleftrightarrow{AB}$	C. triangle ABC
4. AB	D. segment AB
5. $\overrightarrow{AB}$	E. ray starting at A and passing through B
6. $m\angle ABC$	F. ray starting at B and passing through A
7. $\overrightarrow{BA}$	G. line AB
8. $\triangle ABC$	H. angle ABC

Write the meaning of each of the following mathematical statements.

9. $m\angle B = 80°$

____

10. Circle O; $r = 9$ mm

____

11. $\angle XYZ \cong \angle MNP$

____

12. $BC = 4$

____

13. $\overline{DJ} \cong \overline{KL}$

____

14. $DJ = KL$

____

15. $m\angle P = m\angle R$

____

16. $BC = \frac{1}{2}TU$

____

Name ______________________ Class ______________ Date ______________

7D: Visual Vocabulary Practice

For use after Lesson 7-7

Study Skill Use Venn Diagrams to understand the relationship between words whose meanings overlap, such as squares, rectangles, and quadrilaterals or real numbers, integers, and counting numbers.

Concept List

obtuse angle	right triangle	adjacent angles
chord	equilateral triangle	segment
vertical angles	hexagon	pentagon

Write the concept that best describes each exercise. Choose from the concept list above.

1.

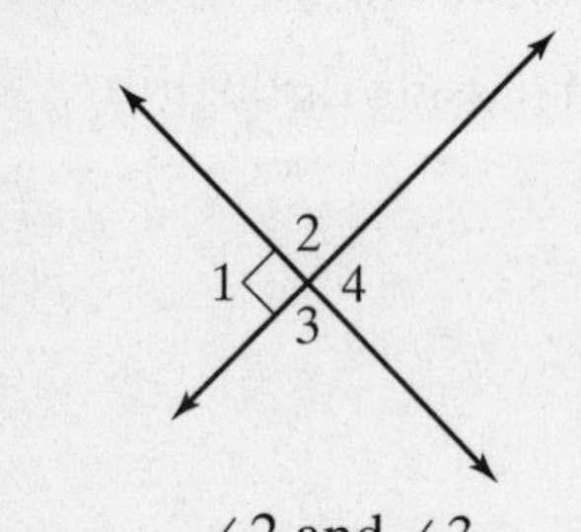

$\angle 2$ and $\angle 3$

____

2.

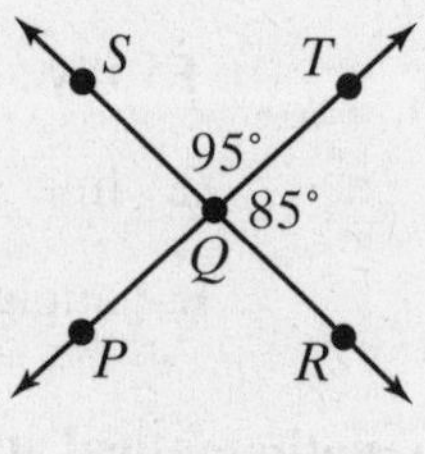

$\angle SQT$

____

3.

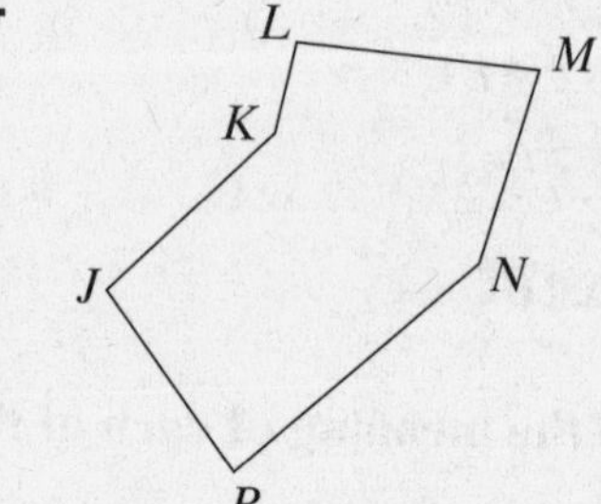

____

4.

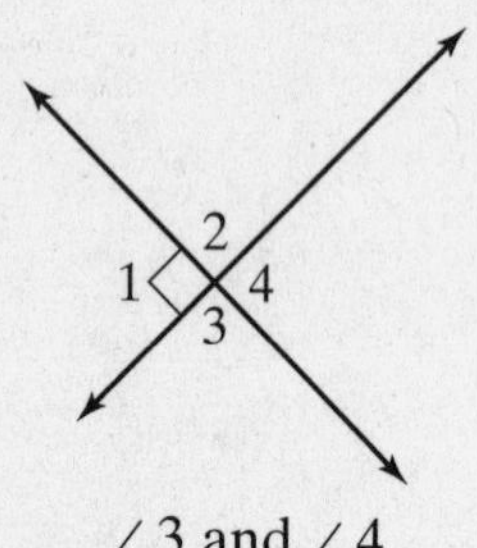

$\angle 3$ and $\angle 4$

____

5.

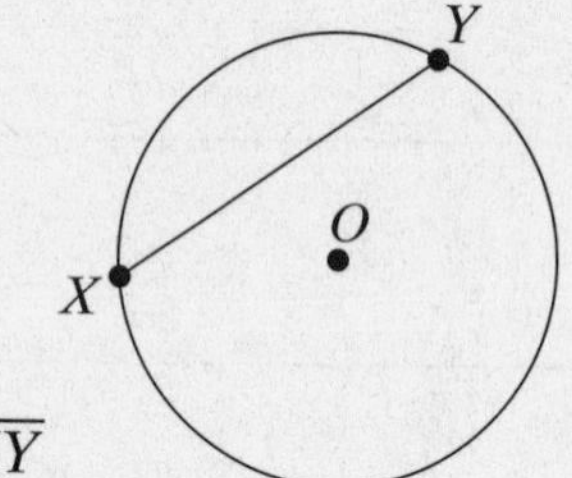

$\overline{XY}$

____

6.

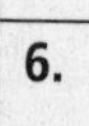

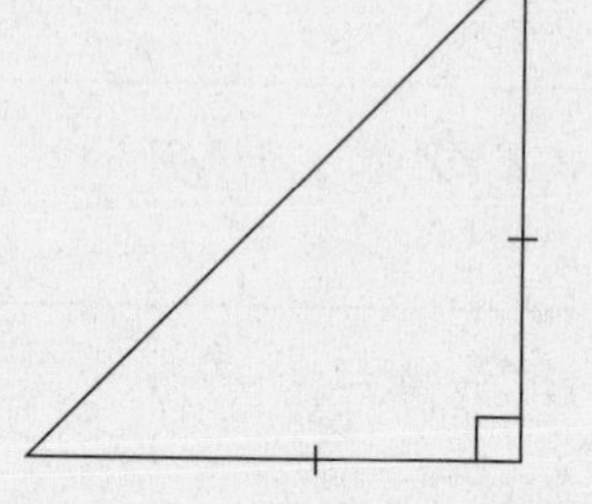

____

7.

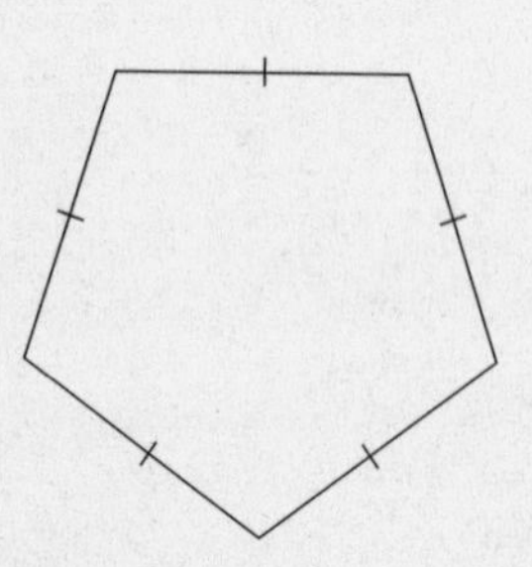

____

8.

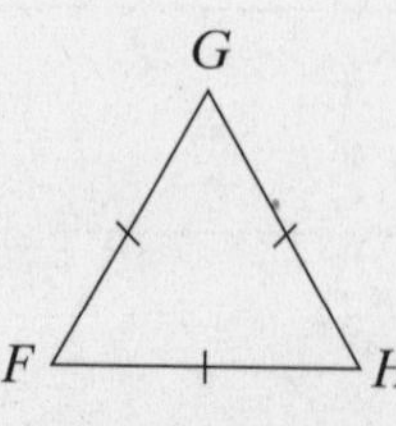

$\overline{FG} \cong \overline{GH} \cong \overline{FH}$

____

9.

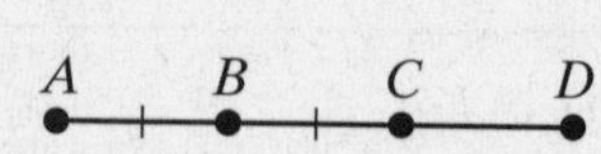

____

7E: Vocabulary Check

For use after Lesson 7-6

Study Skill Strengthen your vocabulary. Use these pages and add cues and summaries by applying the Cornell Notetaking style.

Write the definition for each word or term at the right. To check your work, fold the paper back along the dotted line to see the correct answers.

______________________	regular polygon
______________________	parallel lines
______________________	trapezoid
______________________	acute angle
______________________	circle

Name ______________________ Class ______________ Date ______________

7E: Vocabulary Check (continued)

For use after Lesson 7-6

Write the vocabulary word or term for each definition. To check your work, fold the paper forward along the dotted line to see the correct answers.

a polygon with all sides congruent and all angles congruent ______________________

lines in the same plane that never intersect ______________________

a quadrilateral with exactly one pair of parallel sides ______________________

an angle with measure between 0° and 90° ______________________

the set of points in a plane that are all the same distance from a given point ______________________

Name ______________________ Class ______________ Date ______________

7F: Vocabulary Review Puzzle

For use with the Chapter Review

Study Skill Write assignments down; do not rely only on your memory.

Below is a list of clues grouped by the number of letters in the answer. Identify the word each clue represents, and fit each word into the puzzle grid.

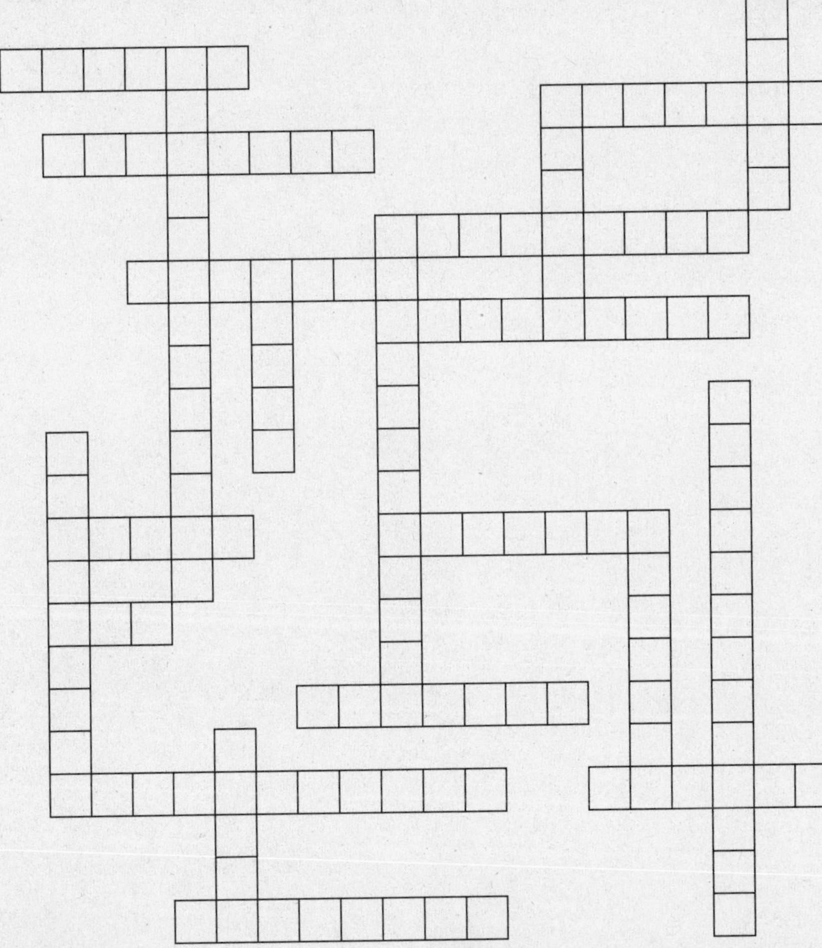

3 letters

- part of a circle

5 letters

- angle that measures between 0° and 90°
- formed by two rays with a common endpoint
- segment that has both endpoints on the circle
- flat surface that extends indefinitely in all directions

6 letters

- point of intersection of two sides on an angle or figure
- set of all points in a plane that are the same distance from a given point
- angle that measures between 90° and 180°

7 letters

- tool used to draw circles and arcs
- polygon with 10 sides
- type of triangle with no congruent sides
- polygon with all sides and angles congruent

8 letters

- point that divides a segment into two segments of equal length
- polygon with 5 sides

9 letters

- sides that have the same length
- type of triangle with at least two sides congruent
- parallelogram with four right angles
- quadrilateral with exacly one pair of parallel sides

11 letters

- triangle with three congruent sides

12 letters

- lines that have exactly one point in common

13 letters

- two angles whose sum is 180°
- two angles whose sum is 90°

Name ____________ Class ____________ Date ____________

Practice 8-1

Perimeter and Area of a Rectangle

Write an equation for the perimeter of each rectangle described below. Use w for the unknown width or l for the unknown length.

1. width = 5 cm

____

2. length = 3.5 ft

____

3. width = 32 m

____

4. Use the equation $P = 10.4 + 2w$ to find the perimeter of a rectangle with a width of 6 m.

____

5. Use the equation $P = 2l + 11.8$ to find the perimeter of a rectangle with a length of 7 ft.

____

For each figure below, write an expression for the area of the shaded region. Then evaluate each expression for $x = 2.5$.

6.

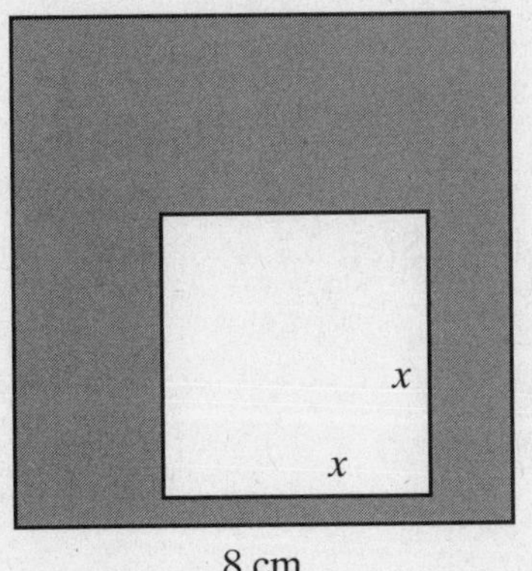

____

____

7.

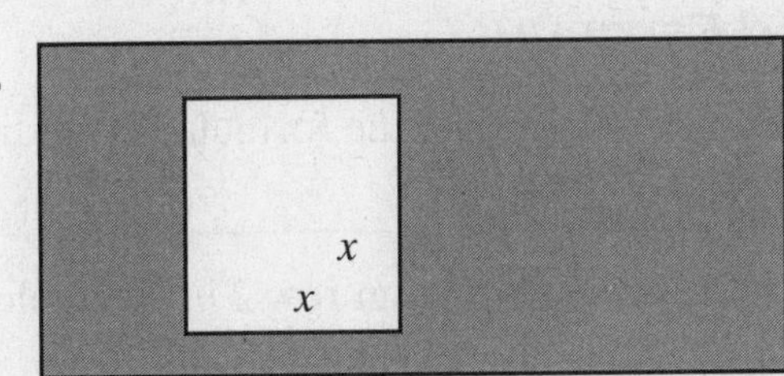

____

____

Use the formula $A = x^2$ to find the area of each square.

8. $x = 6.3$

____

9. $x = \frac{4}{7}$

____

10. $x = 2\frac{1}{3}$

____

11. Use the table at the right.

a. Find the width of the three other rectangles with a perimeter of 16 units.

b. Calculate the area for each rectangle.

c. Describe the rectangle that has the greatest area.

Length	Width	Perimeter	Area
1	7	16	7
2		16	
3		16	
4		16	

____

____

Name ______________________ Class ______________ Date ______________

8-1 • Guided Problem Solving

GPS Exercise 15:

Use the table at the right.

Length	Width	Perimeter	Area
1	9	20	9
2		20	16
3		20	
4		20	
5		20	

a. Find the width of the four other rectangles that also have a perimeter of 20 units.

b. Calculate the area for each rectangle.

c. Describe the rectangle that has the greatest area.

Understand

1. What does the table show? What are you being asked to do?

___

Plan and Carry Out

2. To solve Part (a), write the formula for finding the perimeter of a rectangle.

___

3. Substitute the values from row 2 in the table into your equation from Step 2.

___

4. Solve the equation you wrote in Step 3 to find the width for row 2. Repeat this process for all rows to complete the second column of the table.

5. To solve Part (b), write the formula for the area of a rectangle.

___

6. Substitute values from the table to find the missing areas. Write your answers in the table.

7. To solve Part (c), look at the Area column of the table. Which rectangle has the greatest area? Describe its dimensions.

___

Check

8. Substitute values from the table into the area and perimeter formulas. Are the equations true?

___

Solve Another Problem

9. Make a table showing the widths and areas of the rectangles with lengths 1, 2, and 3 and perimeter of 12. Which rectangle has the greatest area?

___

Practice 8-2

Area of a Parallelogram

Find the area of each parallelogram.

1. 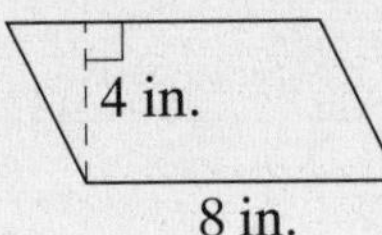

2. 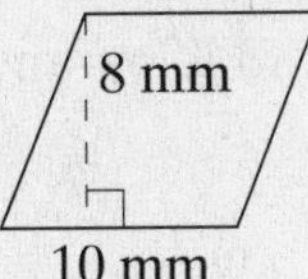

3. 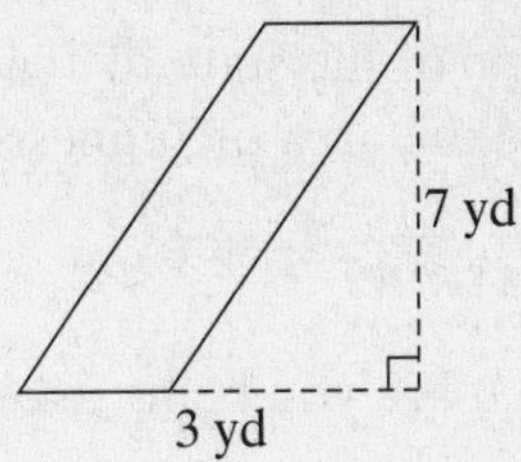

Find the perimeter of each parallelogram.

4. 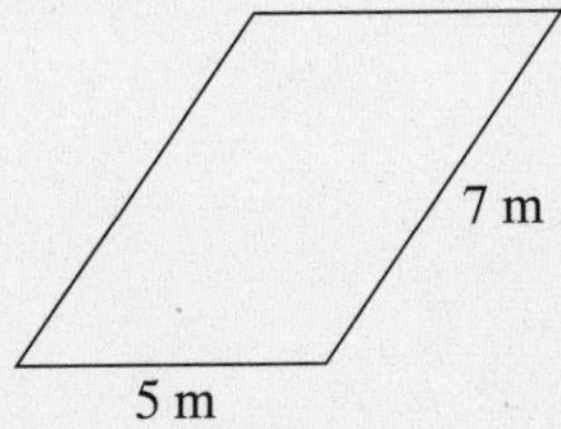

5. 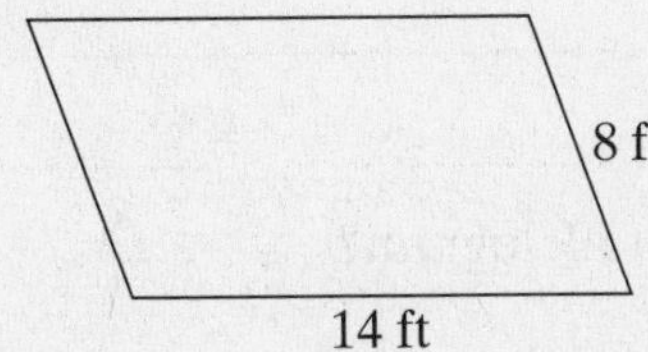

6. 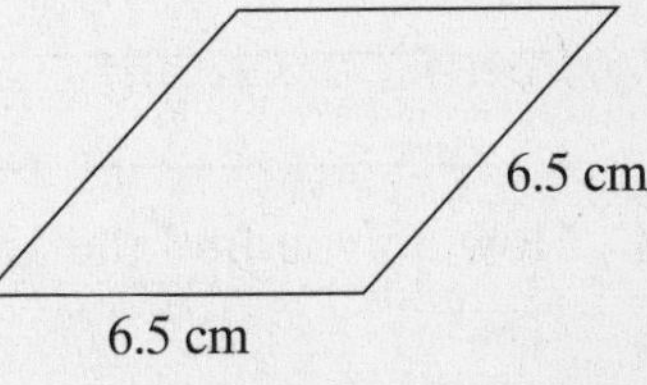

Find each area for base b and height h of a parallelogram.

7. $b = 16$ mm, $h = 12$ mm

8. $b = 23$ km, $h = 14$ km

9. $b = 65$ mi, $h = 4.8$ mi

10. $b = 1.9$ in., $h = 1.5$ in.

Solve.

11. The area of a parallelogram is 6 square units. Both the height and the length of the base are whole numbers. What are the possible lengths of the bases and heights?

12. The perimeter of a parallelogram is 72 m. The base of the parallelogram is 16 m. What is the length of the side of the parallelogram?

13. The area of a certain parallelogram is 288 yd^2. The base is 24 yd. If you double the base and the height, what will be the area of the new rectangle?

14. If you have 36 ft of fencing, what are the bases and side lengths of the different parallelograms you could enclose with the fencing? Consider only whole-number dimensions.

Name ______________________ Class ______________ Date ______________

8-2 • Guided Problem Solving

GPS Exercise 17:

The shape of the state of Tennesee is similar to a parallelogram. Estimate the area of Tennessee.

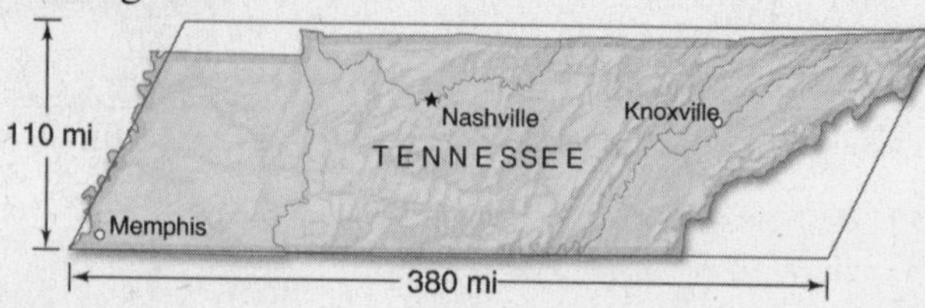

Understand

1. What are you being asked to do?

____

____

2. What shape is Tennessee similar to?

____

____

3. How do you find the area of a parallelogram?

____

____

____

Plan and Carry Out

4. What is the approximate height of Tennessee? __________
5. What is the approximate length of the base of Tennessee? __________
6. Substitute the values into the formula $A = bh$. __________
7. What is the approximate area of Tennessee? __________

Check

8. Is this estimate more or less than the actual area of Tennessee? Explain.

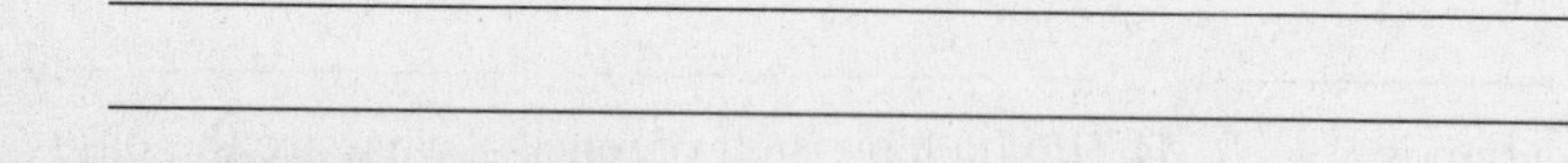

____

Solve Another Problem

9. Tamika's yard is similar to the shape of a parallelogram. Estimate the area of Tamika's yard.

____

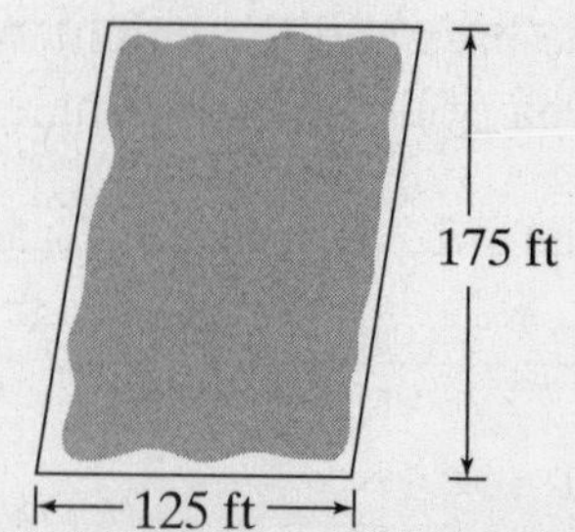

Name ______________ Class ______________ Date ______________

Practice 8-3

Perimeter and Area of a Triangle

Find the perimeter of each triangle.

1. 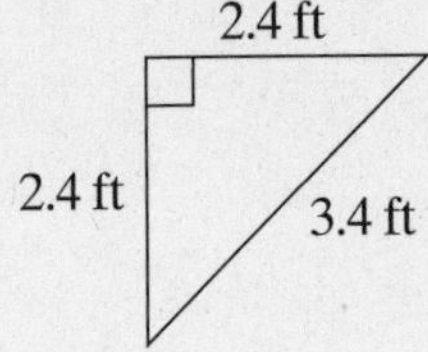

2. 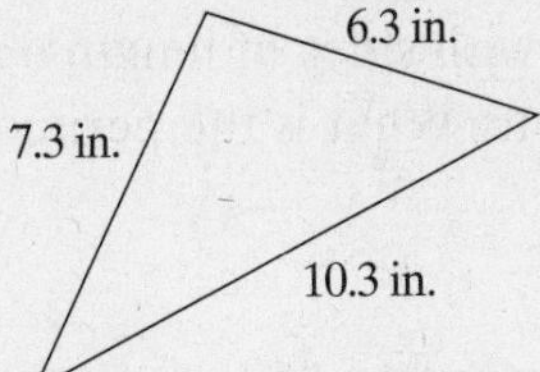

3. 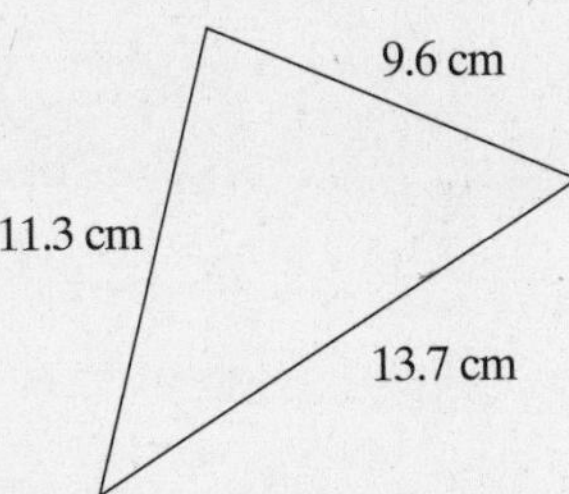

4. 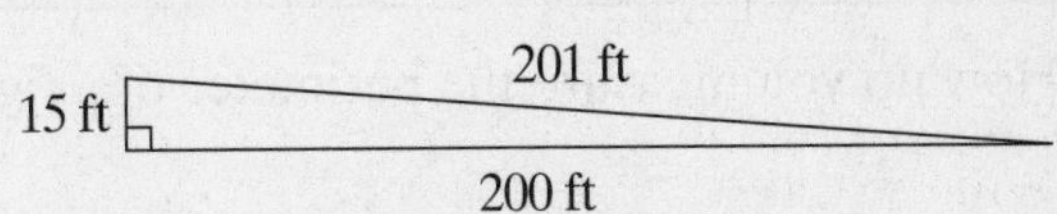

Find the area of each triangle.

5. 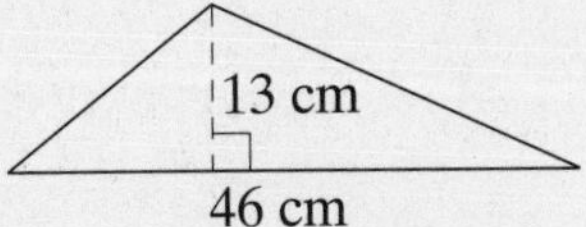

6. 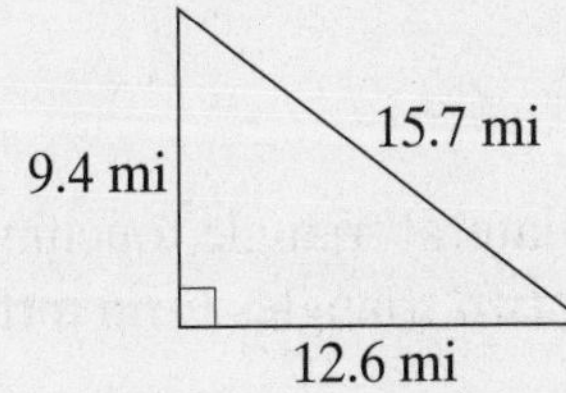

7. 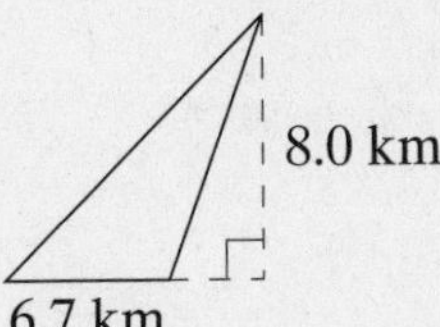

8. 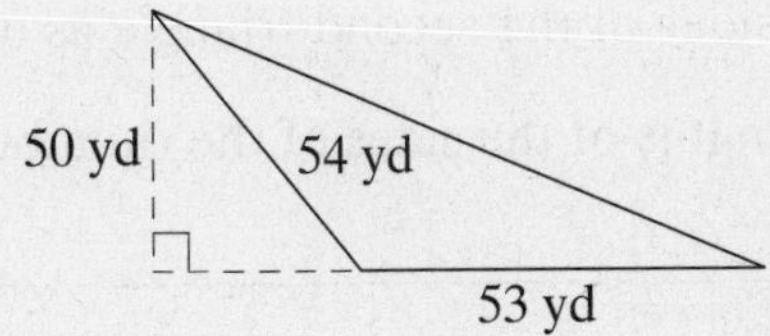

Find the area for base b and height h of each triangle.

9. $b = 5.1$ cm; $h = 7.7$ cm

10. $b = 14$ km; $h = 13$ km

11. $b = 11.5$ mi; $h = 9.2$ mi

Solve.

12. The side of an equilateral triangle has a length of 5.4 m. The height of the triangle is approximately 4.7 m. What are the perimeter and area of this triangle? Round your answers to the nearest tenth.

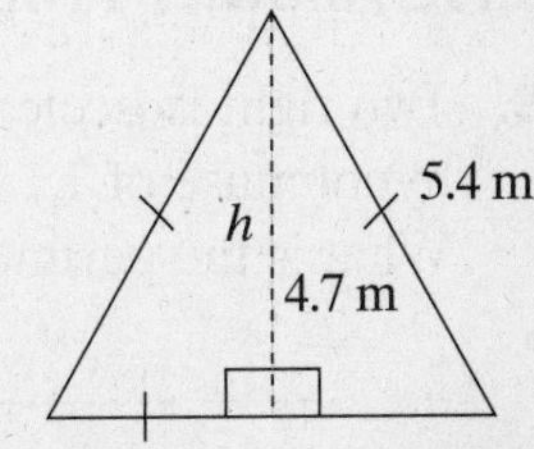

Name ______________________ Class ______________ Date ______________

8-3 • Guided Problem Solving

GPS Exercise 25:

Two equilateral triangles with sides of length 6 inches are joined together to form a rhombus. What is the perimeter of the rhombus?

Understand

1. What are you being asked to do?

____

2. How do you measure the perimeter of a figure?

____

3. What is an equilateral triangle?

____

Plan and Carry Out

4. In the space to the right, draw an equilateral triangle. Label all of its sides as 6 in.

5. Draw another equilateral triangle touching the first equilateral triangle so that the two triangles form a rhombus.

6. Label the sides of the second triangle as 6 in.

7. Add the lengths of the sides of the rhombus to find the perimeter.

____

Check

8. Count the number of sides that the rhombus has. Multiply this number by the length of the sides. Is this number the same as your answer?

____

Solve Another Problem

9. Two right isosceles triangles with legs of 5 in. length and a hypotenuse of 7.1 in. are joined together to make a square. What is the perimeter of the square?

____

Name ______________________ Class ______________ Date ______________

Practice 8-4

Circumference and Area of a Circle

Find the circumference and area of each circle. Round to the nearest tenth.

1.

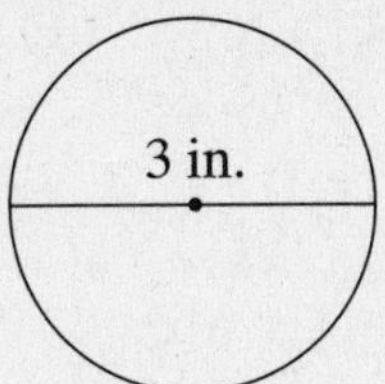

2.

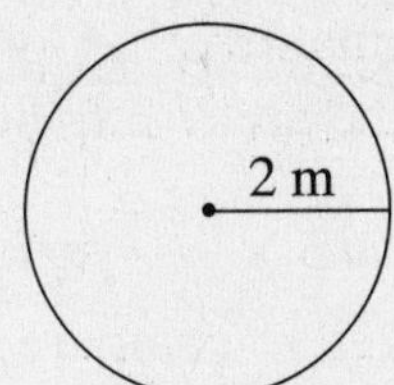

3.

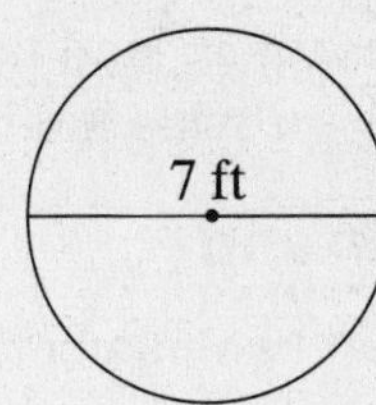

4.

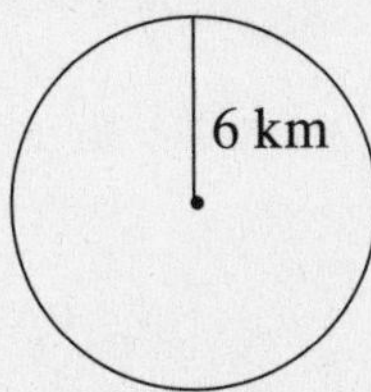

5.

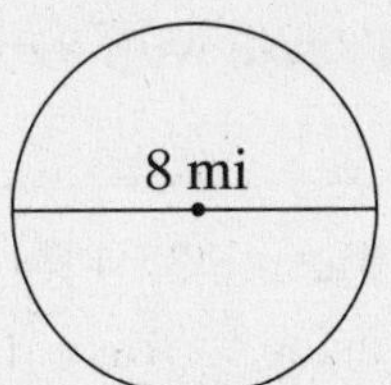

6.

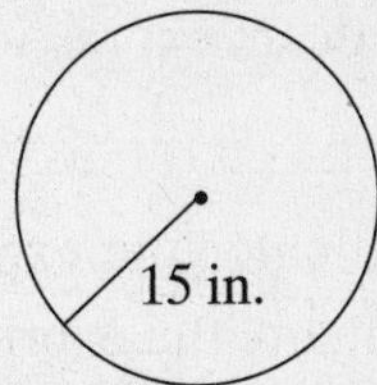

7.

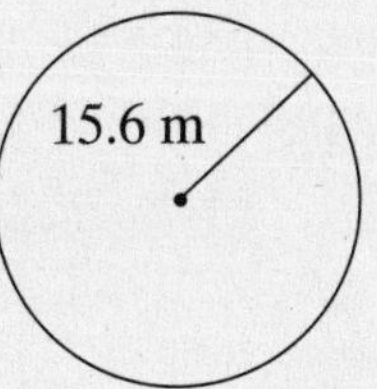

8.

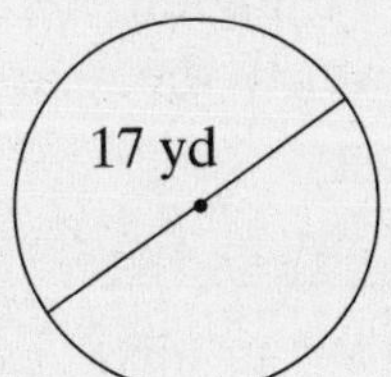

9.

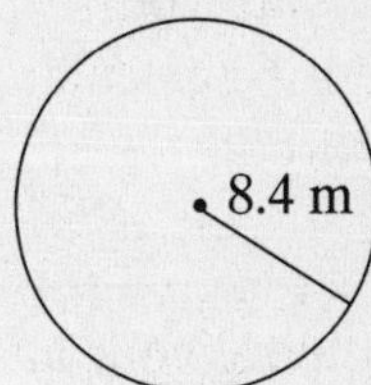

Use $\pi = \frac{22}{7}$ to estimate the circumference and area for each circle. When necessary, round to the nearest tenth.

10. $r = 35$ in.

11. $r = \frac{14}{15}$ km

12. $d = 33$ cm

13. In the diagram at the right, the radius of the large circle is 8 in. The radius of each of the smaller circles is 1 in. Find the area of the shaded region to the nearest square unit.

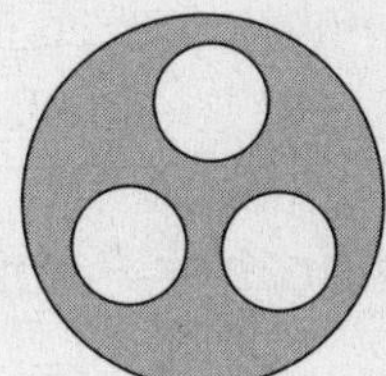

Name ______________________ Class ______________ Date ______________

8-4 • Guided Problem Solving

GPS Exercise 23:

Find the area of a circle with a radius of 12 cm, using 3.14 and $\frac{22}{7}$ as estimates for π. Find the area using a calculator value for π. Does 3.14 or $\frac{22}{7}$ provide the better estimate of the area? Explain.

Understand

1. What two numbers are you being asked to compare?

____

Plan and Carry Out

2. Write an expression for the area of a circle with a radius of 12.

____

3. Evaluate your expression from Step 2 using 3.14 for π. Then evaluate the expression from Step 2 using $\frac{22}{7}$ for π. Round your answers to the nearest hundredth.

____

4. Evaluate your expression from Step 2 using the π key on a scientific calculator. Round your answer to the nearest hundredth.

____

5. Compare your answers from Step 3 to your answer to Step 4. Which of the two is closer to your answer to Step 5?

____

6. Is 3.14 or $\frac{22}{7}$ a more accurate estimate for π? Explain.

____

Check

7. Divide 22 by 7 and round to the nearest ten-thousandth. Compare this number and 3.1400 to the number your calculator uses for π. Which is closer?

____

Solve Another Problem

8. Find the area of a circle with a radius of 7 in., using 3.14 and $\frac{22}{7}$ as estimates for π. Find the area using a calculator value for π. Does 3.14 or $\frac{22}{7}$ provide the better estimate of the area?

____

Name ______________________ Class ______________ Date ______________

Practice 8-5

Three-Dimensional Figures

Name each figure.

1. 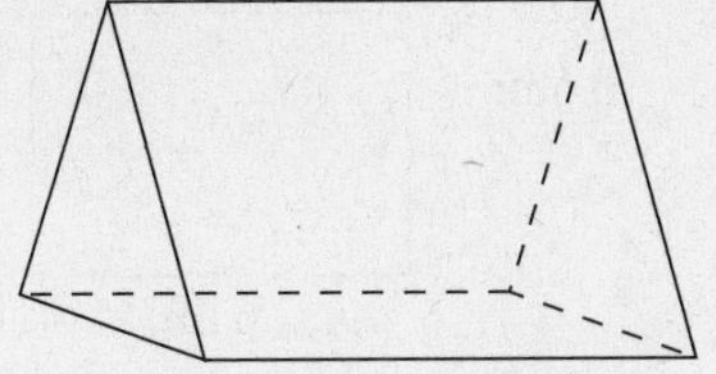

2. 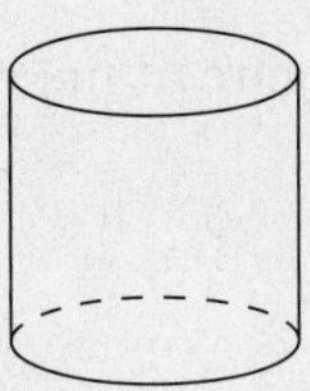

3. 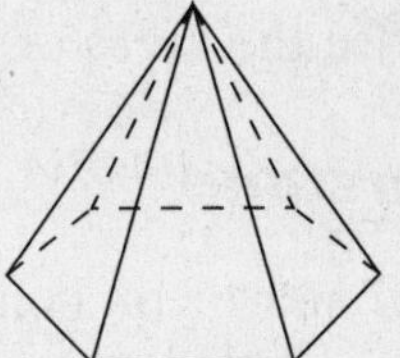

4. 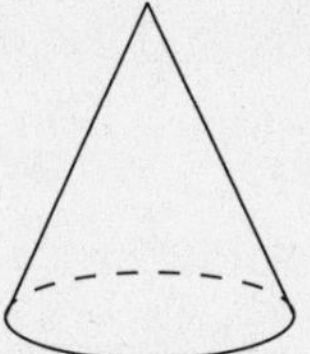

5. 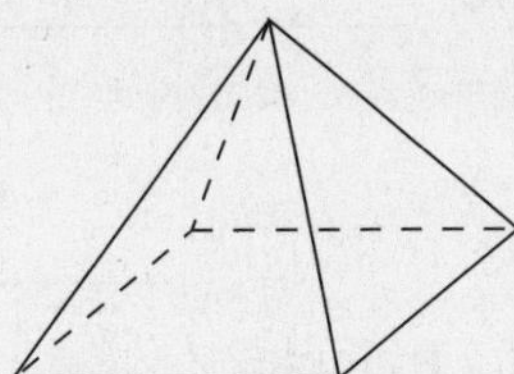

6. 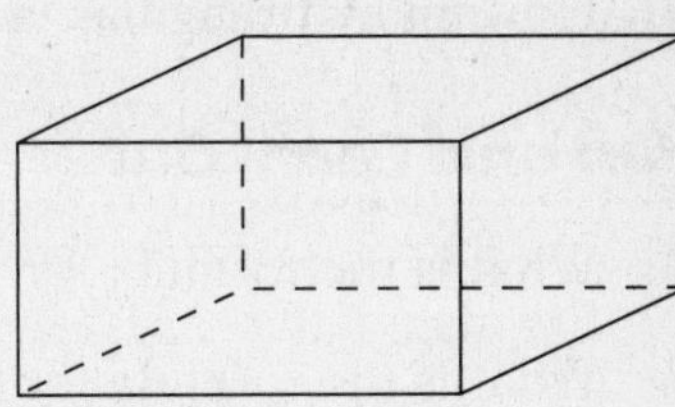

Draw each figure named.

7. a triangular pyramid

8. a square prism

9. a cone

10. a pentagonal pyramid

Name ______________________ Class ______________ Date ______________

8-5 • Guided Problem Solving

GPS Exercise 23:

What are the areas of all the faces of the figure at the right?

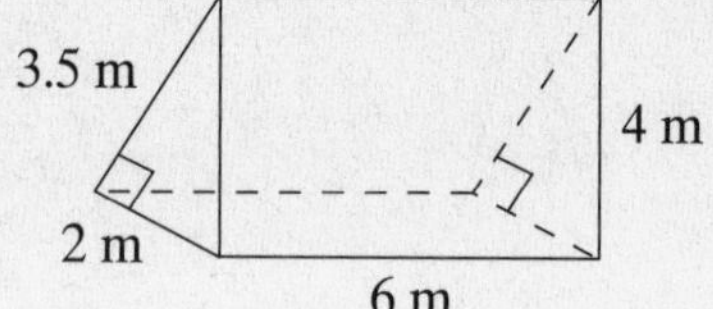

Understand

1. What are you being asked to do?

____

2. How many rectangular faces are there? ______________

3. How many triangular faces are there? ______________

Plan and Carry Out

4. What is the formula for the area of a rectangle? ______________

5. What is the formula for the area of a triangle? ______________

6. What are the dimensions of the triangular faces?

____

7. What is the area of one triangular face? ______________

8. What is the area of all the triangular faces? ______________

9. What are the dimensions of each rectangular face?

____

10. What is the area of each rectangular face?

____

11. Find the total area of the base and faces of the figure.

____

Check

12. Did you find the area of each face? How many faces are there?

____

Solve Another Problem

13. A rectangular solid has a base 11 in., height 15 in., and a length of 6 in. Find the total area of all faces.

____

____

Name ______________________ Class ______________ Date ____________

Practice 8-6

Surface Areas of Prisms and Cylinders

Draw a net for each three-dimensional figure.

1. 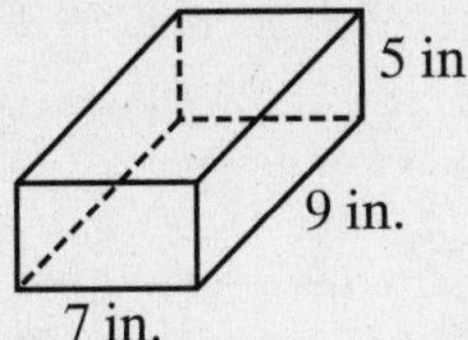

2. 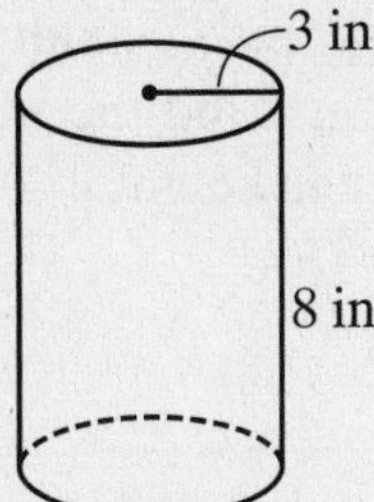

Find the surface area of each prism.

3. 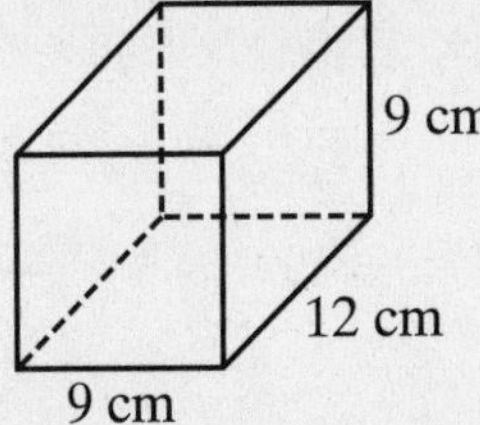

____

4. 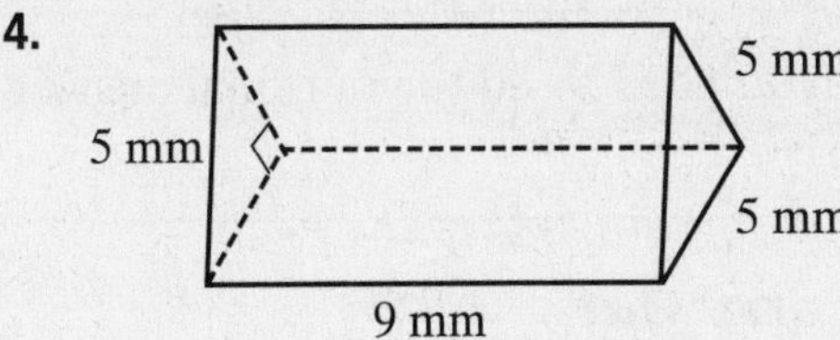

____

5. 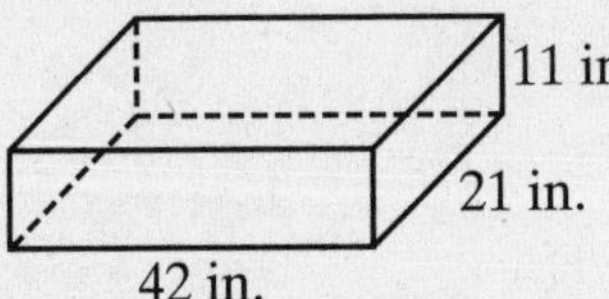

____

6. 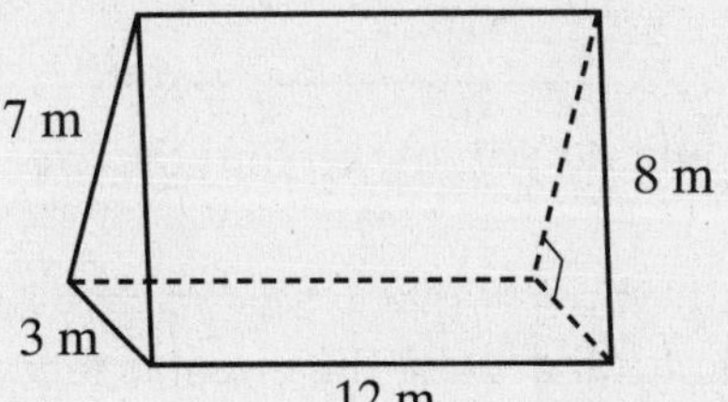

____

Find the surface area of each cylinder. Round to the nearest tenth.

7. 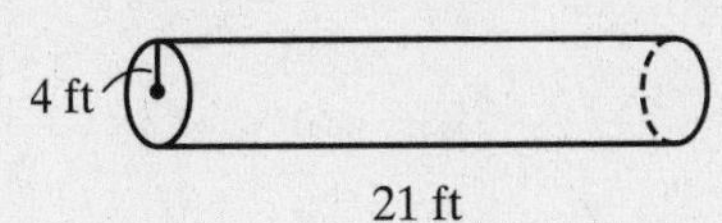

____

8. 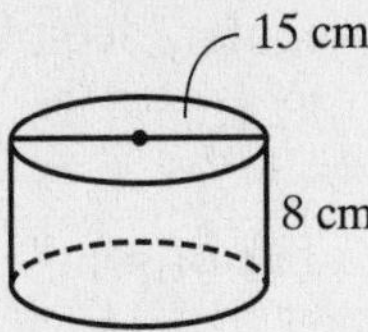

____

9. 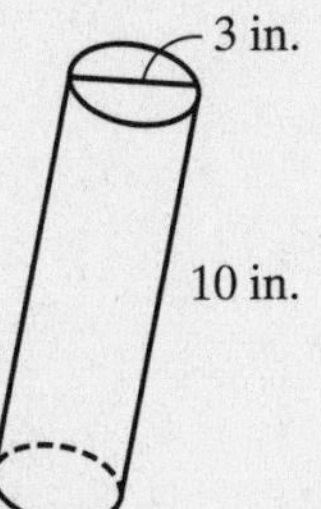

____

10. 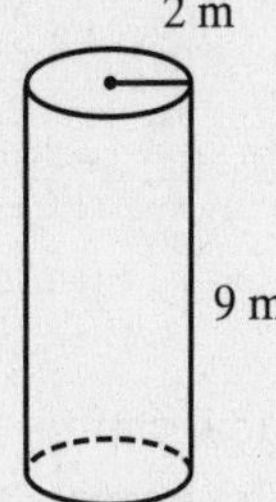

____

Name ______________________ Class ______________ Date ______________

8-6 • Guided Problem Solving

GPS Exercise 23:

A cosmetics company that makes small cylindrical bars of soap wraps the bars in plastic prior to shipping. Find the surface area of a bar of soap if the diameter is 5 cm and the height is 2 cm. Round to the nearest tenth.

Understand

1. What are you being asked to do?

____

2. What do you need to do to your final answer?

____

Plan and Carry Out

3. How do you find the surface area of a cylinder?

____

____

4. What formula do you use to find the area of a circular face?

____

5. What is the total area of the circular faces of a bar of soap?

____

6. What formula do you use to find the area of the rectangular face?

____

7. What is the area of the rectangular face of a bar of soap?

____

8. What is the surface area of a bar of soap? ______________

Check

9. Did you find the area of all the surfaces of a bar of soap? Does your answer check?

____

Solve Another Problem

10. Find the surface area of a cylindrical candle if the diameter is 6 in. and the height is 8 in. Round to the nearest tenth.

____

Name ______________________ Class ______________ Date ____________

Practice 8-7

Volumes of Prisms and Cylinders

Find the volume of each rectangular prism.

1. 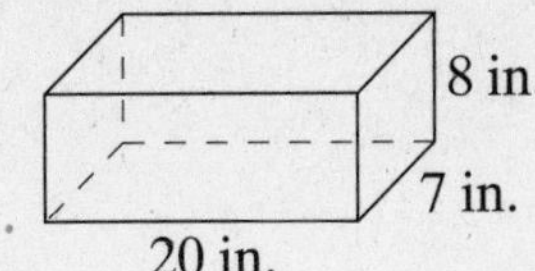

2. 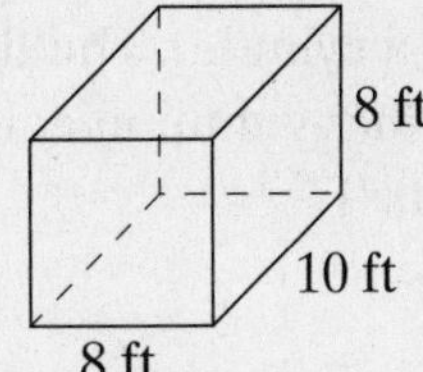

3. 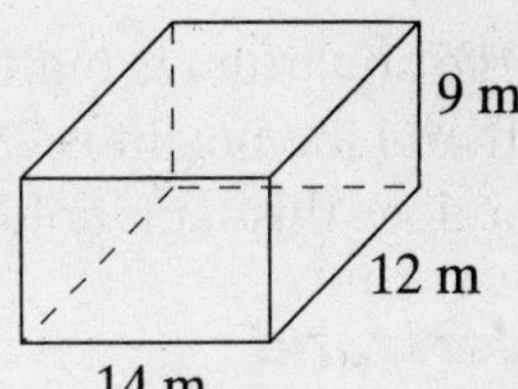

Find the volume of each triangular prism.

4. 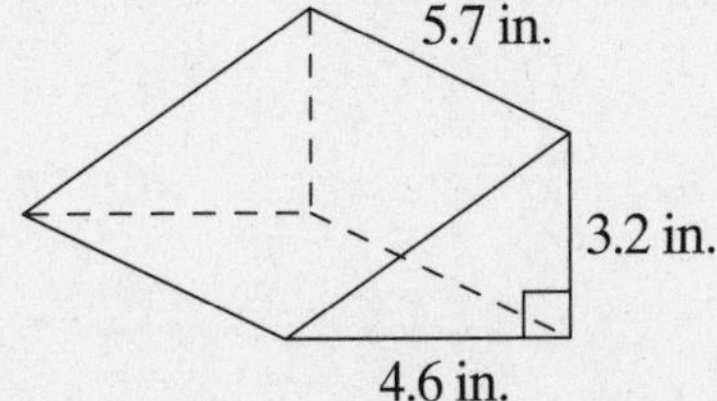

5. 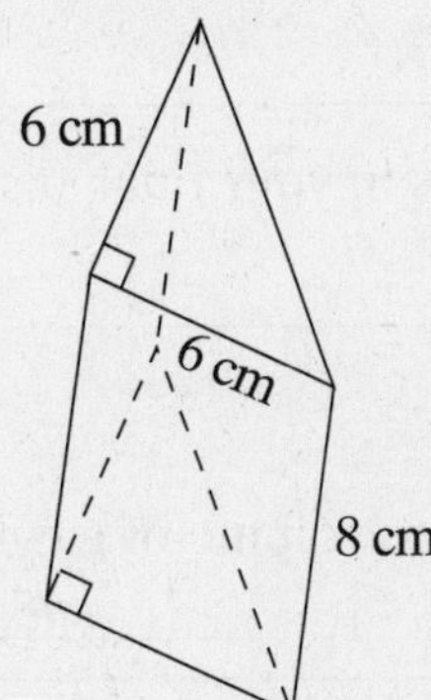

6. 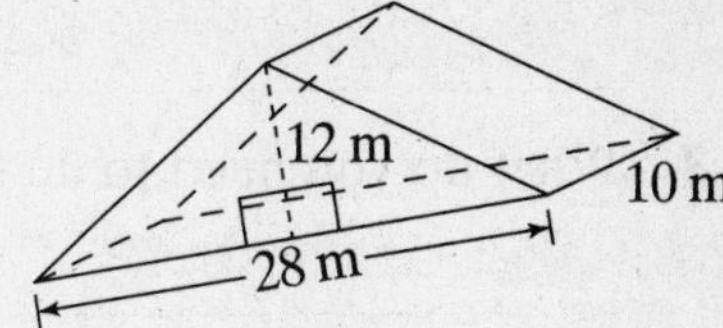

Estimate the volume of each cylinder. Then find the volume to the nearest cubic unit.

7. 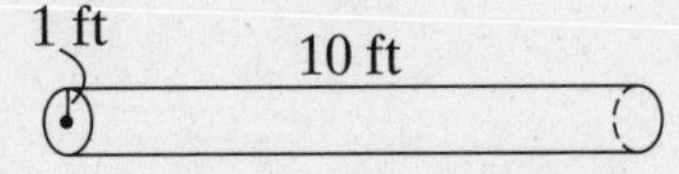

8. 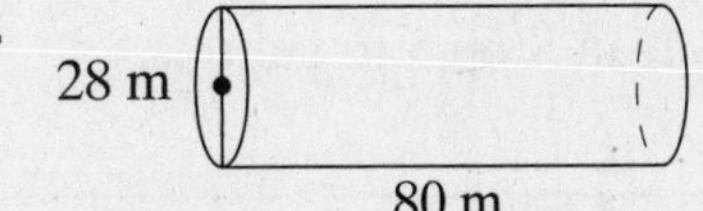

9. 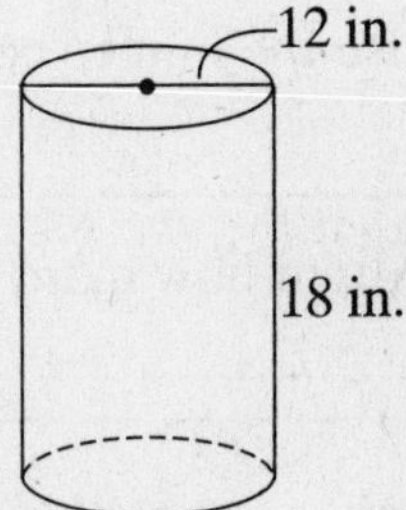

Find the height of each rectangular prism.

10. $V = 122{,}500\ \text{cm}^3$
$l = 50$ cm
$w = 35$ cm

11. $V = 22.05\ \text{ft}^3$
$l = 3.5$ ft
$w = 4.2$ ft

12. $V = 3{,}375\ \text{m}^3$
$l = 15$ m
$w = 15$ m

Name ______________________ Class ______________ Date ______________

8-7 • Guided Problem Solving

GPS Exercise 21:

A large aquarium is built in the shape of a cylinder. The diameter is 203 ft and the height is 25 ft. About how many million gallons of water does this tank hold? (1 gal ≈ 231 in.^{3})

Understand

1. Circle the information you will need to solve the problem.
2. What are you being asked to do?

____

____

3. What do you need to do to the units in your final answer?

____

Plan and Carry Out

4. Write the formula you use to find the volume of a cylinder.

____

5. Find the volume of the aquarium in cubic feet.

____

6. Convert the answer in Step 4 to cubic inches.

____

7. Use the hint to convert the answer in Step 5 to gallons.

____

8. About how many million gallons does the tank hold?

____

Check

9. Estimate the answer by using 3 for π, 200 ft for the diameter, and 1 gal ≈ 230 in.^{3}. Does your answer make sense? Check.

____

____

Solve Another Problem

10. The diameter of a tank is 26 cm, and the height is 58 cm. About how many liters of fuel oil can this steel tank hold? (1,000 cm^3 = 1L)

____

Name ______________________ Class ______________ Date ______________

8A: Graphic Organizer

For use before Lesson 8-1

Study Skill Take a few minutes to relax before and after studying. Your mind will absorb and retain more information if you alternate studying with brief rest intervals.

Write your answers.

1. What is the chapter title? ______________________
2. How many lessons are there in this chapter? ______________________
3. What is the topic of the Test-Taking Strategies page? ______________________
4. Complete the graphic organizer below as you work through the chapter.
   - In the center, write the title of the chapter.
   - When you begin a lesson, write the lesson name in a rectangle.
   - When you complete a lesson, write a skill or key concept in a circle linked to that lesson block.
   - When you complete the chapter, use this graphic organizer to help you review.

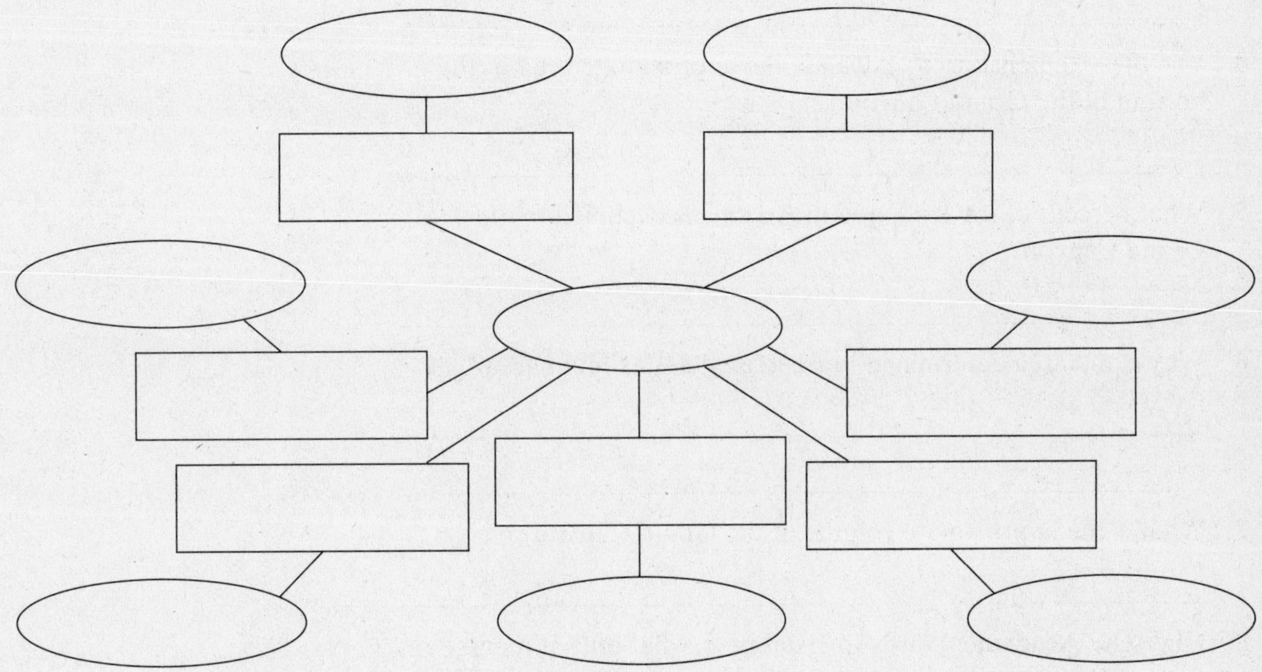

Name ______________________ Class ______________ Date ______________

8B: Reading Comprehension

For use after Lesson 8-6

Study Skill Learning to read for detail takes practice. As you read your notes, underline or highlight important information.

Read the paragraph and answer the questions.

The Grand Canyon was formed by the Colorado River in Arizona. It is estimated to be nearly 10 million years old. With a length of 277 miles, the Grand Canyon is nearly 18 miles wide at its widest point and one mile deep in some places. Arizona, called the Grand Canyon State, has a total land area of approximately 113,000 square miles.

1. What is the paragraph about?

____

2. How old is the Grand Canyon?

____

3. What dimensions are given for the Grand Canyon?

____

4. Use these dimensions to calculate the approximate area of the bottom of the Grand Canyon.

____

5. What percent of the land area in Arizona is occupied by the Grand Canyon?

____

6. Why is the area determined in Exercise 4 a maximum area?

____

____

7. What is the approximate volume of the Grand Canyon?

____

8. **High-Use Academic Words** In Exercise 4, what does it mean to *calculate?*

   a. to determine by mathematical processes　　b. to show that you recognize something

8C: Reading/Writing Math Symbols

For use after Lesson 8-7

Study Skill After completing an assignment, take a break. Then, come back and check your work.

State whether each of the following units represents length, area or volume.

1. cm^2 ____________
2. $in.^3$ ____________
3. mi ____________
4. ft^2 ____________
5. km ____________
6. mm^3 ____________

State whether each expression can be used to calculate length, area, or volume and to what shapes each applies.

7. $\frac{1}{2}bh$ ____________
8. lwh ____________
9. bh ____________
10. πd ____________
11. πr^2 ____________
12. s^2 ____________
13. $2l + 2w$ ____________
14. $\pi r^2 h$ ____________
15. $2\pi r$ ____________

Name ______________________ Class ______________ Date ______________

8D: Visual Vocabulary Practice

For use after Lesson 8-7

Study Skill When interpreting an illustration, look for the most specific concept represented.

Concept List

circumference	base	cone
net	faces	edges
vertices	prism	pyramid

Write the concept that best describes each exercise. Choose from the concept list above.

1.

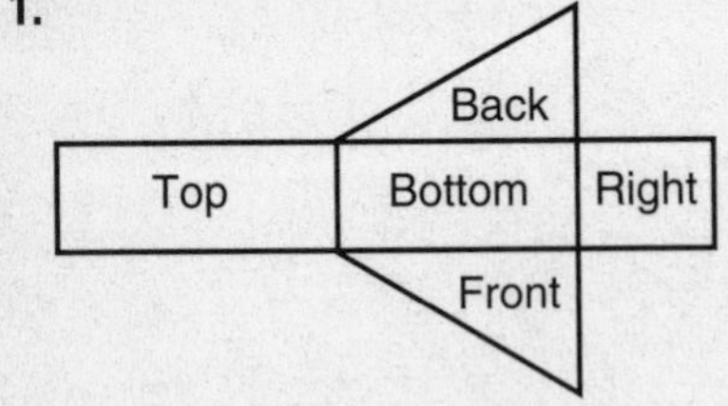

____

2.

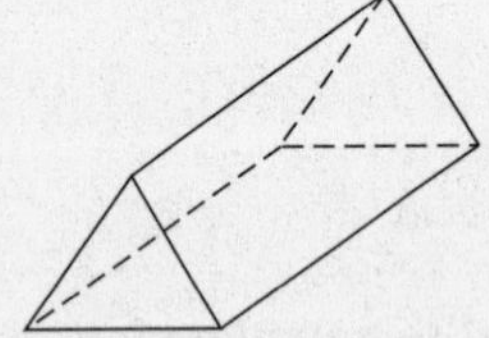

____

3.

Circle P is one for this cylinder.

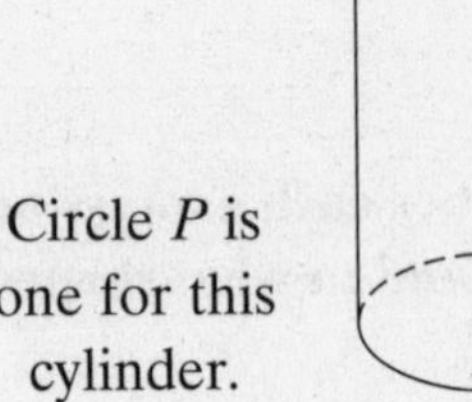

____

4.

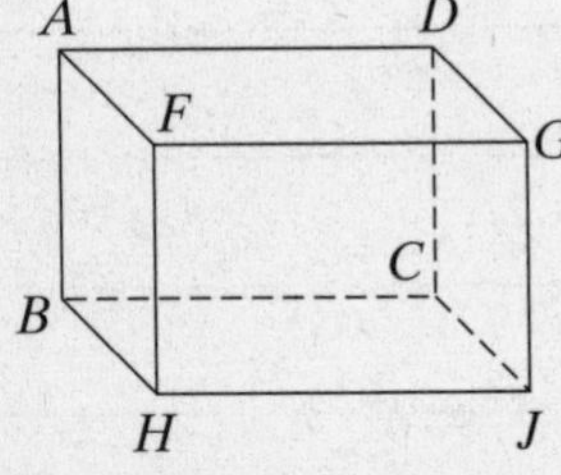

$\overline{AB}$ and $\overline{CJ}$ are examples.

____

5.

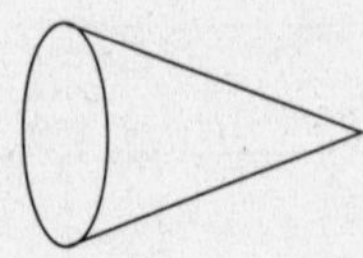

____

6.

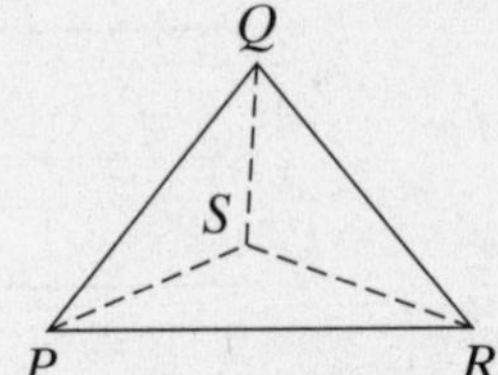

There are four of these in this three-dimensional figure.

____

7.

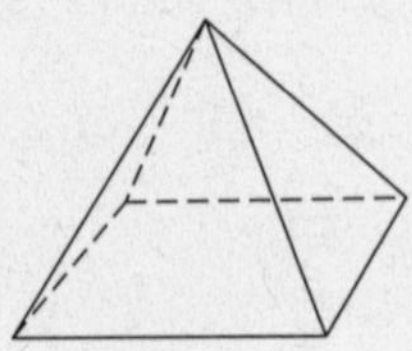

____

8.

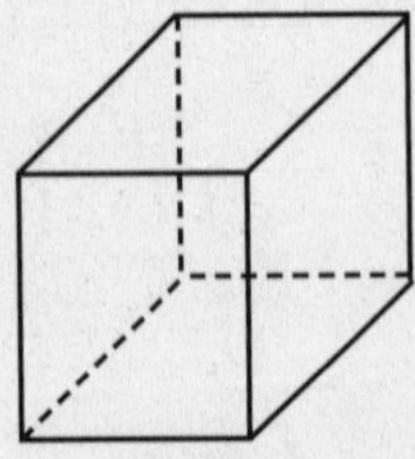

There are six of these in this three-dimensional figure.

____

9.

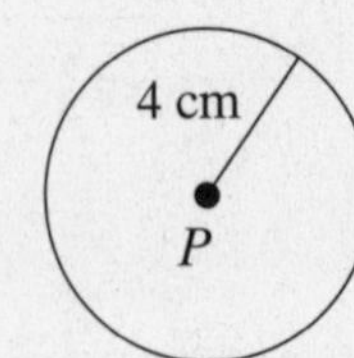

$C \approx 25.1$ cm

____

Name ______________________ Class ______________ Date ______________

8E: Vocabulary Check

For use after Lesson 8-7

Study Skill Strengthen your vocabulary. Use these pages and add cues and summaries by applying the Cornell Notetaking style.

Write the definition for each word or term at the right. To check your work, fold the paper back along the dotted line to see the correct answers.

______________________	net
______________________	face
______________________	area
______________________	volume
______________________	prism

Name ______________________ Class ______________ Date ______________

8E: Vocabulary Check (continued)

For use after Lesson 8-7

Write the vocabulary word or term for each definition. To check your work, fold the paper forward along the dotted line to see the correct answers.

a pattern you can fold to form a three-dimensional figure ______________________

a flat surface of a three-dimensional figure that is shaped like a polygon ______________________

the number of square units a figure encloses ______________________

the number of cubic units needed to fill the space inside a three-dimensional figure ______________________

a three-dimensional figure with two parallel and congruent polygonal faces, called bases ______________________

8F: Vocabulary Review

For use with the Chapter Review

Study Skill Participating in class discussions will help you remember new material. Do not be afraid to express your thoughts when your teacher asks for questions, answers, or discussion.

Circle the word that best completes the sentence.

1. A pentagon with five congruent sides and five congruent angles is (*regular*, *isosceles*).
2. (*Parallel, Skew*) lines lie in the same plane and do not intersect.
3. A (*solution, statement*) is a value of a variable that makes an equation true.
4. Angles with equal measures are (*similar, congruent*).
5. (*Complementary, Supplementary*) angles are two angles whose sum is 90°.
6. A (*circle, sphere*) is the set of all points in space that are the same distance from a center point.
7. The perimeter of a circle is the (*circumference, circumcenter*).
8. The (*area, volume*) of a figure is the number of square units it encloses.
9. A(n) (*isosceles, scalene*) triangle has no congruent sides.
10. A (*rhombus, square*) is a parallelogram with four right angles and four congruent sides.
11. A (*map*, *net*) is a two-dimensional pattern you can fold to form a three-dimensional figure.
12. A (*pyramid, prism*) is a three-dimensional figure with triangular faces that meet at one point.
13. A speed limit of 65 mi/h is an example of a (*ratio, rate*).
14. A (*cone, cylinder*) has two congruent parallel bases that are circles.

Name ______________________ Class ______________ Date ______________

Practice 9-1

Patterns and Graphs

1. The table shows the costs of packages containing writable CDs. Graph the data in the table.

Number of CDs	10	20	50	100	200
Cost ($)	10	15	25	40	75

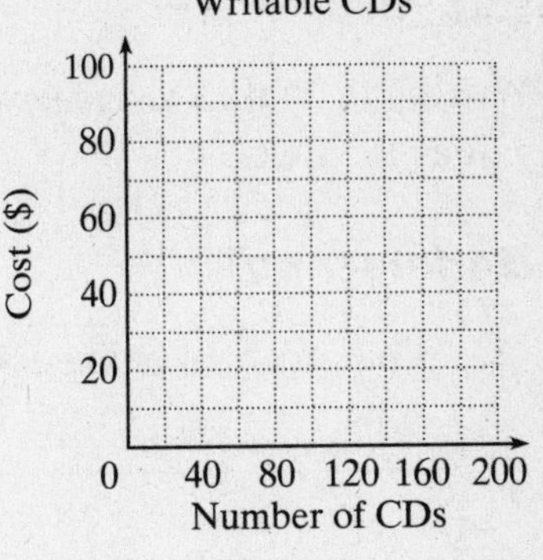

The graph shows the 2005 median income of some year-round workers and the number of years of school. The trend line is shown. Use this graph for Exercises 2–3.

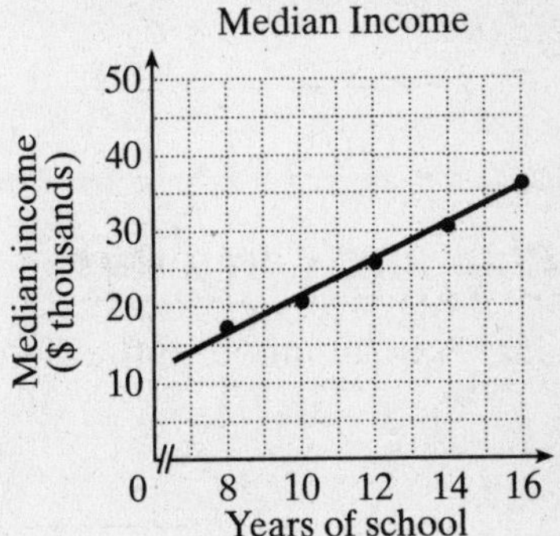

2. Predict the median income for the workers who have spent 20 years in school.

____

3. Do you think you can use this graph to predict the median salary for workers who have spent less than 8 years in school? Explain.

____

____

The table shows average monthly temperatures in degrees Fahrenheit for American cities in January and July. Use this information for Exercises 4–5.

City	Seattle	Boise	Chicago	LA	New York	Anchorage
Jan.	39.1	29.9	21.4	56.0	31.8	13.0
Jul.	64.8	74.6	73.0	69.0	76.4	58.1

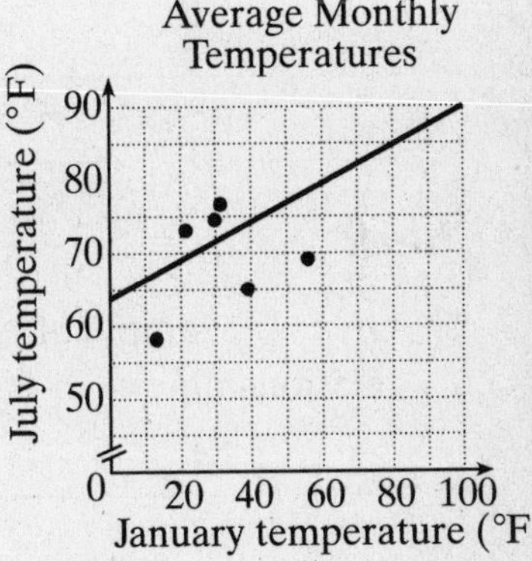

4. Graph the data in the table.

5. Use your graph to estimate the July temperature of a city whose average January temperature is 10°F.

____

Name ________________ Class ________ Date ________

9-1 • Guided Problem Solving

GPS Exercise 16:

Writing in Math Describe what a graph looks like when both sets of values increase.

Understand

1. What are you being asked to do?

____

____

2. What does the phrase *both sets of values* mean?

____

____

Plan and Carry Out

3. As you move to the right, what happens to the horizontal values of the points?

____

4. As you move to the right, what happens to the corresponding vertical values of the points?

____

5. Describe what a graph looks like when both sets of values increase.

____

____

Check

6. Give an example of two quantities that would have this relationship.

____

____

Solve Another Problem

7. Describe what a graph looks like when only the vertical values decrease as the horizontal values increase.

____

____

Name ______________________ Class ______________ Date ______________

Practice 9-2

Patterns and Tables

Complete each table.

1.

Time (h)	1	2	3	4	7
Distance cycled (mi)	8	16	24	32	

2.

Time (min)	1	2	3	4	7
Distance from surface of water (yd)	−3	−2	−1	0	

Write an expression to describe each sequence. Then find the 100th term.

3. 35, 36, 37, . . .

Expression: ____________

100th term: ____________

4. 8, 10, 12, 14, . . .

Expression: ____________

100th term: ____________

Find the values of the missing entries in each table.

5.

m	4	6		10
n	24	26	28	

6.

p	2		10	14
q	1	13	25	

7. A pattern of squares is shown.

a. Sketch the 4th and 5th figure in this pattern. ____________________

b. Make a table comparing the figure number to the number of squares. Write an expression for the number of squares in the nth figure.

c. How many squares would there be in the 80th figure? ____________

Write an expression to describe each sequence. Then find the 20th term.

8. 6, 12, 18, 24, . . .

Expression: ____________

20th term: ____________

9. 3, 6, 9, 12, . . .

Expression: ____________

20th term: ____________

10. One month's average price for ground beef is $2.39 per pound. Using this relationship, make a table that shows the price for 1, 2, 3, and 4 pounds of ground beef.

Name ______________________ Class ______________ Date ______________

9-2 • Guided Problem Solving

GPS Exercise 18:

The table shows costs for violin lessons. Complete the table.

Time (h)	0.5	1	1.5	2
Cost ($)	24.50			

Understand

1. In which row is the cost of a violin lesson?

____

2. What information is given in the first column of the table?

____

3. What are you being asked to do?

____

Plan and Carry Out

4. How much is a 0.5-hour lesson? __________

5. What is the relationship between 0.5 and 1? __________

6. Use the same relationship you found in Step 5 to find the cost of a 1-hour lesson. __________

7. What amount should you add to the answer in Step 6 to find the cost of a 1.5-hour lesson? __________

8. How much does a 1.5-hour lesson cost? __________

9. How much does a 2-hour lesson cost? __________

Check

10. Explain how you could use multiplication in this problem.

____

____

____

Solve Another Problem

11. The table shows costs for math tutoring. Complete the table.

Time (h)	0.5	1	1.5	2
Cost ($)	19.75			

Name ______ Class ______ Date ______

Practice 9-3

Function Rules

Use each function rule. Find y for $x = 1, 2, 3$, and 4.

1. $y = 2x$ ______

2. $y = x + 4$ ______

3. $y = x^2 - 1$ ______

4. $y = -2x$ ______

5. $y = 3x + 1$ ______

6. $y = 8 - 3x$ ______

7. $y = 6 + 4x$ ______

8. $y = x - 5$ ______

9. $y = 2x + 7$ ______

Write a rule for the function represented by each table.

10.

x	y
1	6
2	7
3	8
4	9

______

11.

x	y
1	4
2	8
3	12
4	16

______

12.

x	y
1	−6
2	−9
3	−12
4	−15

______

13.

x	y
1	5
2	7
3	9
4	11

______

14.

x	y
1	4
2	7
3	10
4	13

______

15.

x	y
1	−1
2	−3
3	−5
4	−7

______

16. A typist types 45 words per minute.

a. Write a function rule to represent the relationship between the number of typed words and the time in which they are typed. ______

b. How many words can the typist type in 25 minutes? ______

c. How long would it take the typist to type 20,025 words? ______

Name ______________________ Class ______________ Date ______________

9-3 • Guided Problem Solving

Exercise 23:

Suppose you put $.50 in a piggy bank on July 1, $1.00 on July 2, $1.50 on July 3, and so on. Use n to represent the date. Write a function rule for the amount you put in for any date in July.

Understand

1. What is a function rule?

____

____

2. What are you being asked to do?

____

____

Plan and Carry Out

3. What are the inputs? ______________
4. What are the outputs? ______________
5. What variable represents the inputs? ______________
6. What is the relationship between the amount of money you put in the piggy bank on the first day and number of the day, July 1? July 2?

____

7. What do you do to n to figure out how much money to put in the piggy bank? ______________
8. Write a function rule for the amount, a, you put in for *any* date in July. ______________

Check

9. Check that your rule works with days July 1, 2, and 3.

____

Solve Another Problem

10. Suppose your parents paid you $.10 on December 1, $.20 on December 2, $.30 on December 3, and so on. Use n to represent the date. Write a function rule for the amount your parents will pay you for any date in December.

____

Name ______________________ Class ______________ Date ______________

Practice 9-4

Using Tables, Rules, and Graphs

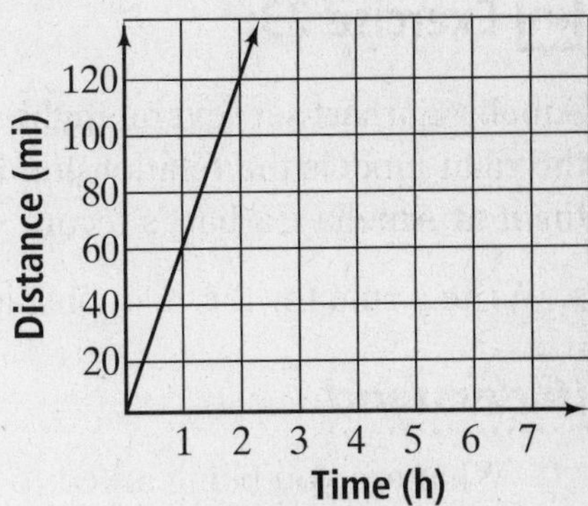

The graph at the right shows the relationship between distance and time for a car driven at a constant speed.

1. What is the speed? ______________

2. Is this a function relationship? ______________

3. If this is a function, write a rule to represent it.

____

4. Make a table for the function, listing six input/output pairs.

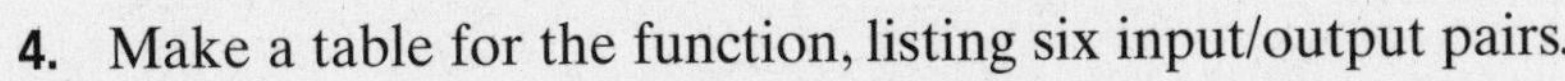

Graph each rule. Use x-values of 1, 2, 3, 4, and 5.

5. $y = -\frac{1}{2}x$

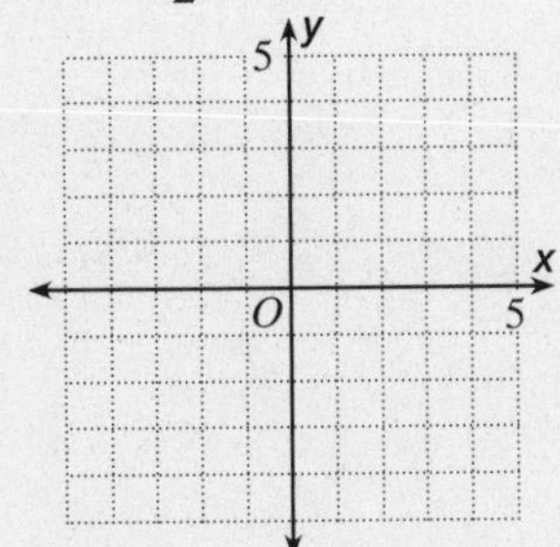

6. $y = -2x + 4$

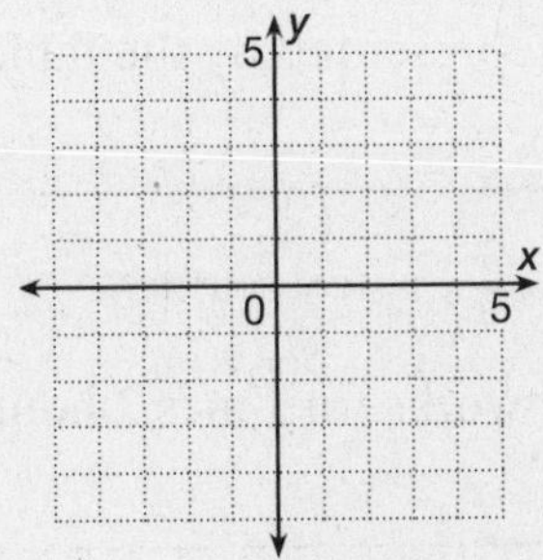

7. The relationship between the amount of time a zebra runs at maximum speed and the distance it covers is shown.

Time (min)	3	6	9	12	15
Distance (mi)	2	4	6	8	10

a. Write an equation to describe this relationship.

____

b. Use the equation to find the distance the zebra would travel in 48 minutes.

____

Name ______________________ Class ______________ Date ______________

9-4 • Guided Problem Solving

GPS Exercise 23:

Amelia Earhart set several flight speed records. The table at the right models the relationship between distance and time for a flight at Amelia Earhart's record speed.

Amelia Earhart's Flight

Time (h)	Distance (mi)
2	362
4	724
6	1,086
8	1,448

a. Write a rule for the relationship represented by the table.

Understand

1. What are you being asked to do?

____

____

Plan and Carry Out

2. How many miles did Earhart travel in 2 h?

____

3. How many miles did Earhart travel in 1 h?

____

4. What are the inputs? What are the outputs?

____

5. Use d to represent distance and t to represent time. Write a rule for the relationship represented by the table.

____

Check

6. Check that your rule works for times 2 hours, 4 hours, and 6 hours.

____

Solve Another Problem

7. On February 20, 1962, John Glenn flew the *Friendship 7* spacecraft on the first manned orbital mission of the United States. He completed three orbits around the earth, reaching a maximum orbital velocity of approximately 17,500 miles per hour. Write a rule for the relationship of Glenn's distance d and time t at this speed.

____

Name ____________ Class ____________ Date ____________

Practice 9-5

Graphing Linear Equations

Tell whether each ordered pair is a solution of $y = x - 4$.

1. $(0, -4)$ ________ 2. $(5, -1)$ ________ 3. $(-3, -7)$ ________ 4. $(-7, -3)$ ________

Find three solutions for each equation.

5. $y = x + 5$ ____________________
6. $y = -x + 7$ ____________________
7. $y = 2x - 1$ ____________________

Graph each linear equation.

8. $y = 3x - 1$

9. $y = -2x + 1$

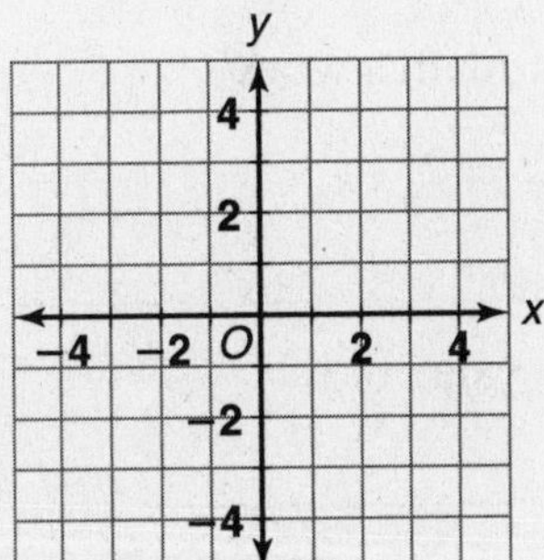

10. $y = 2x - 4$

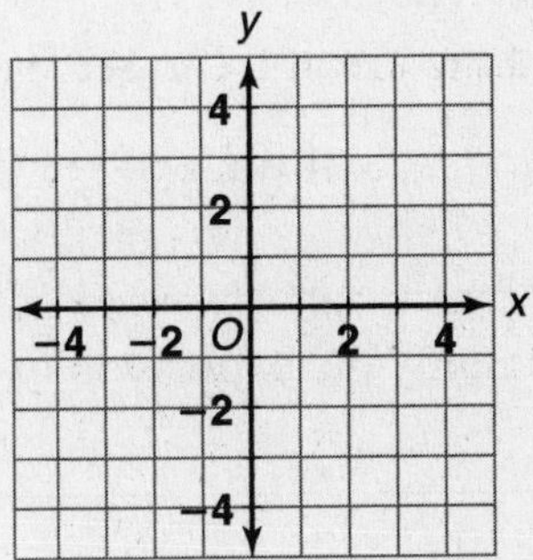

11. The graph of $y = -x$ passes through which quadrants?

____

12. Use the graph below to determine the coordinates of the point that is a solution of the equations of lines p and q.

____

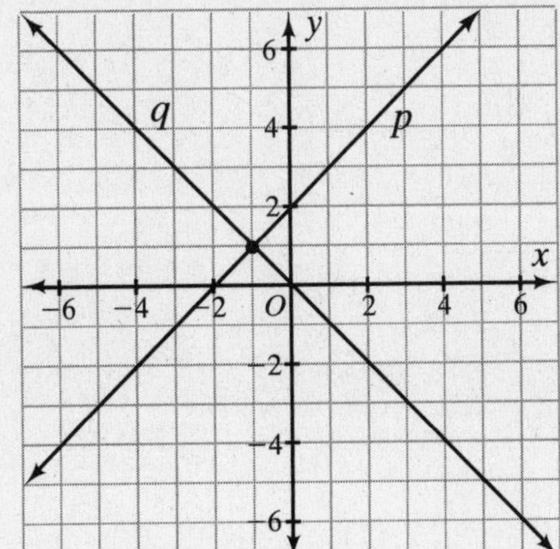

Name ______________________ Class ______________ Date ______________

9-5 • Guided Problem Solving

GPS Exercise 32:

Error Analysis A student says that $(-1, -5)$ is a solution of $y = -3x - 2$. What error do you think the student made?

Understand

1. Is $(-1, -5)$ a correct solution to the equation? How do you know this from just reading the question?

____

____

Plan and Carry Out

To find the error, try to recreate the student's work.

2. First, substitute $x = -1$ into $-3x - 2$.

____

3. Simplify the expression to find the value of y.

____

4. Would your answer be different if you simplified $-3(-1)$ to -3 incorrectly and then subtracted 2? What would you get?

____

5. What mistake do you think the student made?

____

Check

6. What if the student substituted -5 for y and then solved the equation? Solve the problem this way and identify an error the student could make to get $x = -1$.

____

Solve Another Problem

7. A student gives $(2, -9)$ as a solution to the equation $y = 2x - 5$. What error do you think the student made?

____

____

Name ______________________ Class ______________ Date ____________

9A: Graphic Organizer

For use before Lesson 9-1

Study Skill Many skills build on each other, particularly in mathematics. Before you begin a new lesson, do a quick review of the material you covered in earlier lessons. Make sure you ask for help when there are concepts you did not understand or do not remember.

Write your answers.

1. What is the chapter title?

____

2. How many lessons are there in this chapter?

____

3. What is the topic of the Test-Taking Strategies page?

____

4. Complete the graphic organizer below as you work through the chapter.

- In the center, write the title of the chapter.
- When you begin a lesson, write the lesson name in a rectangle.
- When you complete a lesson, write a skill or key concept in a circle linked to that lesson block.
- When you complete the chapter, use this graphic organizer to help you review.

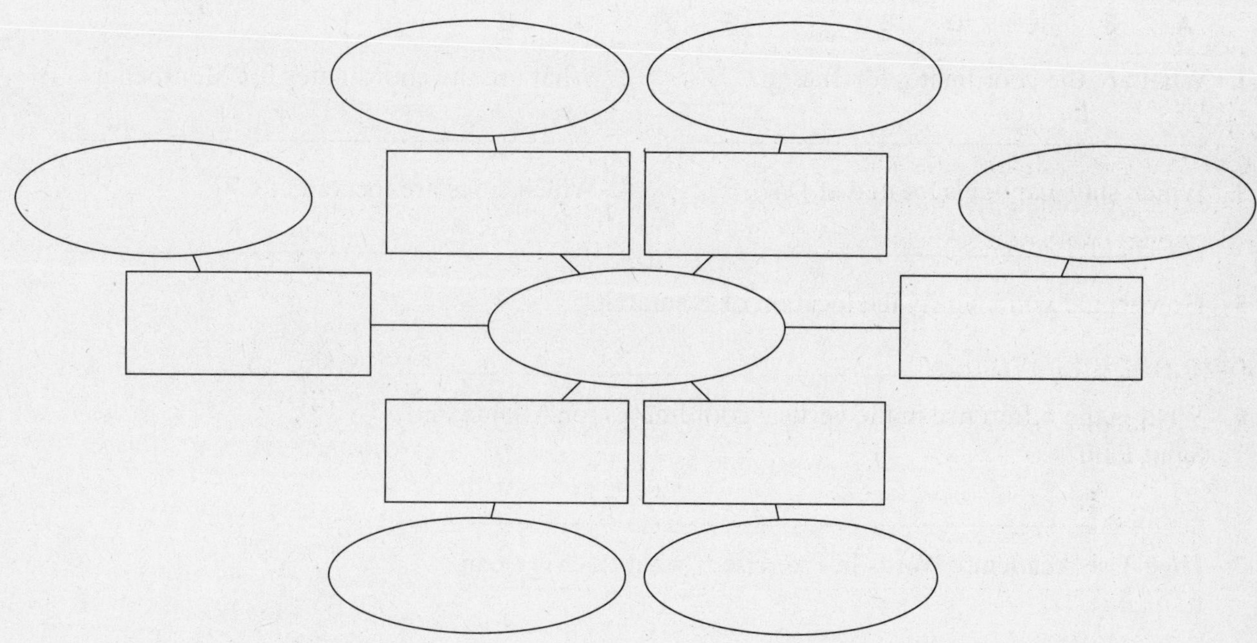

Name ____________________ Class ____________ Date ____________

9B: Reading Comprehension

For use after Lesson 9-4

Study Skill Go to class prepared. Always bring your textbook, notebook or paper, and a pencil, unless your teacher tells you otherwise.

Below is a coordinate map of the midwestern and eastern United States. The horizontal scale uses letters and the vertical scale uses numbers to identify various locations. Use the map to answer the questions below. Letters are typically written first, followed by numbers.

1. What are the coordinates for Tucson?

   ____

2. What are the coordinates for Montpelier?

   ____

3. Which state capital is located at D4?

   ____

4. Which cities are located at C7?

   ____

5. How would you identify the location of Bismarck?

   ____

6. What is the difference in the vertical coordinates for Atlanta and Saint Paul?

   ____

7. **High-Use Academic Words** In Exercise 5, what does it mean to *identify*?

   a. to come together to form a single unit
   b. to show that you recognize something

Name ______________________ Class ______________ Date ______________

9C: Reading/Writing Math Symbols

For use after Lesson 9-4

Study Skill Using mathematical symbols is a great way to take notes more quickly. Other symbols are helpful as well, such as these: @ (at), w/ (with), # (number), and = (equal).

Write each mathematical statement in words.

1. $x^2 = 0.25$

2. $MN = 3$

3. $y = 3x$

4. $(4 + (-7)) = -3$

5. $4:5 = 8:10$

6. $m\angle B \neq 30°$

7. $\frac{x}{3} \neq \frac{6}{9}$

8. $y \neq 3(x^2)$

9. $60\% = \frac{60}{100}$

10. $5^2 = 25$

11. $\triangle EFG \sim \triangle KLM$

12. $\frac{25}{6} \approx 4.17$

13. $y = x + 4$

14. $\frac{2}{3} \neq \frac{4}{6}$

Name ____________________ Class ______________ Date ______________

9D: Visual Vocabulary Practice

For use after Lesson 9-5

High-Use Academic Words

Study Skill When you feel you're getting frustrated, take a break.

Concept List

name	classify	acronym
measure	rule	symbolize
dimensions	abbreviate	property

Write the concept that best describes each exercise. Choose from the concept list above.

1. $a + b = b + a$

____

2.

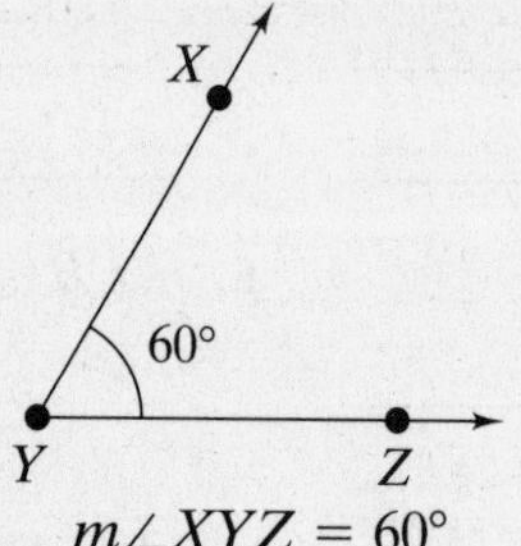

$m\angle XYZ = 60°$

____

3. Trapezoids, rectangles, and parallelograms are all quadrilaterals; circles and octagons are not.

____

4. $l \times w \times h$

____

5. Write oz for ounces.

____

6.

is equal to	$=$
is similar to	$\sim$
is less than	$<$

____

7.

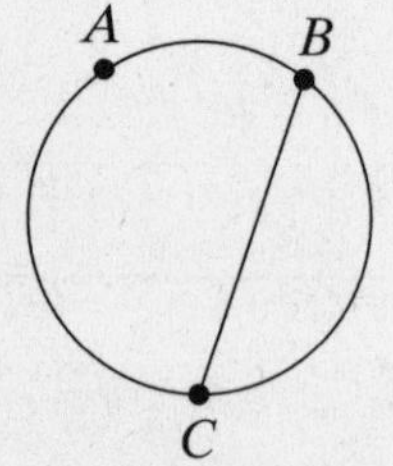

Three arcs are $\overset{\frown}{AB}$, $\overset{\frown}{ABC}$, and $\overset{\frown}{BC}$.

____

8. $f(x) = 2x + 1$

____

9. Write GCD for greatest common divisor.

____

9E: Vocabulary Check

For use after Lesson 9-5

Study Skill Strengthen your vocabulary. Use these pages and add cues and summaries by applying the Cornell Notetaking style.

Write the definition for each word or term at the right. To check your work, fold the paper back along the dotted line to see the correct answers.

______________________	ordered pair
______________________	linear equation
______________________	origin
______________________	function
______________________	sequence

Name ______________________ Class ______________ Date ______________

9E: Vocabulary Check (continued)

For use after Lesson 9-5

Write the vocabulary word or term for each definition. To check your work, fold the paper forward along the dotted line to see the correct answers.

a pair (x, y) that gives the coordinates of a point ______________________

an equation where the graph of the solutions lies on a line ______________________

the point where the x-axis and y-axis meet ______________________

a relationship that assigns exactly one output value for each input value ______________________

a set of numbers that follow a pattern ______________________

Name ______________________ Class ______________ Date ______________

9F: Vocabulary Review Puzzle

For use with the Chapter Review

Study Skill Have a dictionary or a textbook's glossary available while you are studying. Look up any unknown words.

Find the words in the puzzle from the definitions. Circle them. Words can be forwards, backwards, up, down, or diagonally.

Y	R	A	T	N	E	M	E	L	P	M	O	C	I	P	I	A	U	D
B	X	T	F	Q	X	E	L	A	P	I	C	N	I	R	P	B	Y	L
F	S	N	Y	E	Q	D	P	D	I	A	M	E	T	E	R	R	E	X
C	I	X	Z	G	C	T	A	O	L	W	X	H	R	M	V	F	P	S
Q	C	Y	N	A	M	N	S	F	I	P	B	B	O	M	U	P	I	E
B	O	S	D	J	R	F	E	L	I	N	E	A	R	P	Y	H	D	Q
U	N	L	M	G	O	U	N	R	H	N	A	C	C	O	U	Q	Q	U
V	E	A	R	C	V	N	G	P	E	E	O	R	U	J	F	P	S	E
T	H	W	L	H	O	C	I	C	E	F	C	G	O	C	W	U	E	N
N	V	W	Y	Q	L	T	L	O	H	Y	M	N	A	P	Z	D	Q	C
I	G	E	U	P	U	I	X	N	Z	L	I	U	A	X	T	D	U	E
O	T	L	D	X	M	O	D	G	G	V	P	L	C	L	E	W	E	I
P	P	C	R	J	E	N	I	R	U	I	M	L	C	R	A	H	N	C
D	V	R	O	N	N	K	M	U	J	S	O	Z	R	O	I	B	C	Z
I	U	I	H	O	D	R	A	E	X	S	J	Q	I	E	J	C	E	L
M	G	C	C	G	K	B	R	N	P	E	R	I	M	E	T	E	R	C
J	E	B	A	A	Y	T	Y	T	T	Y	S	M	Y	E	O	F	F	B
R	I	B	Z	C	Q	P	P	Q	U	X	I	Z	A	D	L	E	E	R
S	C	X	C	E	W	X	K	H	O	Q	R	J	J	E	P	E	A	X
A	O	O	Q	D	D	E	L	G	N	A	U	M	Q	W	B	T	E	Y

Definitions

- three dimensional figure with only one base
- the total distance around a figure
- a polygon with 10 sides
- set of numbers that follows a pattern
- a segment passing through the center of a circle, with endpoints on the circle
- the number of cubic units needed to fill the space inside a figure
- an equation where the graph of all solutions lies on a line
- set of all points in a plane that are the same distance from a given point
- a polygon with six sides
- this figure is made of two rays with a common endpoint
- a part of a circle
- a set of numbers that follow a pattern
- the principal plus interest
- distance around a circle
- segment that has both endpoints on the circle
- figures that have the same size and shape
- two angles whose sum is 90 degrees
- relationship that assigns exactly one output value for each input value
- the amount of money that you deposit or borrow
- a figure with one vertex and one circular base

Practice 10-1

Making Data Displays

Use the table at the right for Exercises 1 and 2.

Trampoline Sales		
Month	**2005**	**2006**
January	17	15
February	25	22
March	30	33
April	24	30
May	30	35

1. Make a bar graph to display trampoline sales in 2005.

2. Make a line graph to display trampoline sales in 2006.

3. The list below shows the height of the players on a basketball team in inches.

72	74	72	78	67	80	72	75	78	74	75	70	82

Make a frequency table and a histogram of the data above.

4. The list below shows the amounts that different people spent at a grocery store.

\$54.17	\$10.35	\$112.53	\$78.30	\$189.01	\$42.04	\$62.59
\$50.31	\$4.92	\$92.48	\$63.38	\$29.57	\$48.05	\$145.20

Make a frequency table and a histogram of the data above using four intervals.

5. a. Make a graph to display the data shown in the table at the right.

b. What kind of graph did you use? Explain your reasoning.

____

____

August Rainfall	
Town	**Rainfall (in.)**
Brownsville	3.5
Lafayette	5
Tillery	2
Grady	7

Name ______________________ Class ______________ Date ____________

10-1 • Guided Problem Solving

GPS Exercise 10:

a. Make a histogram using each set of data below.

Age of Contestants

Intervals	Years
20–34	21, 28, 25
35–49	39, 36
50–64	57, 55

Age of Contestants

Intervals	Years
20–29	21, 28, 25
30–39	39, 36
40–49	
50–59	57, 55

b. Compare the histograms. Do you think the data is better represented using 3 or 4 intervals? Explain your reasoning.

Understand

1. What are you being asked to do?

____

Plan and Carry Out

2. On a separate sheet of paper, make a histogram using the first table above.
3. Make a histogram using the second table above.
4. Look at the histograms you drew. What information is available in the second graph that is not available in the first graph?

____

5. For this data, do you think it is more useful to use 3 or 4 intervals? Explain your reasoning.

____

____

Check

6. Compare the total number of participants in the two tables. Did you find the same number for each graph?

____

Solve Another Problem

7. Make a table of the same data set using 8 equal-sized intervals. Do you think that a histogram using this table would represent the data better than the histograms above? Explain your reasoning.

____

Name ______________________ Class ______________ Date ______________

Practice 10-2

Analyzing Data Displays

Use the bar graph at the right for Exercises 1–3.

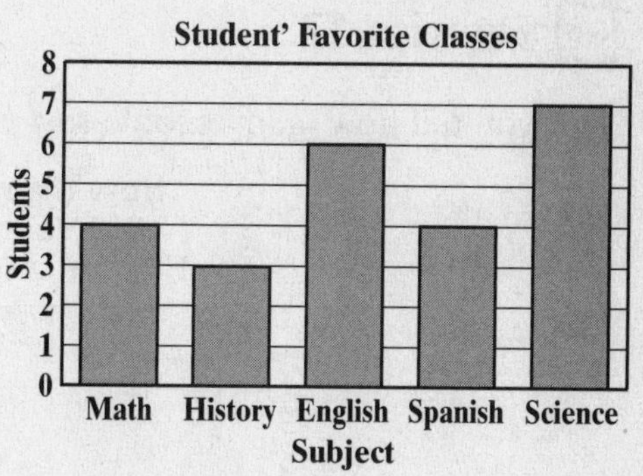

1. How many students' favorite class was math or science?

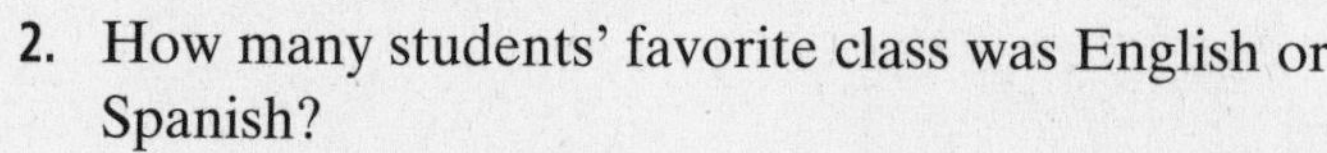

2. How many students' favorite class was English or Spanish?

3. How many more students like English best than like math best?

Use the line graph at the right for Exercises 4–6.

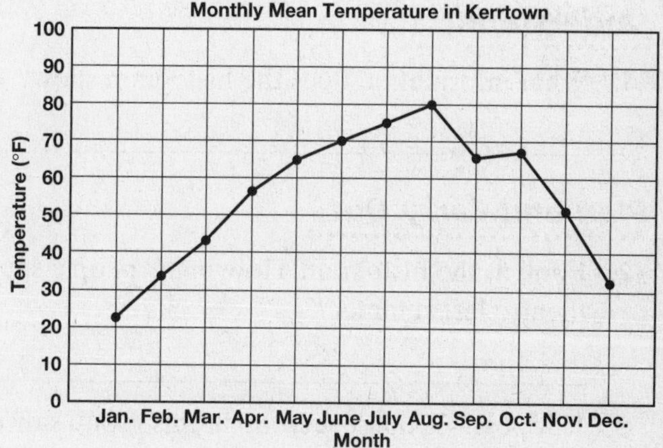

4. Between which two months did the mean temperature in Kerrtown change the least?

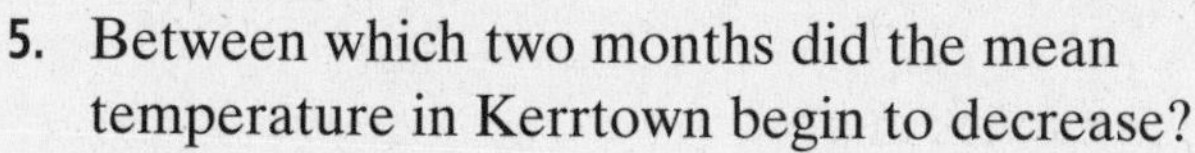

5. Between which two months did the mean temperature in Kerrtown begin to decrease?

6. In which month was the mean temperature in Kerrtown greatest?

Use the histogram at the right for Exercises 7–9.

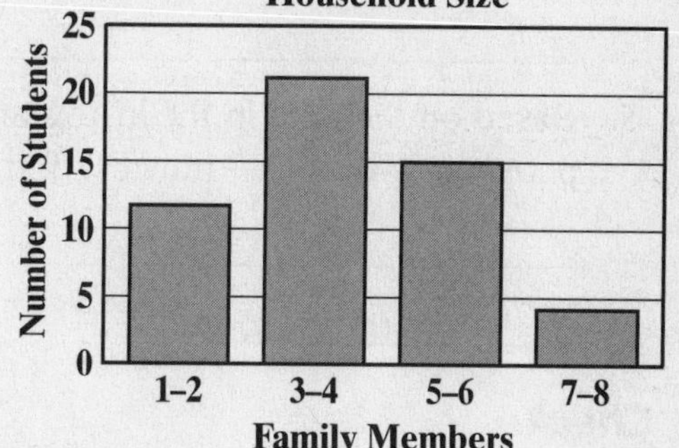

7. About how many students have families with fewer than 5 members?

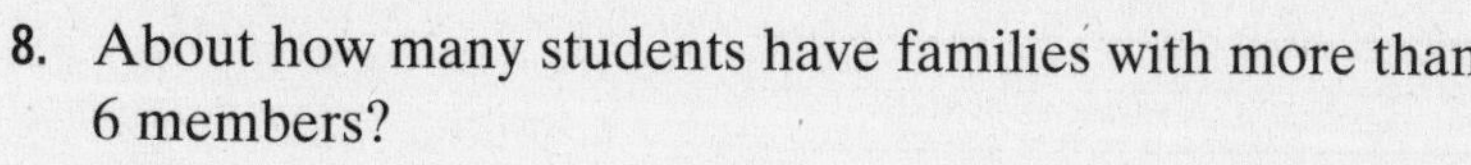

8. About how many students have families with more than 6 members?

9. Is it possible to tell how many students have 4 or 5 people in their families? Explain.

Name ______________________ Class ______________ Date ____________

10-2 • Guided Problem Solving

GPS Exercise 12:

Can you tell how many people saw exactly 7 movies? Explain.

Understand

1. What information does the histogram show?

____

Plan and Carry Out

2. Look at the histogram. How many people saw 6–7 movies in a theatre last summer?

____

3. Is it possible that everyone in this group saw exactly 6 movies?

____

4. Is it possible that everyone in this group saw exactly 7 movies?

____

5. Based on the data in the histogram, can you tell how many people saw exactly 7 movies? Explain.

____

____

Check

6. Based on the data in the histogram, list two different possibilities for how many people saw exactly 7 movies last summer.

____

Solve Another Problem

7. Using the histogram above, is it possible to tell how many people did not see any movies in the theatre last summer? Explain.

____

Name ________________ Class ________________ Date ________________

Practice 10-3

Sampling

For each population, decide when to survey each member or to take a sample. Explain your answer.

1. all ten-year-olds in a swimming pool

____

2. construction workers in the state of Colorado

____

3. all girls in a classroom

____

For each situation, decide which sampling method was used.

4. survey classmates based on names drawn from a hat

____

5. survey everybody playing basketball on one court

____

6. survey every 15th customer at a barber shop

____

Decide which method better represents the population. Explain.

7. You want to know the median height of the 7th graders at your school.
   a. Find the height of everyone in your math class.
   b. Find the height of the 20 oldest students in 7th grade.

____

8. You want to know the average age of people in the mall.
   a. Survey everybody in the pet store.
   b. Survey every 15th person who enters the mall.

____

9. Every tenth customer at a bakery gets a free roll. Explain why using systematic sampling to survey customer satisfaction might not represent the population well.

____

____

____

Name ______________________ Class ______________ Date ______________

10-3 • Guided Problem Solving

GPS Exercise 15:

Suppose you want to know which baseball team is considered to be the best. You ask everyone seated in your section of the ballpark.

a. Is this a random sample? Explain.

b. How might your results differ if you asked every 12th visitor at a tourist attraction?

Understand

1. What is a sample of a population?

____

Plan and Carry Out

2. Is there a chance that asking everyone in your section of the ballpark favors a certain group of people?

____

3. Will surveying everyone in your section of the ballpark provide a random sample?

____

4. Do people from many different areas of the country visit tourist attractions?

____

5. Is the area in which someone lives likely to influence which baseball team is his or her favorite?

____

6. Explain how a survey of people's favorite baseball teams might show different results if given to every 12th person at a tourist attraction instead of to visitors at a specific baseball stadium.

____

Check

7. Is it possible for a survey to be both systematic and random?

____

Solve Another Problem

8. Monica wants to conduct a survey to find out how often people go to the movies. Would her sample be more random if she asked everyone on her block or every 10th visitor to a movie theatre?

____

Name ______________________ Class ______________ Date ____________

Practice 10-4

Surveys and Samples

Is each survey question fair or biased? If the question is biased, rewrite it to make it fair.

1. Do you prefer comedy or science fiction movies?

   ____

2. Do you prefer taking a noisy bus or getting exercise by walking to school?

   ____

3. Do you prefer to go to the movies or read a book?

   ____

4. Would you rather live in a dirty city or on a peaceful farm?

   ____

5. Do you prefer greasy pizza or healthy vegetables?

   ____

The following surveys are biased. Explain how each survey is biased and how the results of each survey might differ if the survey was less biased.

6. **Question:** Should the school day be even longer than it already is?
   Sampling Method: random sampling of teachers at the end of the day at LeBron Middle School

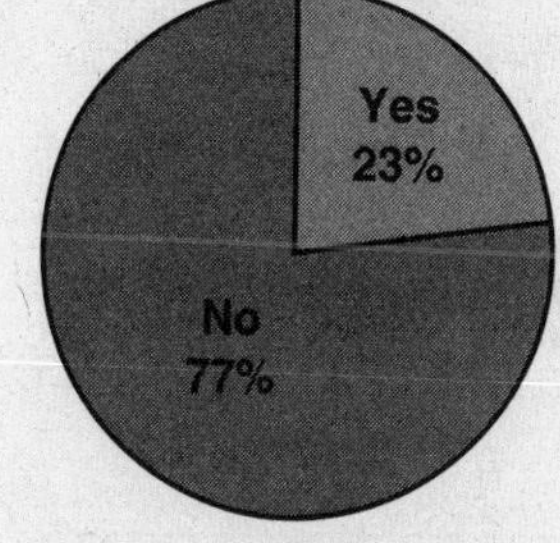

   ____

   ____

   ____

7. **Question:** Do you prefer Mexican food, Chinese food, or Italian food?
   Sampling Method: survey every 10th customer at a Chinese market

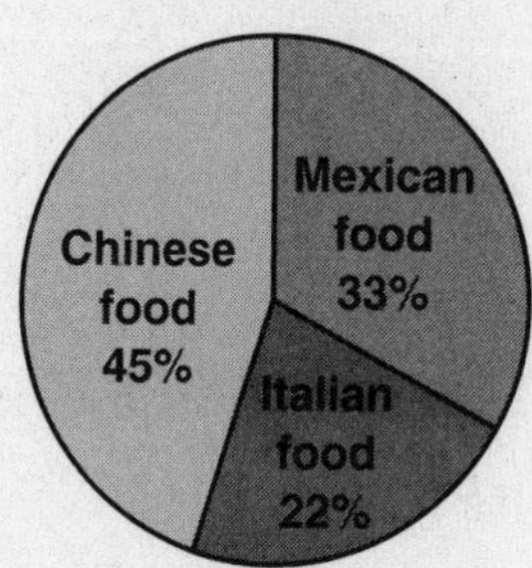

   ____

   ____

   ____

Name ______________________ Class ______________ Date ______________

10-4 • Guided Problem Solving

GPS Exercise 12:

Students conducted a survey. They asked "How many hours per week do you read?" They took the sample by asking every 10th person who entered the library. Their results are shown below.

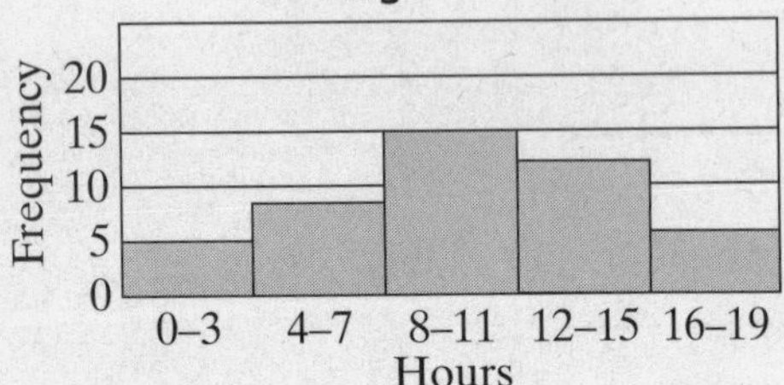

a. Was the question *biased* or *fair*?
b. Explain why the sampling method was biased.
c. Describe a sampling method that better represents the general population.

Understand

1. What does it mean to say that a survey is *biased*?

____

Plan and Carry Out

2. Are people entering a library likely to read for more hours per week than members of the general population? ______________
3. Was the survey in the question *biased* or *fair*? ______________
4. What is a sampling method? ______________
5. Why is the sampling method in this survey biased?

____

6. Think of a place to conduct the survey in which people would not be more or less likely to read more hours per week than members of the general population. For this location, describe a sampling method that would better represent the population.

____

Check

7. Do the results of the survey seem different from what you would reasonably expect? ______________

Solve Another Problem

8. Ronaldo wants to conduct a survey to find out how often people eat at restaurants. Would his sample be more random if he asked every 5th visitor to a grocery store or every 10th person he saw at a fair? Explain.

____

Name ________________ Class ________________ Date ________________

Practice 10-5

Using Graphs to Persuade

The table below shows the number of students enrolled in swimming classes for 2001 to 2003.

1. Use the data to create a double line graph that emphasizes the increase in the number of students enrolled in summer swim classes.

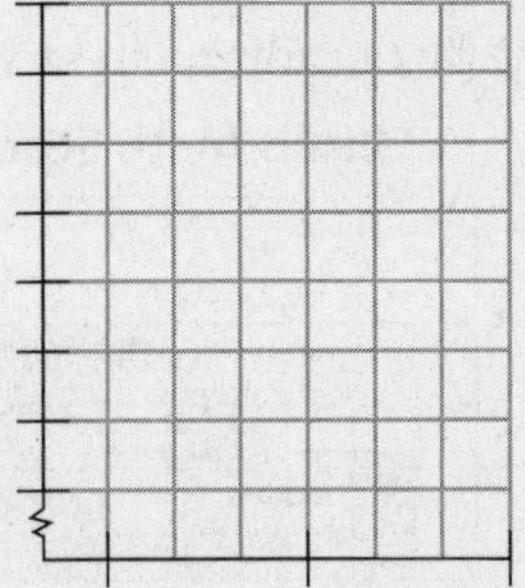

Swim Class Enrollment		
Year	**Boys**	**Girls**
2001	375	360
2002	400	395
2003	410	420

2. Use the data again to create a second double line graph that does not emphasize the increase in the number of students enrolled in the summer swim classes.

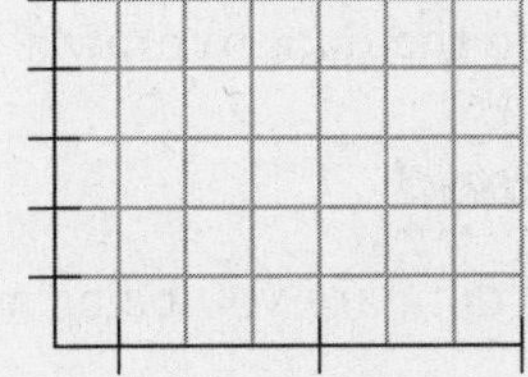

3. Which graph could be used to request additional reserved times for swim classes at the pool?

____

____

Use the graph at the right for Exercises 4–6

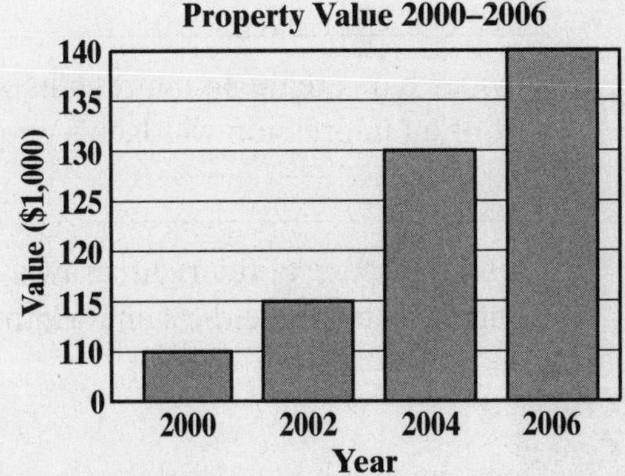

4. How is the graph misleading?

____

____

5. Redraw the graph so that it is not misleading by using a break in the vertical scale.

6. Redraw the graph so that it is not misleading by starting the vertical scale at 0.

Name ______________________ Class ______________ Date ______________

10-5 • Guided Problem Solving

GPS Exercise 15:

Jack made this graph to show his parents his math test scores.

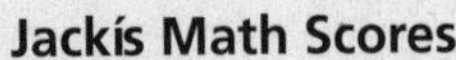

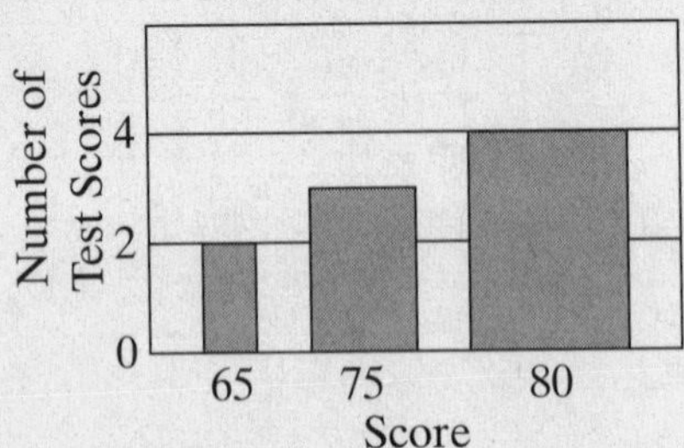

a. Why is this graph misleading?

b. What impression was Jack trying to create with his graph?

c. Use the data to draw a graph that does not mislead.

Understand

1. What data are you being asked to analyze?

____

Plan and Carry Out

2. What is different about the three bars in Jack's graph?

____

3. Why is the graph misleading?

____

4. If wider bars create an impression of added importance, what sort of an impression will Jack's graph create?

____

5. Using the space at the right, draw a graph for Jack's test scores using bars that have the same width.

Check

6. Does the graph you drew above look like a normal bar graph?

____

Solve Another Problem

7. Are the numbers on the *y*-axis in Jack's graph also misleading? Why or why not?

____

____

Name ______________________ Class ______________ Date ____________

Practice 10-6

Using Data to Persuade

Use the table at the right for Exercises 1–3.

1. The table at the right shows the amount of time each person took to complete four different 75-yard dashes on different days. Can you use this data to show that Sam is the fastest runner? Explain.

75-Yard Dash Times				
Name	**Time (seconds)**			
Sam	17	15	14	16
Janis	12	19	22	18
Dave	13	28	13	13

____

2. Can you use this data to show that Janis is the fastest runner? Explain.

____

3. Can you use this data to show that Dave is the fastest runner? Explain.

____

4. If the three runners raced again, who do you think would probably win? Explain your reasoning.

____

Use the table at the right for Exercises 4–5.

5. After comparing grades with his friends Wanda and Julia, John told his parents that he has the highest grade of the three friends. How is this misleading?

Test Grades			
	Test 1	**Test 2**	**Test 3**
John	76	96	65
Wanda	81	85	86
Julia	92	95	82

____

____

6. What do you think is the fairest way to analyze how well John is doing compared to his friends?

____

7. A survey taken at the mall shows that 65% of people prefer watching movies to reading books. Describe a biased sampling method that could be used to make it appear that more people prefer reading books to watching movies.

____

____

Name ______________________ Class ______________ Date ____________

10-6 • Guided Problem Solving

GPS Exercise 8:

Businesses often advertise sales using outliers. Explain how this can be misleading, and why it is a common practice.

Understand

1. What is an outlier?

____

Plan and Carry Out

2. In a sale, which prices could be considered outliers?

____

3. How can advertising a sale using an outlier be misleading?

____

4. Why would a business want to advertise a discount that is greater than the average discount for a sale?

____

5. Why do you think it is a common practice to advertise sales with outliers?

____

Check

6. Does a low price on a given item influence you to shop at a store?

____

Solve Another Problem

7. What kind of outlier would a business *not* want to use to advertise a sale?

____

____

Name ______________________ Class ______________ Date ______________

10A: Graphic Organizer

For use before Lesson 10-1

Study Skill As you learn new skills, practice them regularly. Each time you work a problem, it should seem easier than the time before. Keep a list of problems that you want to spend extra time practicing.

Write your answers.

1. What is the chapter title?

____

2. How many lessons are there in this chapter?

____

3. What is the topic of the Test-Taking Strategies page?

____

____

4. Complete the graphic organizer below as you work through the chapter.
   - In the center, write the title of the chapter.
   - When you begin a lesson, write the lesson name in a rectangle.
   - When you complete a lesson, write a skill or key concept in a circle linked to that lesson block.
   - When you complete the chapter, use this graphic organizer to help you review.

Name ______________________ Class ______________ Date ____________

10B: Reading Comprehension

For use after Lesson 10-1

Study Skill Take short breaks between assignments.

Read the paragraph and answer the questions.

In 1945, the first electronic computer was built. ENIAC, which stands for Electronic Numerical Integrator and Calculator, was able to do 5,000 additions per second. Current computers are capable of doing 100,000 times as many additions per second. ENIAC weighed approximately 30 tons and had a length of 40 feet and a width of 45 feet. Present-day computer notebooks weigh about 3 pounds. Unlike modern computers, which use microprocessors composed of thousands or millions of transistors, ENIAC used vacuum tubes to process data. It had about 18,000 tubes, each the size of a small light bulb.

1. What does the acronym ENIAC stand for?

   ____

2. How many years ago was ENIAC built?

   ____

3. How many additions could ENIAC perform per second?

   ____

4. How many additions per second do current computers perform?

   ____

5. How much area did ENIAC cover?

   ____

6 How many pounds did ENIAC weigh?

   ____

7. How many times more does ENIAC weigh than today's notebook computers?

   ____

8. What do today's modern computers use to process data?

   ____

9. **High-Use Academic Words** In Exercise 1, what does the word *acronym* mean?

   a. a certain way in which something appears

   b. a word formed from the first letters of several other words

Name ______________________ Class ______________ Date ______________

10C: Reading/Writing Math Symbols

For use after Lesson 10-4

Study Skill Make a realistic study schedule. Plan ahead when your teacher assigns a long-term project.

Some mathematical symbols have multiple meanings. Explain the meaning of the bar (−) in each of the following.

1. $2.\overline{3}$ ______________________
2. $11 - 15$ ______________________
3. $\overline{GH}$ ______________________
4. $3 + (-7)$ ______________________
5. $\frac{1}{5}$ ______________________

The bar (−) takes on different meanings when used with other symbols. Explain the meaning of each symbol below.

6. $=$ ______________________
7. $\leq$ ______________________
8. $\cong$ ______________________
9. $\stackrel{?}{=}$ ______________________
10. $\neq$ ______________________

When they are vertical, the bars also take on different meanings. Explain the meaning of these symbols.

11. $| \quad |$, as in $|-3| = 3$

____

12. $\|$, as in $m \parallel n$

____

Name ______________________ Class ______________________ Date ______________________

10D: Visual Vocabulary Practice

For use after Lesson 10-6

Study Skill When interpreting an illustration, notice the information that is given and also notice what is not given. Do not make assumptions.

Concept List

biased question	bar graph	histogram
frequency table	random sampling	population
systematic sampling	line graph	misleading graph

Write the concept that best describes each exercise. Choose from the concept list above.

1.

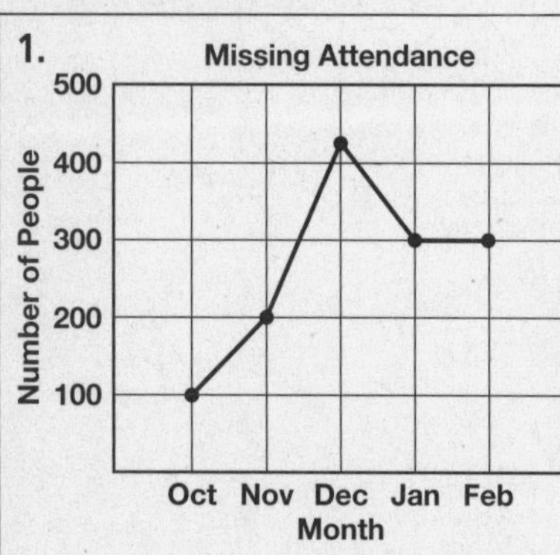

____

2.

Number of Passengers	Frequency
0–9	/
10–19	///
20–29	///

____

3. Sandy conducted a survey at her college. She chose a random sample from all freshmen and asked how much time they study each week. The freshmen class represents this for the survey.

____

4.

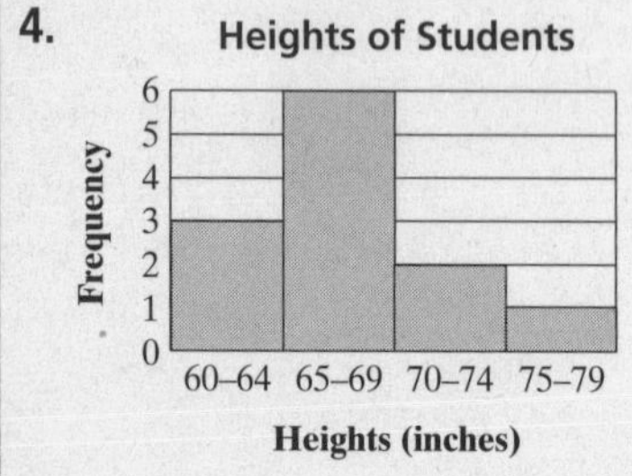

____

5. To conduct a survey of students in his school, Anthony wrote the names of all of the students on cards. Then, without looking, he chose 25 names.

____

6.

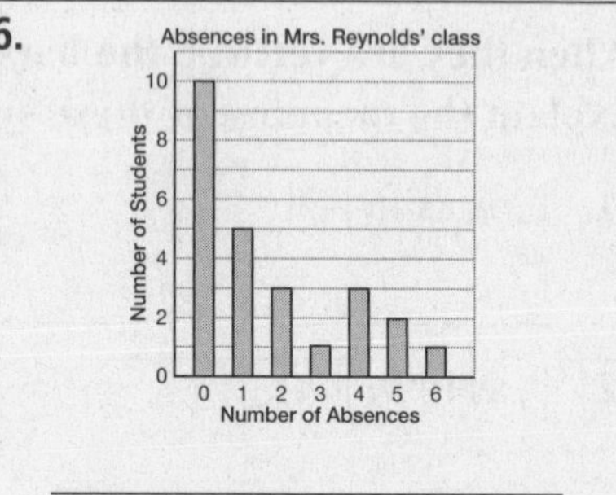

____

7. "Do you prefer lovable dogs or lazy cats?"

____

8.

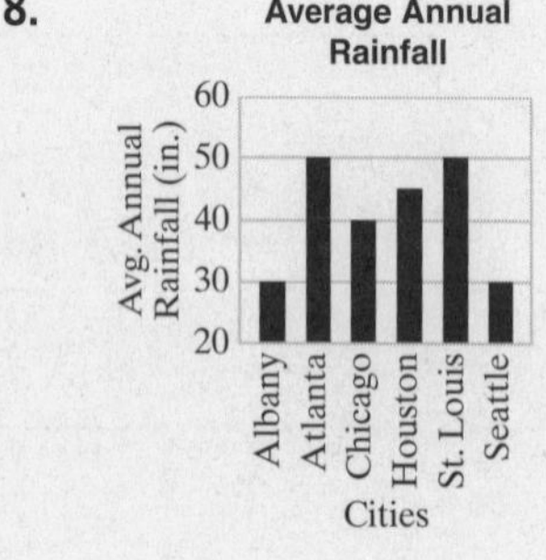

____

9. Derrick conducted a survey using the customers at a local ice cream shop. Derrick chose every 5th and 8th customer entering the shop to represent this.

____

Name ______________________ Class ______________ Date ____________

10E: Vocabulary Check

For use after Lesson 10-6

Study Skill Strengthen your vocabulary. Use these pages and add cues and summaries by applying the Cornell Notetaking style.

Write the definition for each word or term at the right. To check your work, fold the paper back along the dotted line to see the correct answers.

______________________	biased question
______________________	bar graph
______________________	histogram
______________________	sample
______________________	random sample

Name ______________________ Class ______________ Date ______________

10E: Vocabulary Check (continued) For use after Lesson 10-6

Write the vocabulary word or term for each definition. To check your work, fold the paper forward along the dotted line to see the correct answers.

a question that makes an unjustified assumption or makes one answer appear better than the other ______________________

a graph that uses vertical or horizontal bars to show comparisons ______________________

a bar graph with no spaces between the bars, where the height of each bar shows the frequency of data within that interval ______________________

a part of the population that is used to represent the whole population ______________________

a sample where each member of the population has an equal chance of being selected ______________________

Name ______________________ Class ______________ Date ______________

10F: Vocabulary Review

For use with the Chapter Review

Study Skill Take notes while you study. Use a highlighter to emphasize important material in your notes.

Circle the term that correctly completes each sentence.

1. In (*systematic, random*) sampling, every member of a population has an equal chance of being selected.
2. A question that makes an unjustified assumption is (*biased, random*).
3. A (*function, sequence*) is a set of numbers that follows a pattern.
4. A (*line graph, bar graph*) is usually used to show change over time.
5. You can use a (*bar, circle*) graph to easily compare amounts.
6. The (*mean, median*) is the middle number in a data set when the values are written in order from least to greatest.
7. The (*mode, range*) of a data set is the difference between the greatest and least data values.
8. (*Convenience, Systematic*) sampling selects a sample in the easiest way possible.
9. The heights of the bars in a (*bar graph, histogram*) show the frequency of data within an interval.
10. (*Principal, Interest*) is the amount of money borrowed or deposited.
11. The (*area, surface area*) of a prism is the sum of the areas of the faces.
12. (*Circumference, Area*) is the distance around a circle.
13. A line segment that has both endpoints on a circle is a (*radius, chord*).
14. A (*function, sequence*) is a relationship that assigns exactly one output value for each input value.

Name ______________________ Class ______________ Date ____________

Practice 11-1

Probability

You spin a spinner numbered 1 through 10. Each outcome is equally likely. Find the probabilities below as a fraction, decimal, and percent.

1. *P*(9)
2. *P*(even)
3. *P*(number greater than 0)
4. *P*(multiple of 4)

There are eight blue marbles, nine orange marbles, and six yellow marbles in a bag. You draw one marble at random. Find each probability.

5. *P*(blue marble) ______________________
6. *P*(yellow marble) ______________________
7. What marble could you add or remove so that the probability of drawing a blue marble is $\frac{1}{3}$?

____

A box contains 12 slips of paper as shown. Each slip of paper is equally likely to be drawn. Find each probability.

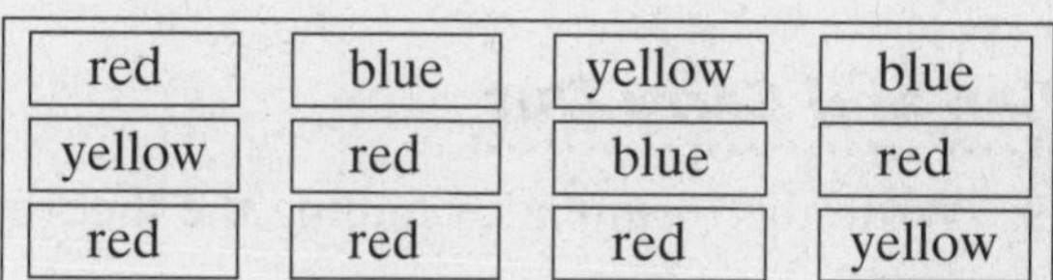

red	blue	yellow	blue
yellow	red	blue	red
red	red	red	yellow

8. *P*(red)
9. *P*(blue)
10. *P*(yellow)
11. *P*(red or blue)
12. *P*(red or yellow)
13. *P*(blue or yellow)
14. *P*(not red)
15. *P*(not blue)
16. *P*(not yellow)

You select a letter randomly from a bag containing the letters S, P, I, N, N, E, and R. Find the probability of each event.

17. selecting an N
18. selecting an S

Name ______________________ Class ______________ Date ______________

11-1 Guided Problem Solving

GPS Exercise 23:

The U.S. House of Representatives has 435 members. Each member's name is put into a hat and one name is chosen at random. Find *P*(California) as a decimal to the nearest hundredth.

U.S. House of Representatives

State	Number	State	Number
California	53	Illinois	19
Pennsylvania	19	Texas	32

SOURCE: U.S. Census Bureau. Go to **PHSchool.com** for a data update. Web Code avg-9041

Understand

1. What are you being asked to do?

____

2. Circle the information you will need to solve the problem.

Plan and Carry Out

3. Write the formula for finding the theoretical probability of an event.

____

4. How many representatives come from California?

____

5. How many representatives are there in the entire House of Representatives?

____

6. Substitute the values from Steps 4 and 5 into the probability formula from Step 3.

____

7. Convert the fraction from Step 6 to a decimal. Round the decimal to the nearest hundredth.

____

Check

8. Is your answer between 0 and 1? ______________

Solve Another Problem

9. Using the table above, find *P*(Illinois). Write your answer as a decimal rounded to the nearest hundredth.

____

Name ______________________ Class ______________ Date ______________

Practice 11-2

Experimental Probability

Suppose you observe the color of socks worn by students in your class: 12 have white, 4 have black, 3 have blue, and 1 has red. Find each experimental probability.

1. *P*(white) ____________
2. *P*(red) ____________
3. *P*(blue) ____________
4. *P*(black) ____________
5. *P*(yellow) ____________
6. *P*(black or red) ____________

Use the data in the table at the right for Exercises 7–12. Find each experimental probability.

Favorite Snack Survey Results

Snack	Number of Students
Fruit	8
Granola	2
Pretzels	3
Chips	7
Carrots	5

7. *P*(fruit) ____________
8. *P*(granola) ____________
9. *P*(pretzels) ____________
10. *P*(carrots) ____________
11. *P*(not fruit) ____________
12. *P*(granola or chips) ____________
13. Do an experiment to find the probability that a word chosen randomly in a book is the word *the.* How many words did you look at to find *P*(the)? What is *P*(the)?

    ____

14. Suppose the following is the result of tossing a coin 5 times:

    heads, tails, heads, tails, heads

    What is the experimental probability for heads?

    ____

Solve.

15. The probability that a twelve-year-old has a brother or sister is $\frac{1}{4}$. Suppose you survey 300 twelve-year-olds. About how many do you think will have a brother or sister? ____________
16. a. A quality control inspector found flaws in 13 out of 150 sweaters. Find the probability that a sweater has a flaw. Round to the nearest tenth of a percent. ____________

    b. Suppose the company produces 500 sweaters a day. How many will not have flaws? ____________

    c. Suppose the company produces 600 sweaters a day. How many will have flaws? ____________

Name ______________________ Class ______________ Date ____________

11-2 • Guided Problem Solving

GPS Exercise 11:

a. The probability that a male human is colorblind is 8%. Suppose you interview 1,000 males. About how many would you expect to be colorblind?

b. **Reasoning** Will you always get the same number? Explain.

Understand

1. What does it mean to be colorblind?

____

2. What are you being asked to do in part (a)?

____

____

Plan and Carry Out

3. Find 8% of 1,000. ____________________

4. How many males out of 1,000 would you expect to be colorblind?

____

5. Will you always get exactly this number? Explain.

____

____

____

Check

6. How could you find the answer another way?

____

Solve Another Problem

7. The probability of a person being left-handed is about 11%. Suppose you interview 500 people. About how many would you expect to be left-handed?

____

Name ______________________ Class ______________ Date ____________

Practice 11-3

Sample Spaces

Make a table to show the sample space and find the number of outcomes. Then find the probability.

1. A theater uses a letter to show which row a seat is in, and a number to show the column. If there are eight rows and ten columns, what is the probability that you select a seat at random that is in column 1? ____________

Make a tree diagram. Then find the probability.

2. A coin is tossed three times.
   a. Make a tree diagram that shows all the possible outcomes of how the coin will land.
   b. Find the probability that the coin will land heads up all three times or tails up all three times. ____________

Use the counting principle.

3. A pizza company makes pizza in three different sizes: small, medium, and large. There are four possible toppings: pepperoni, sausage, green pepper, and mushroom. How many different kinds of pizza with one topping are available? ____________
4. You can choose from three types of sandwiches for lunch and three types of juice. How many possible lunch combinations of sandwich and juice can you have? ____________

Susan has red, blue, and yellow sweaters. Joanne has green, red, and white sweaters. Diane's sweaters are red, blue, and mauve. Each girl has only one sweater of each color and will pick a sweater to wear at random. Find each probability.

5. *P*(each girl chooses a different color) ____________
6. *P*(each girl chooses the same color) ____________
7. *P*(two girls choose the same color, and the third chooses a different color) ____________
8. *P*(each girl chooses a red sweater) ____________

Name ____________________ Class ____________ Date ____________

11-3 • Guided Problem Solving

GPS Exercise 22:

a. **Clothes** James has four sweatshirts (red, blue, black, and green) and four caps in the same colors. How many different sweatshirt-and-cap combinations does James have?

b. Suppose he grabs a sweatshirt and a cap without looking. What is the probability that they will *not* be the same color?

Understand

1. Circle the information you will need to solve the problem.
2. How do you find probability?

____

____

Plan and Carry Out

3. How many different sweatshirts are there? __________
4. How many different caps are there? __________
5. Using the counting principle, how many different sweatshirt-and-cap combinations does James have? __________
6. How many same color sweatshirt-and-cap combinations outfits does James have? __________
7. How many different color sweatshirt-and-cap combinations does James have? __________
8. What is the probability that they will *not* be the same color? __________

Check

9. How else could you find the total number of sweatshirt-and-cap combinations?

____

Solve Another Problem

10. a. Joseph has three pairs of shoes (white, brown, and black) and four pairs of socks (white, brown, black, and blue). How many sock/shoe pairs are there?

    b. If Joseph selects a pair of shoes and a pair of socks without looking, what is the probability they will be the same color?

____

Name ____________________ Class ____________ Date ____________

Practice 11-4

Compound Events

Each letter in the word MASSACHUSETTS is written on a card. The cards are placed in a basket. Find each probability.

1. What is the probability of selecting two S's if the first card is replaced before selecting the second card?

____

2. What is the probability of selecting two S's if the first card is not replaced before selecting the second card?

____

You roll a fair number cube twice. Find each probability.

3. *P*(3, then 5)

____

4. *P*(2, then 2)

____

5. *P*(5, then 4, then 6)

____

6. *P*(6, then 0)

____

Four girls and eight boys want to be president or vice president of the Student Council. To be fair, a teacher puts their names in a hat and selects two. Find each probability.

7. Find the probability that two boys are elected.

____

8. Find the probability that two girls are elected.

____

9. Find the probability that the president is a boy and the vice president is a girl.

____

10. Find the probability that the president is a girl and the vice president is a boy.

____

A box contains ten balls, numbered 1 through 10. Marisha draws a ball. She records its number and then returns it to the bag. Then Penney draws a ball. Find each probability.

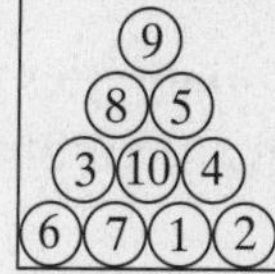

11. *P*(9, then 3)

____

12. *P*(even, then odd)

____

13. *P*(odd, then 2)

____

14. *P*(the sum of the numbers is 25)

____

15. *P*(prime, then composite)

____

16. *P*(a factor of 8, then a multiple of 2)

____

Name ______________________ Class ______________ Date ______________

11-4 Guided Problem Solving

GPS Exercise 23:

A bag contains 3 blue marbles, 4 red marbles, and 2 white marbles. Three times you draw a marble and return it. Find *P*(red, then white, then blue).

Understand

1. What are you being asked to do?

____

2. Circle the information you will need to solve the problem.

Plan and Carry Out

3. How many times will you pick a marble?

____

4. Are these events dependent or independent?

____

5. What is the probability that you will draw a red marble?

____

6. What is the probability that you will draw a white marble?

____

7. What is the probability that you will draw a blue marble?

____

8. Multiply the probabilities from Steps 5–7 by one another. What is P(red, then white, then blue)?

____

Check

9. Is your answer between 0 and 1? ______________

Solve Another Problem

10. In the situation above, find *P*(red, then red, then blue).

____

Name ______________________ Class ______________ Date ______________

Practice 11-5

Disjoint Events

Are the events disjoint? Explain.

1. Rolling a 4 or a number less than 3 on a number cube

____

____

2. Eating dinner or doing homework at 7 P.M.

____

____

3. Flipping "heads" on a coin or rolling a 6 on a number cube

____

____

4. Taking the bus or walking to school

____

____

5. Being good at math and being a fast reader

____

____

6. Spinning a 2 or an even number on a spinner

____

____

Find each probability for one spin of the spinner at right.

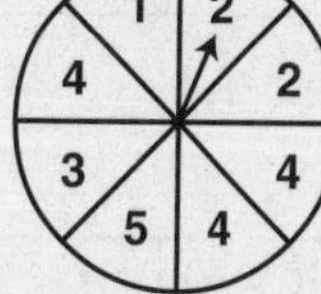

7. P(even or 5) ______________

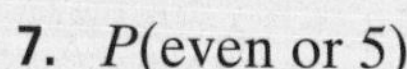

8. P(4 or 1) ______________

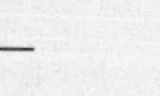

9. P(5 or a multiple of 2) ______________

10. P(1 or prime) ______________

Suppose you select a letter from the alphabet at random. Find each probability.

11. P(vowel or Z) ______________

12. P(letter in CAT or letter in DOG) ______________

13. P(letter in BATH or the letter P) ______________

14. P(one of the first 3 letters of the alphabet or one of the last 5 letters of the alphabet) ______________

15. Pablo has a CD collection of 3 country music CDs, 6 rock CDs, and 5 classical CDs. If he grabs a CD at random, what is the probability that it is a classical or rock CD?

____

Name ____________ Class ____________ Date ____________

11-5 Guided Problem Solving

GPS Exercise 28:

The figure at the right is a regular *dodecahedron*, a solid with 12 faces. Find *P*(multiple of 5 or multiple of 6) for one roll of the dodecahedron.

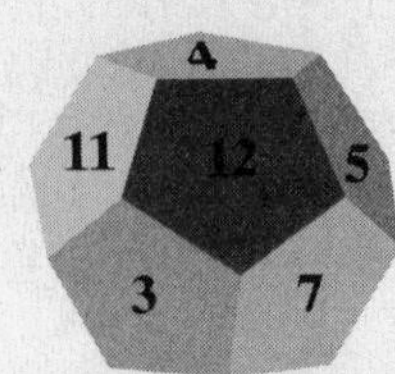

Understand

1. What are you being asked to do?

____

Plan and Carry Out

2. Are rolling a multiple of 5 and rolling a multiple of 6 disjoint events?

____

3. Write the formula for finding the probability of two disjoint events.

____

4. What is *P*(multiple of 5)?

____

5. What is *P*(multiple of 6)?

____

6. Add the two probabilities together using the formula from Step 3. What is *P*(multiple of 5 or multiple of 6)?

____

Check

7. List the possible favorable outcomes for this probability. Divide the number of possible favorable outcomes by the number of all possible outcomes. Is this fraction equal to your answer from Step 6?

____

Solve Another Problem

8. In the situation above, find *P*(7, or multiple of 2).

____

Name ______________________ Class ______________ Date ______________

11A: Graphic Organizer

For use before Lesson 11-1

Study Skill As your teacher presents new material in the chapter, keep a paper and pencil handy to write down notes and questions. If you miss class, borrow a classmate's notes so you will not fall behind.

Write your answers.

1. What is the chapter title?

   ____

2. How many lessons are there in this chapter?

   ____

3. What is the topic of the Test-Taking Strategies page?

   ____

4. Complete the graphic organizer below as you work through the chapter.
   - In the center, write the title of the chapter.
   - When you begin a lesson, write the lesson name in a rectangle.
   - When you complete a lesson, write a skill or key concept in a circle linked to that lesson block.
   - When you complete the chapter, use this graphic organizer to help you review.

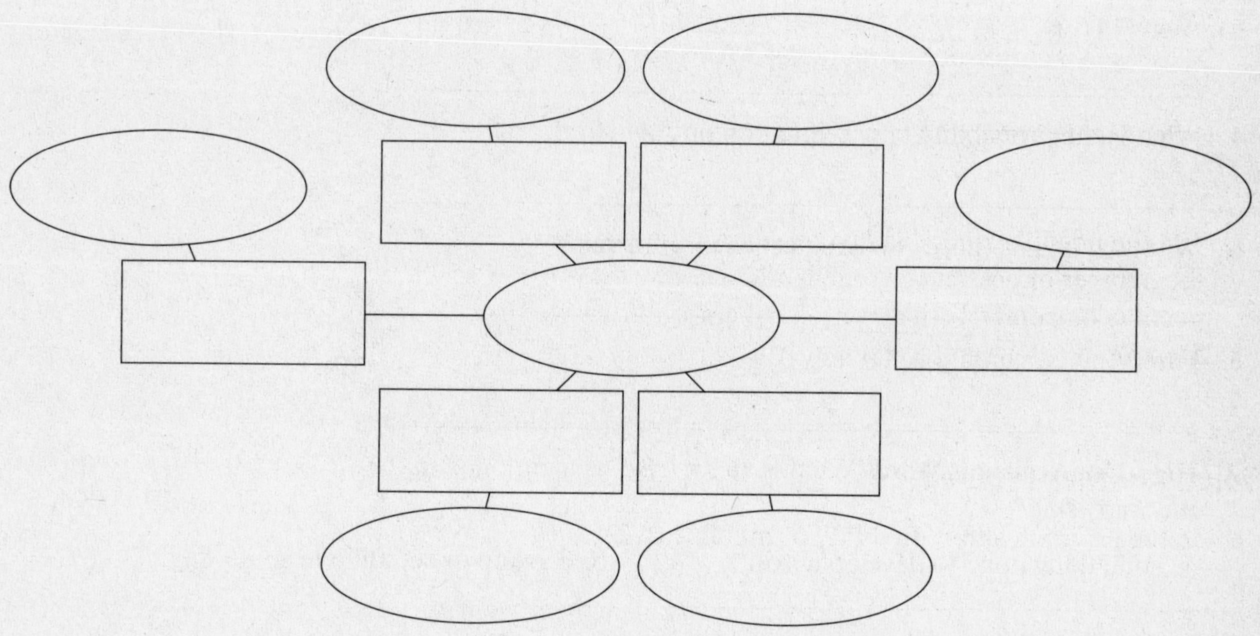

Name ________________ Class ________________ Date ________________

11B: Reading Comprehension

For use after Lesson 11-2

Study Skill When you complete a math exercise, always make sure your answer makes sense.

Below is an 8-day forecast of weather conditions. Use the table to answer the questions.

Date	Weather Prediction	High/Low Temp (°F)	% Chance of Precipitation
July 26 evening	Isolated T-Storms	67°	30%
July 27	PM T-Storms	87° / 71°	40%
July 28	Partly Cloudy	91° / 71°	20%
July 29	Scattered T-Storms	90° / 64°	40%
July 30	Partly Cloudy	87° / 65°	20%
July 31	Partly Cloudy	87° / 60°	20%
Aug 01	Partly Cloudy	83° / 59°	20%
Aug 02	Partly Cloudy	87° / 60°	0%

1. For what dates does the table give weather forecasts?

____

2. On which date might there be isolated thunderstorms?

____

3. What is the difference between the high and low temperature on August 1?

____

4. What is the probability of precipitation on July 30?

____

5. What day(s) has (have) the greatest chance for rain?

____

6. Find *P*(no precipitation) for July 31.

____

7. **High-Use Academic Words** What is an *exercise*, as mentioned in the study skill?

   a. something done to develop a skill b. a group or set alike in some way

Name ______________________ Class ______________ Date ______________

11C: Reading/Writing Math Symbols

For use after Lesson 11-5

Study Skill Write assignments down; do not rely only on your memory.

Write the meaning of each mathematical expression.

1. $P(A)$ ______________________
2. $P(\text{not } A)$ ______________________
3. $P(A, \text{ then } B)$ ______________________ ______________________
4. $P(A \text{ or } B)$ ______________________

You are selecting marbles from a bag that contains green, yellow, and red marbles. Explain the meaning of each mathematical expression.

5. $P(\text{red})$ ______________________
6. $P(\text{not green})$ ______________________
7. $P(\text{red, then yellow})$ ______________________
8. $P(\text{green or yellow})$ ______________________

Write each statement using appropriate mathematical symbols.

9. the probability of event *C* occurring ______________________
10. the probability of rolling an odd number on a number cube ______________________
11. the probability of event *D*, and then event *E* occurring ______________________
12. the probability of rolling a 6 or a prime number on a standard number cube ______________________
13. the number of possible outfits created by choosing one shirt and one pair of pants from 5 shirts and 6 pairs of pants ______________________

Name ______________________ Class ______________ Date ______________

11D: Visual Vocabulary Practice

For use after Lesson 11-5

High-Use Academic Words

Study Skill Mathematics is like learning a foreign language. You have to know the vocabulary before you can speak the language correctly.

Concept List

counting principle	complement	independent events
disjoint events	compound event	dependent events
outcome	experimental probability	sample space

Write the concept that best describes each exercise. Choose from the concept list above.

1. $P(A \text{ or } B) = P(A) + P(B)$ for these events __________________	**2.** Flipping a coin and then rolling a number cube is an example of this. __________________	**3.** A jar contains 2 red marbles, 1 blue marble, and 1 green marble. You draw one marble and record the color. This is represented by the set {red, blue, and green}. __________________
4. $P(A, \text{then } B) = P(A) \cdot P(B)$ for these events __________________	**5.** If you flip a coin, then flipping heads is an example of this. __________________	**6.** Pedro draws a card from a standard 52-card deck. He then rolls a six-sided number cube. The total number of possible outcomes is $52 \cdot 6 = 312$. __________________
7. $\frac{\text{number of times an event occurs}}{\text{total number of trials}}$ __________________	**8.** $P(A, \text{then } B) = P(A) \cdot P(B \text{ after } A)$ for these events __________________	**9.** Renee rolls a six-sided number cube. If an event represents rolling an even number, then this is represented by the set {1, 3, 5}. __________________

Name ______________________ Class ______________ Date ______________

11E: Vocabulary Check

For use after Lesson 11-5

Study Skill Strengthen your vocabulary. Use these pages and add cues and summaries by applying the Cornell Notetaking style.

Write the definition for each word or term at the right. To check your work, fold the paper back along the dotted line to see the correct answers.

______________________	sample space
______________________	event
______________________	disjoint events
______________________	theoretical probability
______________________	experimental probability

Name ________________ Class ____________ Date ____________

11E: Vocabulary Check (continued)

For use after Lesson 11-5

Write the vocabulary word or term for each definition. To check your work, fold the paper forward along the dotted line to see the correct answers.

the collection of all possible outcomes in an experiment ________________

a collection of possible outcomes ________________

two events that cannot happen together ________________

the ratio of the number of favorable outcomes to the number of possible outcomes ________________

the ratio of the number of times an event occurs to the total number of trials ________________

Name ________________ Class ________________ Date ________________

11F: Vocabulary Review Puzzle

For use with the Chapter Review

Study Skill When using a word bank, read the words first. Then answer the questions.

Complete the crossword puzzle. Use the words from the following list.

parallelogram	net	decagon	equation	mode
convenience	symmetry	variable	discount	prime
independent	probability	dependent	outcome	slope

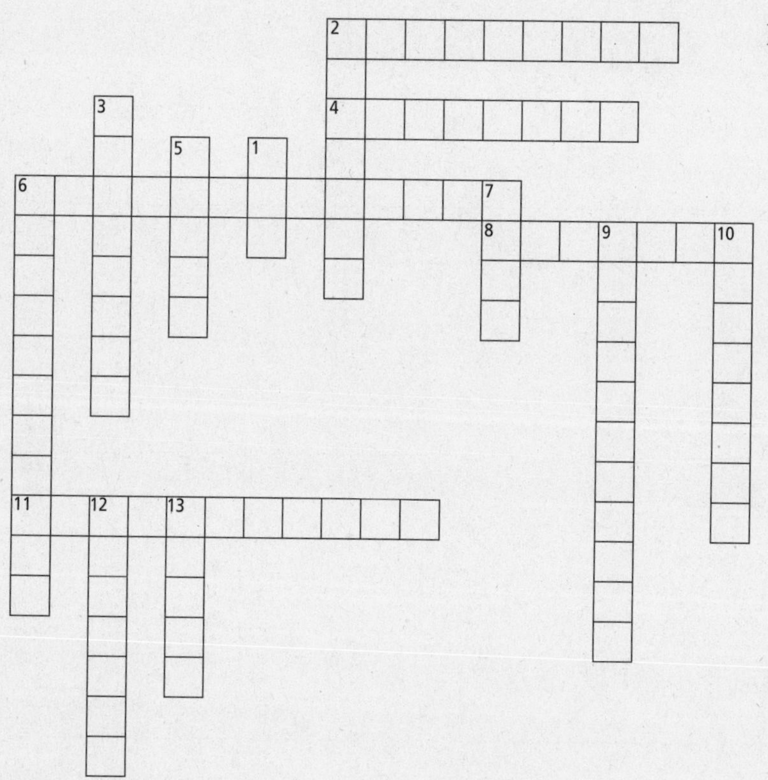

ACROSS

2. Events are ______________ if the occurrence of one event affects the probability of the occurrence of another event.
4. A figure has ___________ if one side of the figure is the mirror image of the other side.
6. four-sided figure with two sets of parallel lines
8. possible result of an action
11. Events are ____________ if the occurrence of one event does not affect the probability of the occurrence of another event.

DOWN

1. a 2-dimensional pattern you can fold to form a 3-dimensional figure
2. difference between the original price and the sale price
3. letter that stands for a number
5. ratio that describes the steepness of a line
6. the ratio of favorable outcomes to the total number of possible outcomes gives the theoretical ______________.
7. number that occurs most often in a data set
9. ______________ sampling is a method that selects samples in the easiest way possible.
10. mathematical statement with an equal sign
12. polygon with ten sides
13. whole number with only two factors, itself and the number one